W9-BXR-820

JOSEPH CASE
HIGH SCHOOL
SWANSEA
MASS.

THE MATHEMATICS OF MATRICES

A BLAISDELL BOOK IN THE PURE AND APPLIED SCIENCES

The Mathematics of Matrices

A FIRST BOOK OF MATRIX THEORY AND LINEAR ALGEBRA

---

by Philip J. Davis
BROWN UNIVERSITY

BLAISDELL PUBLISHING COMPANY
A DIVISION OF GINN AND COMPANY
Waltham, Massachusetts · Toronto · London

Library of Congress Catalog Card Number: 64-24818

To Ernie *and to* Joe
and once again
to
Handy

Preface

IT IS INEVITABLE in an age of rapid change to tell children about the horse drawn wagons of one's youth, and it is equally inevitable in writing a text that makes matrix theory available to young students for one's thought to turn to the position of the subject a few years back. A generation ago, the subject was taught as an intermediate level or first-year graduate course in college, and was taken by majors in mathematics and theoretical physics. Before long, I suspect, the educated man on the street may be making bad jokes about matrix inversion and characteristic values, the way he now does about Pythagoras' Theorem or the Binomial Formula.

This is not a case of how the mighty have fallen; on the contrary, it is a wonderful example of the gradual dissemination of knowledge that has been going on since antiquity when the ancient scientific élite yielded their secrets of arithmetic. It should make anyone who loves mathematics both proud and humble, simultaneously.

A number of reasons can be advanced for the study of matrices and linear algebra as a one-semester course. In the first place, this theory is basic and of wide applicability to advanced work in pure and applied mathematics. In the second place, since the rules of matrix algebra are similar—but not altogether similar—to the rules of ordinary algebra, its study can serve as a review or a consolidation of ordinary algebra, and can lend new insights to old processes.

In composing this text I have been guided by the principle that "sufficient unto the day is the rigor, generality, and notation thereof." This means, in practice, that I have tried not to be tediously doctrinaire about rigor, generality, and notation, but have tried to allow the subject matter to carry as much of them as seemed possible without their gaining the upper hand. I have avoided the use of the sigma sign for summation, thinking that the notation of matrix algebra is itself sufficiently burdensome to the beginner. I have not proved any theorem involving "the general case" by means of mathematical induction. The arguments used in these cases will be convincing without induction; and the teacher who wants to drill on the technique of induction will therefore find ample opportunity to do so at these spots.

The learning of matrices at the elementary level consists of four things; (1) the notation and terminology; (2) the formal algebra; (3) the interpretations of matrices; and (4) the applications of matrices. I have tried to arrange the material in such a way that the four aspects are intermingled in an easy and natural association. When one goes to a foreign land, say to Japan, it would be foolish to avoid communicating with the Japanese until one had learned the subtleties of Haiku poetry.

I approach the subject of matrices with the eye of the analyst and the experience of the applied mathematician. For this reason, I tend to regard matrix theory as mathematical grammar, and not as fiction or belles-lettres. On the other hand, I have been associated over the years with a number of very distinguished algebraists who regard matrix theory, like virtue, as its own reward. This association has led me to appreciate the role of matrices in algebra, and I hope that I have given this aspect sufficient emphasis.

The present book presupposes that the student knows algebra, plane geometry, plane analytic geometry, and trigonometry, all in modest amounts. I am using these terms in the old-fashioned sense, for in the present state of flux, I have no way of telling what is being taught in high schools and under what name.

The core of the course consists of the first six chapters. Chapter 8 and 9 should be taught if time permits. Chapter 7 has been included for flavor and philosophy, while Chapter 10 provides additional material for projects, essays, et cetera.

A word is in order about the working of the problems. In conformity with the spirit of the text, the directive "Prove" or "Show" should be interpreted with flexibility. It might mean anything from "give a few plausible arguments" to "prove in the strict sense of a polished formal argument." Similarly, when propositions to be proved have been phrased very generally, they should be construed as meaning anything from "prove in the case $n = 2$ and with specific numerical coefficients" to "prove in the really general case." The teacher must be guided by the level of mathematical sophistication of his class.

The School Mathematics Study Group (SMSG) has been instrumental in introducing matrix theory into the secondary curriculum. I am indebted to them for having pioneered a textbook on the subject. This book has been of great help to me in planning my own work, and I have, in a large measure, followed their recommendations as to subject matter and pace. Other texts that I have found useful have been referred to in the Bibliography.

I would like to thank Dr. Morris Newman for a number of fruitful discussions and Mr. Robert Rourke for numerous fine suggestions.

I am particularly indebted to Mrs. Persis Redgrave of the Norwich Connecticut Free Academy. Mrs. Redgrave undertook to teach a section of high school seniors from an early version of my manuscript and out of her class experiences have come a number of changes as well as a teachers' manual.

I am indebted to the editors of Blaisdell Publishing Company for the opportunity they have given me to contribute to their distinguished series of mathematical texts.

PHILIP J. DAVIS

Contents

"We have made oblongs and stood them upon squares.
This is our triumph."

VIRGINIA WOOLF

THE MATHEMATICS OF MATRICES

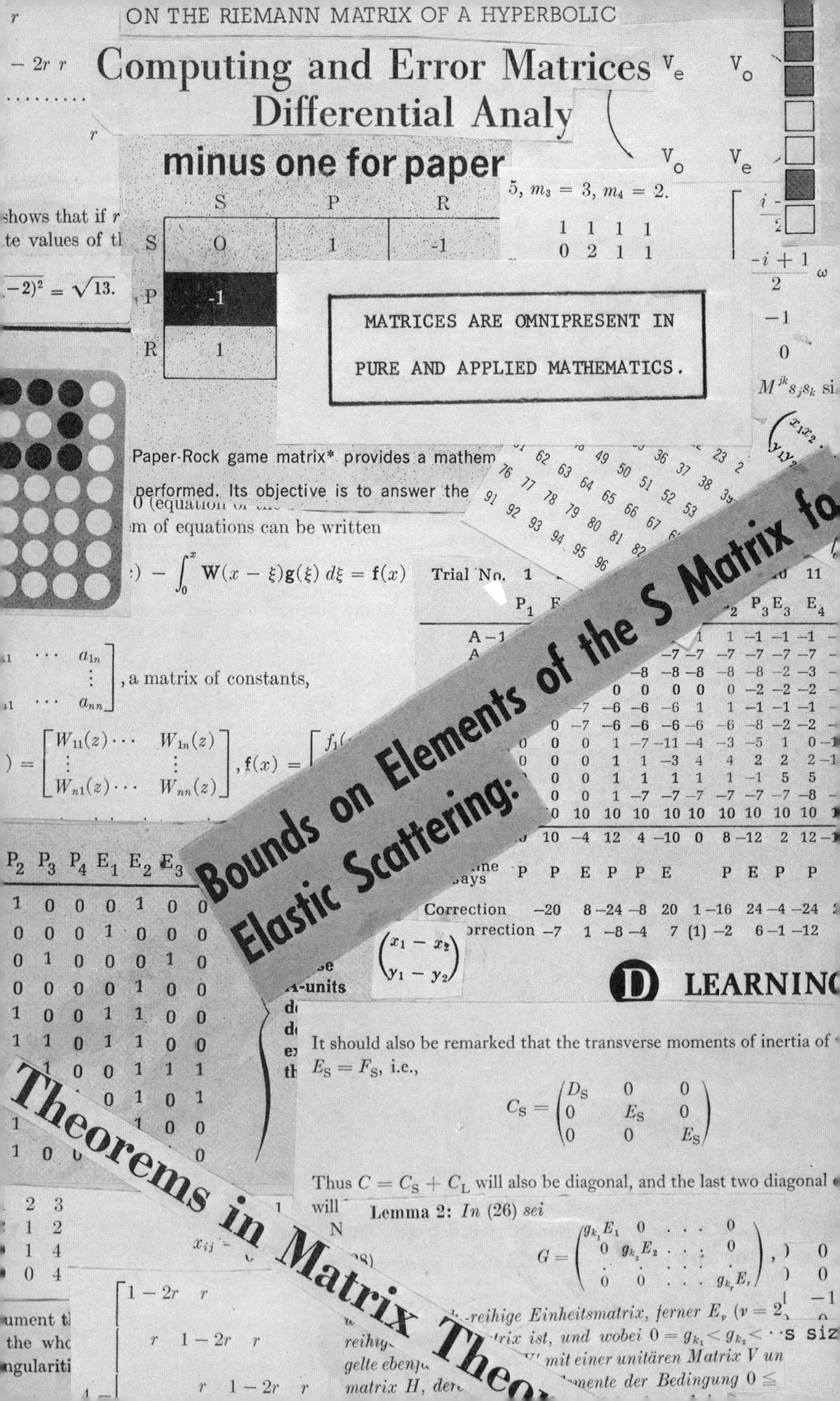

ON THE RIEMANN MATRIX OF A HYPERBOLIC
Computing and Error Matrices
Differential Analy
minus one for paper
MATRICES ARE OMNIPRESENT IN
PURE AND APPLIED MATHEMATICS.
Paper-Rock game matrix* provides a mathem
performed. Its objective is to answer the
m of equations can be written
, a matrix of constants,
Bounds on Elements of the S Matrix fo
Elastic Scattering:
Trial No.
Correction
LEARNING
It should also be remarked that the transverse moments of inertia of
Thus C = CS + CL will also be diagonal, and the last two diagonal
Lemma 2: In (26) sei
Theorems in Matrix Theo

CHAPTER 1

What is a Matrix

1.1 In the Beginning

The roots of most mathematical ideas can be traced back several centuries with ease, and this is true of the objects that go by the name of matrices. But in a strict sense, matrices first saw the light of day in 1850 when the famous English mathematician James Joseph Sylvester (Figure 1.1) wrote down an oblong arrangement of terms and proceeded to extract from it certain rows and columns to form squares. Sylvester had a penchant

FIGURE 1.1 *James Joseph Sylvester in Academic Regalia*

for giving fancy names to the objects he dealt with, and he called his rectangular arrangement a *matrix*. The choice of word was an appropriate one, for one of its common meanings is a place in which something develops or originates. It did not take long before mathematicians recognized that rectangular arrays are a convenient device for extending the common notions of number; Sir William Rowan Hamilton made contributions to the subject in 1853 as did Arthur Cayley in 1858.

The theory of matrices is, in the main, a part of algebra, and in the half century that followed Sylvester, matrices were a plaything of the algebraists. But it became increasingly clear that matrices possessed a utility that extended beyond the domain of algebra and into other regions of mathematics. More than this, it was found that they were exactly the means necessary for expressing many ideas of applied mathematics. For instance, in 1925, Heisenberg introduced them into the mathematics of quantum mechanics. Today matrices are omnipresent in pure and applied mathematics. Wherever there are vast numbers of interlocking relationships that must be handled it is reasonable to guess that matrices will appear on the scene and lend their strength to facilitate the process.

Despite the fundamental position they now occupy in the vocabulary of theoretical science, it has only been in the last two decades that the rank and file of working scientists have learned their language. In this period also, the new electronic computers arrived, and were able to perform matrix arithmetic which would have been impossible in the age of adding machines run by gears. The combination of the power of abstraction embodied in the theory of matrices, plus the possibility of carrying out the necessary computation when concrete problems are at hand, have secured for the theory of matrices an audience that now extends into high school.

1.2 What is a Matrix

A *matrix* is a rectangular array or a table of numbers. $\begin{pmatrix} 6 & 3 & 0 \\ 2 & 1 & -7 \end{pmatrix}$ is a matrix. Here is another matrix: $\begin{pmatrix} 43 & 6 \\ 9 & 0 \\ -7/2 & \pi \end{pmatrix}$. This simple definition will serve as a start. But matrices are more than arrays of numbers. The individual numbers stand in very special relationship to one another, and their totality constitutes a mathematical object that will be manipulated according to certain rules and regulations, interpreted in a variety of ways, and applied in still others.

One can look up the definition of a cat in a dictionary and find that a cat is "a domesticated carnivorous mammal." But in order to know what a cat really is, what it looks like, how it feels, how it operates, and to get some inkling of its rôle in the universe, you have to live with one for a while. Matrices are like cats in this respect; this whole book constitutes an elaboration of the above definition.

The individual numbers in the array are called the *elements* (or *entries*) of the matrix. The elements may be positive or negative integers. Or they may be fractions (that is, rational numbers), irrational numbers, or imaginary numbers (that is, complex numbers). The elements may be algebraic expressions involving one or more variables, or functions that are more complicated than this. Thus,

$$\begin{pmatrix} \sqrt{2} & -\frac{1}{2} \\ x^4 + 6 & -q \end{pmatrix} \quad \text{and} \quad \begin{pmatrix} 0 & (x-a)^{-1} \\ (x-b)^{-1} & (x-c)^{-1} \end{pmatrix}$$

are also matrices.

1.3 The Order of a Matrix

The *rows* of a matrix are the arrays of numbers that go across the page. The *columns* of a matrix are the arrays of numbers that go down the page. Thus, in the matrix

$$\begin{pmatrix} 6 & 2 \\ 3 & 4 \end{pmatrix},$$

the first row is 6 2. The second row is 3 4. The first column is $\begin{matrix} 6 \\ 3 \end{matrix}$, the second column is $\begin{matrix} 2 \\ 4 \end{matrix}$.

A matrix that has m rows and n columns is called an $m \times n$ matrix (read: m by n). In the tag, "$m \times n$," the number of rows is always specified first, and the number of columns second. The tag $m \times n$ is called the *order* of the matrix. Two matrices are considered to be of the same order if they have the same number of rows and have the same number of columns.

A matrix may consist of a single row, such as

$$(3 \quad 9 \quad 12 \quad -6).$$

The order of this matrix is 1×4. Or it may consist of a single column, such as

$$\begin{pmatrix} 3 \\ 9 \\ 12 \\ -6 \end{pmatrix}.$$

The order of this matrix is 4×1. Even though these two matrices have the same elements in the same linear order, the two matrices are considered to be different because the elements in one run across and the elements in the other run down. A matrix might even consist of a single element, as for example

$$(60).$$

The order of this matrix is 1×1, and it is considered to be a totally different object from the number sixty which constitutes its sole element.

A matrix that consists of one row is called a *row matrix* or a *row vector;* a matrix that consists of a single column is called a *column matrix* or a *column vector.* In later chapters, we shall have an opportunity to observe the special way in which vectors enter into the theory.

Matrices such as

$$\begin{pmatrix} 5 & 6 & 7 & 8 \\ 2 & 7 & 9 & 0 \\ -5 & 1 & 5 & 6 \\ 9 & 11 & 5 & 8 \end{pmatrix},$$

which have the same number of rows as columns are called *square matrices.* An $n \times n$ square matrix is said to be of *order* n. There is no doubt that square matrices and row or column matrices are the most important types.

A square matrix has, of course, two diagonals. It turns out in practice that the diagonal extending from the upper left to the lower right is more important than the other diagonal, and it carries a special name. It is called the *principal diagonal* (*or main diagonal*) of the matrix and its elements are called the *diagonal elements* (Figure 1.2).

$$\begin{pmatrix} \mathbf{1} & 2 & 3 \\ 6 & \mathbf{6} & 4 \\ 2 & 1 & \mathbf{7} \end{pmatrix}$$

FIGURE 1.2 *The Principal Diagonal of a Square Matrix*

PROBLEMS

1. How many elements does an $m \times n$ matrix have?
2. A matrix has 180 elements. What are its possible orders?
3. A matrix has thirteen elements. What are its possible orders?
4. How many elements does an $n \times n$ matrix have that are not on the principal diagonal?

5. Given an $m \times n$ matrix. How many interior elements does it have? (that is, elements that are in neither the first or last rows or columns).

6. Find a formula for the number of elements that a square matrix of order n has below its main diagonal.

7. Four matrices have orders $m \times n$, $m \times (q - n)$, $(p - m) \times n$, and $(p - m) \times (q - n)$. Show they can be placed contiguously so as to form a $p \times q$ matrix.

1.4 Various Ways of Writing Matrices

In this book, matrices will be written by placing parentheses around the rectangular array of numbers. But other notations will be found and should be mentioned. Some authors prefer square brackets. For example,

$$\begin{bmatrix} 2 & 1 & 3 \\ 2 & 9 & 1 \\ 2 & 0 & 2 \end{bmatrix}.$$

In older books, double bars were sometimes employed:

$$\begin{Vmatrix} 2 & 1 & 2 \\ 2 & 9 & 1 \\ 2 & 0 & 2 \end{Vmatrix}.$$

Capital letters are used to designate matrices:

$$A = \begin{pmatrix} 2 & 9 \\ 6 & 0 \end{pmatrix} \qquad B = \begin{pmatrix} 3 & -3 \\ 4 & -4 \end{pmatrix}.$$

This useful shorthand device calls attention to the fact that the array of numbers is to be considered as an object in its own right, and the notation is important in the development of the algebra of matrices.

Occasionally, it may be necessary to separate the elements of the matrix for clarity, and commas are employed:

$$\begin{pmatrix} 21, & 16, & -57 \\ -70, & 33, & -21 \end{pmatrix}.$$

It may happen that we would like to talk about a matrix and its elements without having any specific numbers in mind. Two notational devices may be used. The first device is to fill in the element positions with arbitrary letters. For example,

$$\begin{pmatrix} a & b & c & d \\ e & f & g & h \end{pmatrix}.$$

The second device is to use a single letter with a set of double subscripts:

$$\begin{pmatrix} a_{11} & a_{12} & a_{13} & a_{14} \\ a_{21} & a_{22} & a_{23} & a_{24} \\ a_{31} & a_{32} & a_{33} & a_{34} \end{pmatrix}.$$

The subscripts of the letter a are not to be interpreted as eleven, twelve, thirteen, fourteen, twenty-one, et cetera; they are to be thought of as consisting of two integers, the first of which indicates the number of the row in which the element is found, and the second indicates the number of the column. With this technique, the general matrix consisting of m rows and n columns may be written as

$$\begin{pmatrix} a_{11} & a_{12} & a_{13} & \cdots & a_{1n} \\ a_{21} & a_{22} & a_{23} & \cdots & a_{2n} \\ \cdot & \cdot & \cdot & & \cdot \\ \cdot & \cdot & \cdot & & \cdot \\ a_{m1} & a_{m2} & a_{m3} & \cdots & a_{mn} \end{pmatrix}.$$

It would be preferable to separate the integers in the subscript with a comma: $a_{m,n}$; for mn without a comma suggests either a product: m times n, or a two digit number. But this refinement causes typographical difficulties, and is done only when needed for absolute clarity.

The general matrix of m rows and n columns is further abbreviated as

$$A = (a_{ij})_{m \times n}.$$

The tag $m \times n$ outside the parenthesis gives the dimensions of the rectangle and is added for clarity. When matters are clear as they stand, the tag may be omitted and one writes

$$A = (a_{ij}).$$

The quantity a_{ij} is frequently known as *the element in the* i, j *position.*

It is important to become familiar with the double subscript notation. By way of practice, one should verify that the ith row of an $m \times n$ matrix has elements (or consists of the row vector)

$$(a_{i1} \ \ a_{i2} \ \ a_{i3} \cdots a_{in}).$$

The jth column of an $m \times n$ matrix consists of the column vector

$$\begin{pmatrix} a_{1j} \\ a_{2j} \\ \cdot \\ a_{mj} \end{pmatrix}.$$

The elements on the principal diagonal of an $n \times n$ matrix are a_{11}, a_{22}, $\cdots$, a_{nn}. The general diagonal element located in the ith row and ith column can be written as a_{ii}. The elements

$$\begin{matrix} a_{ij} & a_{i,j+1} \\ a_{i+1,j} & a_{i+1,j+1} \end{matrix}$$

are four adjacent elements (in a general position) and form a 2×2 square matrix extracted from the original matrix.

A matrix is completely specified once its elements have been written down. But often a formula takes the place of the complete exhibition of elements. Thus, if one writes that the elements a_{ij} of a 3×4 matrix A are given by

$$a_{ij} = 1, \quad \text{for} \quad 1 \leqq i \leqq 3, 1 \leqq j \leqq 4$$

we can reconstruct the matrix as

$$A = \begin{pmatrix} 1 & 1 & 1 & 1 \\ 1 & 1 & 1 & 1 \\ 1 & 1 & 1 & 1 \end{pmatrix}.$$

Here is a second example. A is a 4×4 matrix whose general element a_{ij} is given by

$$a_{ij} = 0 \qquad \text{if} \qquad i \neq j$$

and

$$a_{ij} = i \qquad \text{if} \qquad i = j.$$

By following this prescription, we find that

$$A = \begin{pmatrix} 1 & 0 & 0 & 0 \\ 0 & 2 & 0 & 0 \\ 0 & 0 & 3 & 0 \\ 0 & 0 & 0 & 4 \end{pmatrix}.$$

PROBLEMS

1. Use the double subscript notation and write down the elements of the second last column of a general $m \times n$ matrix.
2. Given a square $n \times n$ matrix. Use the double subscript notation and write down the elements of the diagonal that is not the principal diagonal.
3. Construct the 5×5 matrix whose elements a_{ij} are given by $a_{ij} = i + j$.
4. Construct the 5×5 matrix whose elements a_{ij} are given by $a_{ij} = ij$. Are the matrices in Problems 3 and 4 familiar? (Notice that the symbol ij is used in two senses here. On the left-hand side, it designates a double subscript, whereas on the right-hand side, it designates a product.)

5. Construct the 6×6 matrix whose elements a_{ij} are given by a_{ij} = minimum of i and j.

6. A checkerboard is placed with a black square in the upper left-hand corner. A 1 is placed in each black square and a 0 is placed in each red square. Find a formula for the elements of the resulting matrix.

7. Construct a 6×6 matrix whose elements a_{ij} are given by a_{ij} = least common multiple of i and j.

8. Construct a 6×6 matrix whose elements b_{ij} are given by b_{ij} = greatest common divisor of i and j.

9. Refer to problems 7 and 8 and show that $a_{ij}b_{ij} = ij$. Can you prove a general theorem here?

10. The famous Pascal triangle

$$\begin{matrix} 1 \\ 1 & 1 \\ 1 & 2 & 1 \\ 1 & 3 & 3 & 1 \\ \cdot \\ \cdot \\ \cdot \\ \cdot \end{matrix}$$

that occurs in the Binomial Theorem as the coefficients of $(a + b)^n$, can be put in the form of a matrix:

$$\begin{pmatrix} 1 & 1 & 1 & 1 & 1 & \cdots \\ 1 & 2 & 3 & 4 & 5 & \cdots \\ 1 & 3 & 6 & 10 & 15 & \cdots \\ 1 & 4 & 10 & 20 & 35 & \cdots \\ \cdot & \cdot & \cdot & \cdot & \cdot \\ \cdot & \cdot & \cdot & \cdot & \cdot \end{pmatrix}.$$

The matrix should be considered to be of unlimited extent in each direction. Use the fact that the elements satisfy the equations $a_{ij} = a_{i,j-1} + a_{i-1,j}$ to fill in this matrix to 7×7.

11. In Problem 10, make use of known expressions for the binomial coefficients to produce a formula for a_{ij}.

12. Construct the 6×6 matrix whose elements a_{ij} are given by $a_{ij} = (i - j)^2$.

13. Use "inspection" to derive a formula for the elements of the matrix

$$\begin{pmatrix} 1 & 1 & 1 & 1 & 1 & 1 & \cdot & \cdot \\ 1 & 2 & 3 & 4 & 5 & 6 \\ 1 & 4 & 9 & 16 & 25 & 36 \\ 1 & 8 & 27 & 64 & 125 & 216 \\ \cdot \\ \cdot \\ \cdot \end{pmatrix}.$$

14. Construct the 4×4 matrix whose elements a_{ij} are given by $a_{ij} = i^2j + j^2i$. Are the elements symmetric about the principal diagonal? Could you have predicted this without any numerical computation?

1.5 Tabulations of Information as Matrices

In talking about matrices, we shall for the most part, think of their elements as pure numbers or mathematical expressions and not concern ourselves with where they came from. But in practical applications, the elements of matrices come from the external world and have physical or economic or social meaning. Newspapers and statistical abstracts are full of such tabulations. The purpose of this section is to call attention to a number of ways in which matrices may be used as carriers of information.

Example 1:

Citrus Production – State of Limonia
Units: 1000 Crates

	ORANGES	LEMONS	LIMES	GRAPEFRUIT	CITRONS
1959	2,746	2,006	207	953	22
1960	2,804	2,301	199	1,007	30
1961	3,173	2,098	450	1,202	33
1962	3,240	2,498	356	1,288	31

Information on citrus production in Limonia over a period of four years has been expressed as a 4×5 matrix. Occasionally, such tabulations carry column totals or row totals. The total of the first column gives the total number of crates of oranges produced over the four year period. The total of the first row would give the total number of crates of all kinds produced in 1959. This figure might not be a very significant one in view of possible differences in size, weight, value, et cetera, between the various types of fruit crated. In order to lend significance to such a total, it might be appropriate to multiply each row entry by the corresponding value per crate or weight per crate. This process, which is known as *matrix multiplication*, will be presented abstractly and developed in a later chapter.

Example 2: The State of Limonia has only four post offices: Altamonte, Bonaventura, Cielo Azul, and Delmar. Post office records show the following deliveries of mail over the year 1962. The units are hundreds of bags.

	ALTAMONTE	BONAVENTURA	CIELO AZUL	DELMAR
ALTAMONTE	62	81	4	6
BONAVENTURA	73	75	10	9
CIELO AZUL	5	8	1	2
DELMAR	7	10	2	2

We have expressed this post office information as a 4×4 matrix, but it requires further elucidation. An entry a_{ij} means that $100\,a_{ij}$ bags of mail were delivered from the ith post office to the jth post office. Thus, 1000 bags of mail went from Bonaventura to Cielo Azul. The element a_{ii} on the main diagonal gives the number (in hundreds of bags) of letters written by the residents of the ith district and addressed to their co-residents in the ith district. Row sums and column sums have simple interpretations.

Example 3: The 1963 figures show

	ALTAMONTE	BONAVENTURA	CIELO AZUL	DELMAR
ALTAMONTE	65	80	5	7
BONAVENTURA	75	74	11	9
CIELO AZUL	8	9	1	1
DELMAR	4	9	3	1

If we wanted to compile the mail exchange matrix that covered the two year period 1962–1963, all we would have to do would be to add together the corresponding entries of the two matrices. This process is known as *matrix addition*, and will be developed later.

Example 4: A road map of Pennsylvania has a mileage chart from which the following matrix was extracted.

	ALLEN-TOWN	AL-TOONA	BALTI-MORE	BETH-LEHEM	BING-HAMTON
ALLENTOWN	0	199	136	5	134
ALTOONA	199	0	159	205	216
BALTIMORE	136	159	0	141	254
BETHLEHEM	5	205	141	0	129
BINGHAMTON	134	216	254	129	0

If we designate the elements by a_{ij}, notice that $a_{ij} = a_{ji}$. Why? Hence it would suffice (as in some road maps) to tabulate either the portion of the map above the principal diagonal or the portion below the principal diagonal.

Matrices can also be used to tabulate information that occurs within mathematics itself. Here are two examples of this.

Example 5: A *permutation* of a set of objects in a definite order is a rearrangement of the objects into another definite order. If Algernon, Barbara, Charles, and Dwight—standing from left to right in this order—change their order so that it becomes Barbara, Charles, Algernon, Dwight, then this change is called a permutation. It can be symbolized in the following way:

$$\begin{aligned} A &\to B \\ B &\to C \\ C &\to A \\ D &\to D. \end{aligned}$$

The symbol "$A \to B$" should be read "A is replaced by B." In a permutation, it is not necessary for an object to be replaced by a different object. This is exemplified by $D \to D$.

Numerous permutations are possible. A can be replaced by one of the objects A, B, C, or D. After having made this replacement, B can be replaced by one of the three remaining objects. C can then be replaced by one of the two remaining objects. The last object that remains replaces D. Hence, there are $4 \times 3 \times 2 \times 1 = 24$ different permutations of four objects. It is a general rule that there are

$$n(n-1)(n-2)\ldots 3\cdot 2\cdot 1$$

different permutations of n objects. This product is abbreviated by $n!$, and is read "n factorial."

Here are the six (that is, $3 \times 2 \times 1$) permutations of three objects A, B, and C.

1	2	3	4	5	6
$A \to A$	$A \to A$	$A \to B$	$A \to B$	$A \to C$	$A \to C$
$B \to B$	$B \to C$	$B \to A$	$B \to C$	$B \to A$	$B \to B$
$C \to C$	$C \to B$	$C \to C$	$C \to A$	$C \to B$	$C \to A$

A permutation of n objects can be represented by a $n \times n$ matrix in the following way: if the ith object replaces the jth object, the element a_{ij} will be set equal to 1. If the ith object does not replace the jth object, the element a_{ij} will be set equal to 0. In the permutation $A \to B$, $B \to C$, $C \to A$, $D \to D$, and if A, B, C, D are the first, second, third, fourth objects respectively, the second object replaces the first, the third replaces the second, the first replaces the third, and the fourth replaces the fourth. Hence $a_{21} = 1$, $a_{32} = 1$, $a_{13} = 1$, $a_{44} = 1$ and all the other elements are zero. This permutation is therefore represented by the matrix

$$\begin{pmatrix} 0 & 0 & 1 & 0 \\ 1 & 0 & 0 & 0 \\ 0 & 1 & 0 & 0 \\ 0 & 0 & 0 & 1 \end{pmatrix}.$$

There is one permutation that accomplishes exactly nothing, or rather what it accomplishes is that each object is replaced by the same object. This means that

$$\begin{aligned} A &\to A \\ B &\to B \\ C &\to C \\ D &\to D. \end{aligned}$$

The associated matrix is

$$\begin{pmatrix} 1 & 0 & 0 & 0 \\ 0 & 1 & 0 & 0 \\ 0 & 0 & 1 & 0 \\ 0 & 0 & 0 & 1 \end{pmatrix}.$$

Notice that in each of these matrices there is precisely one 1 in each column. For each object is replaced by exactly one object. And there is precisely one 1 in each row, for each object is itself a replacement precisely once.

Example 6: An arrangement of points connected by lines, such as those given in Figure 1.3, is called a *graph*. This usage of the word "graph" is to be distinguished from the more common usage that refers to a curve depicting the variation of a quantity.

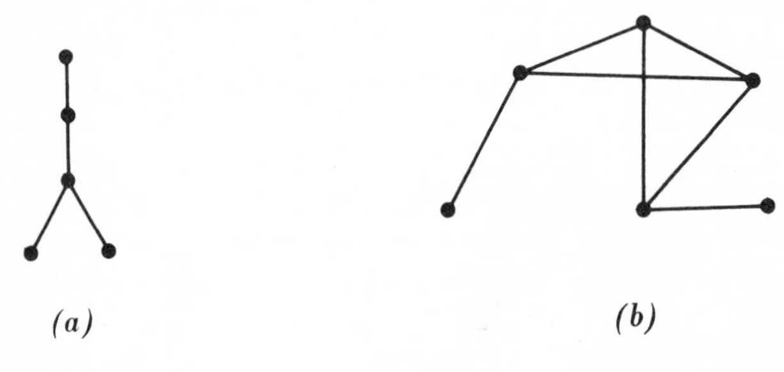

FIGURE 1.3

In certain problems, the important information in such a figure may not be the location of the points and lines, or their lengths, but simply whether or not two given points are connected by a line segment. This information may be conveyed by a matrix. Number the points, and construct a square matrix whose elements a_{ij} are given by the following rule:

$a_{ij} = 1$ if the ith point is connected to the jth point by a line segment;

$a_{ij} = 0$ if it is not.

Thus, numbering the points of Figure 1.3(b) as in Figure 1.4, we may represent it

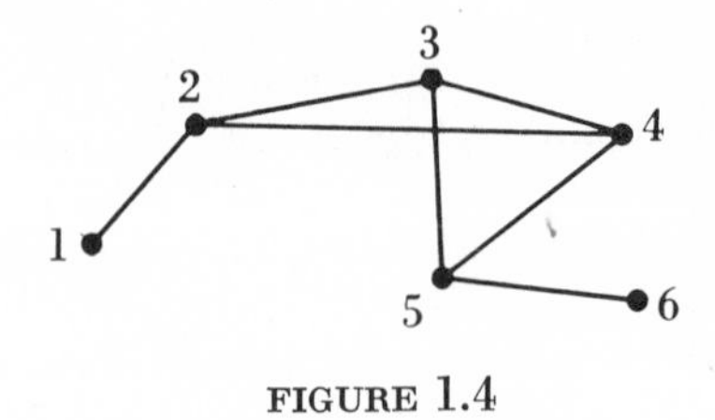

FIGURE 1.4

by the matrix

$$
\begin{array}{c}
\\ 1 \\ 2 \\ 3 \\ 4 \\ 5 \\ 6
\end{array}
\begin{array}{c}
\begin{array}{cccccc} 1 & 2 & 3 & 4 & 5 & 6 \end{array} \\
\begin{pmatrix}
0 & 1 & 0 & 0 & 0 & 0 \\
1 & 0 & 1 & 1 & 0 & 0 \\
0 & 1 & 0 & 1 & 1 & 0 \\
0 & 1 & 1 & 0 & 1 & 0 \\
0 & 0 & 1 & 1 & 0 & 1 \\
0 & 0 & 0 & 0 & 1 & 0
\end{pmatrix}
\end{array}.
$$

We have assumed that no point is joined to itself. Notice that $a_{ij} = a_{ji}$. Why? Such a matrix is called an *incidence matrix* of the graph. The row sums are simply the total number of lines that issue from the respective point. What are the column sums?

PROBLEMS

1. The final record of the American League baseball clubs at the end of the 1961 season is given below as a 10×10 matrix in which the element a_{ij} is the number of games that the ith team won from the jth team.

	N.Y.	DET.	BALT.	CHI.	CLEV.	BOS.	MINN.	L.A.	K.C.	WASH.
NEW YORK	0	10	9	12	14	13	14	12	14	11
DETROIT	8	0	9	12	12	10	11	14	12	13
BALTIMORE	9	9	0	11	9	11	11	8	13	14
CHICAGO	6	6	7	0	12	9	9	10	14	13
CLEVELAND	4	6	9	6	0	13	10	10	8	12
BOSTON	5	8	7	9	5	0	11	11	10	10
MINNESOTA	4	7	7	9	8	7	0	9	11	8
LOS ANGELES	6	4	10	8	8	7	8	0	9	10
KANSAS CITY	4	6	5	4	9	8	7	9	0	9
WASHINGTON	7	5	4	5	6	8	9	8	9	0

Interpret the row sums. Interpret the column sums. Notice that if $i \neq j$, then $a_{ij} + a_{ji}$ always equals eighteen. Explain. Compute the season average of Washington and of New York.

2. Construct a 4×4 matrix that tabulates the mutual distances of the vertices of a square whose side is one unit long.

3. Construct an 8×8 matrix that tabulates the mutual distances of the vertices of a cube whose side is one unit long.

4. A certain geometrical figure has four vertices P, Q, R, and S. The matrix of mutual distances is

$$\begin{array}{c} \\ P \\ Q \\ R \\ S \end{array} \begin{array}{c} \begin{array}{cccc} P & Q & R & S \end{array} \\ \begin{pmatrix} 0 & 1 & 1 & 1 \\ 1 & 0 & 1 & 1 \\ 1 & 1 & 0 & 1 \\ 1 & 1 & 1 & 0 \end{pmatrix} \end{array}.$$

Identify the figure.

5. Designate the elements of the matrix in Example 4 by a_{ij}. Why might one expect that $a_{ij} + a_{jk} \geq a_{ik}$? Test out a few of these inequalities.

6. Work out all possible permutations of two objects and construct their associated matrices. Do the same for permutations of three and of four objects.

7. A 6×6 conversion table for lengths has rows and columns labelled inches, feet, yards, miles, centimeters, and kilometers in the same order. If the elements of the matrix are designated by a_{ij}, prove that $a_{ij}a_{ji} = 1$.

8. Construct incidence matrices for the graphs in Figure 1.5.

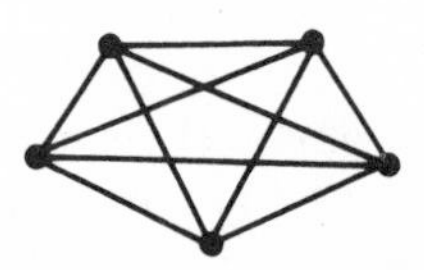

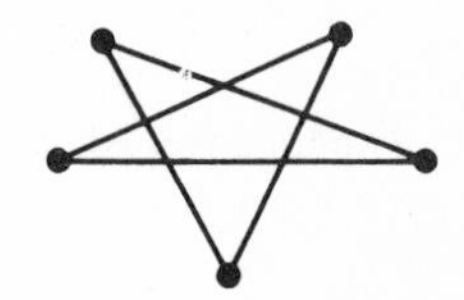

FIGURE 1.5

9. Construct a graph whose incidence matrix is

$$\begin{pmatrix} 0 & 0 & 1 & 0 & 0 \\ 0 & 0 & 1 & 0 & 0 \\ 1 & 1 & 0 & 1 & 1 \\ 0 & 0 & 1 & 0 & 0 \\ 0 & 0 & 1 & 0 & 0 \end{pmatrix}.$$

10. *Times Square Matrices.* Animated signs sometimes consist of a rectangular array of light bulbs. The bulbs that are on form crude pictures or letters. Represent a bulb that is on by a 1 and a bulb that is off by a 0, and form matrices to represent various capital letters.

11. A message on an animated sign moves one column to the right per second. At the beginning of the first second, suppose that the message has the matrix (a_{ij}). At the beginning of the second second the message has the matrix (b_{ij}). Then show that $b_{ij} = a_{i,j-1}$. What is the formula to describe the beginning of the nth second? What if the message moves one column to the right and one row down per second?

12. The famous Latin word square

R	O	T	A	S
O	P	E	R	A
T	E	N	E	T
A	R	E	P	O
S	A	T	O	R

is "magic" in two ways. If a_{ij} denotes the symbol in the i,jth position, show that $a_{ij} = a_{ji}$ and that $a_{ij} = a_{6-i,6-j}$.

13. The magic square in Problem 12 has eight different symbols in it. Show that a 5×5 square that has all the symmetries $a_{ij} = a_{ji}$ and $a_{ij} = a_{6-i,6-j}$ can have at most nine different symbols. What about a 6×6 square?

14. Here is a conversion table for the currency of four countries

	MOLNAR	DOLNAR	PESCO	RHEE
MOLNAR	1	2	7/8	5
DOLNAR	1/2	1	7/16	5/2
PESCO	8/7	16/7	1	40/7
RHEE	1/5	2/5	7/40	1

Show that if the elements are called a_{ij}, $a_{ij}a_{jk} = a_{ik}$. Hence, show that $a_{ij}a_{jk}a_{kp}a_{pq} = a_{iq}$, et cetera.

15. In Problem 14, show that the whole table can be reconstructed from the information contained in either one row or one column. What other information would be sufficient to reconstruct the whole table?

16. An automobile manufacturer advises rotating tires after 6000 miles as indicated in Figure 1.6.

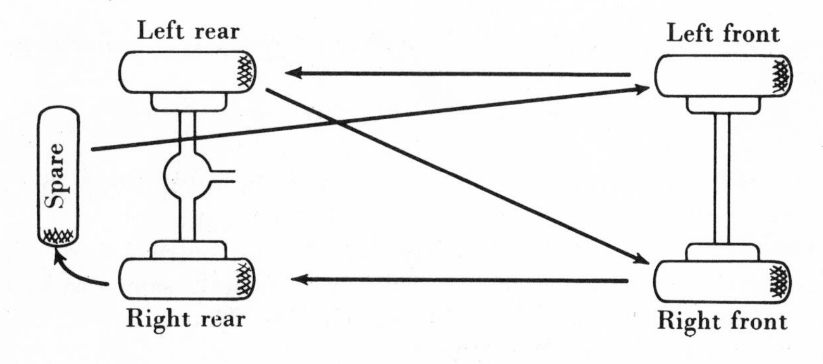

FIGURE 1.6

Express this information in matrix form. If this rotation is carried out twice in succession, where do the tires go?

1.6 When Two Matrices are Equal

Since matrices are objects that are interesting in their own right—quite apart from their elements—we must lay down a rule to tell us when two matrices are to be considered equal to one another.

Two matrices will be considered equal if they have the same order and if corresponding elements are equal. Thus, we shall write

$$\begin{pmatrix} 2 & 1 & 3 \\ 6 & 9 & 8 \end{pmatrix} = \begin{pmatrix} 1+1 & 1 & 2+1 \\ 9-3 & 3^2 & 2^3 \end{pmatrix}.$$

This definition can be expressed in symbols.

"I hate definitions," said one of d'Israeli's fictional characters, and this author sympathizes with his point of view. But formal mathematics proceeds with calculated steps from definition to proof, and so it will be convenient for us to introduce formal definitions from time to time.

Definition: *If* A *is an* m $\times$ n *matrix with elements* $\mathrm{a_{ij}}$ *and* B *is a* p $\times$ q *matrix with elements* $\mathrm{b_{ij}}$, *then we shall write*

$$A = B$$

if and only if m = p, n = q *and*

$$a_{ij} = b_{ij} \quad \textit{for} \quad 1 \leq \mathrm{i} \leq m \quad \textit{and} \quad 1 \leq \mathrm{j} \leq \mathrm{n}.$$

Notice that if we write

$$\begin{pmatrix} a & b \\ c & d \end{pmatrix} = \begin{pmatrix} 1 & 6 \\ 9 & 8 \end{pmatrix},$$

then this single matrix equation implies the four separate ordinary equations

$$a = 1, b = 6, c = 9, d = 8.$$

Part of the strength of matrix rotation derives from just this fact, that one matrix equation can stand for many ordinary equations.

The equality sign "=" when written between two matrices is essentially a new symbol, and one should note that it behaves in the same way as does the ordinary equality relating ordinary numbers. That is to say, matrix equality has these three properties:

1. It is *reflexive*. This means that for any matrix A, $A = A$.
2. It is *symmetric*. This means that if $A = B$, then $B = A$.
3. It is *transitive*. This means that if A, B and C are matrices, then $A = B$, and $B = C$ together imply that $A = C$.

These facts are readily established from the definition of the equality of matrices and from the corresponding truths regarding ordinary equality. The three properties above allow us to manipulate the equality sign between matrices in the manner to which we have been long accustomed.

PROBLEMS

1. Which of the following statements are true? $(0, 0) = (0, 0, 0)$; $(0 - 0, 0) = (0 - 0, 0 - 0)$; $\begin{pmatrix} 1-1, & 2-2 \\ x-x, & 1-1 \end{pmatrix} = (0)$.

2. If $x^2 + x + 1 = 0$, show that

$$\begin{pmatrix} x^2 + x & 1 \\ x & 0 \end{pmatrix} = \begin{pmatrix} -1 & -x^2 - x \\ x & 0 \end{pmatrix}.$$

3. If

$$\begin{pmatrix} x & 2x + y \\ x + z & 2y + w \end{pmatrix} = \begin{pmatrix} 6 & 2 \\ 4 & 3 \end{pmatrix},$$

find the values of x, y, z, w.

4. If

$$\begin{pmatrix} x + y + z + w & x + y + 2z + w \\ x + 2y + z + w & 2x + y + z + w \end{pmatrix} = \begin{pmatrix} 7 & 6 \\ 6 & 6 \end{pmatrix},$$

find the values of x, y, z, w.

5. Show that it is impossible to find x and y such that

$$\begin{pmatrix} x + y & x + 2y \\ x - y & x - 2y \end{pmatrix} = \begin{pmatrix} 5 & 6 \\ 3 & 0 \end{pmatrix}.$$

1.7 Switching Rows and Columns: The Transpose of a Matrix

If we switch around the elements of a matrix so that its rows become columns and vice versa, we obtain a second matrix that is called the *transpose* of the original matrix. For example, the 2×3 matrix

$$\begin{pmatrix} 0 & 2 & 4 \\ 9 & -1 & 6 \end{pmatrix}$$

becomes the 3×2 matrix

$$\begin{pmatrix} 0 & 9 \\ 2 & -1 \\ 4 & 6 \end{pmatrix}$$

when transposed. Notice what happens to the elements. The element a_{11} becomes the element b_{11} in the transpose. The element a_{12} becomes the element b_{21}, et cetera. The two integers in the subscript are merely switched around. There is a special notation used to indicate the process of transposition; a prime, "$'$", placed after the matrix symbol indicates its transpose. In symbols, then, if A is an $m \times n$ matrix, A' is an $n \times m$ matrix. If $A = (a_{ij})$ and $A' = (b_{ij})$, then,

$$b_{ij} = a_{ji}.$$

The symbol A'' means the transpose of the transpose of A. One transposition turns rows into columns; a second transposition turns them back again into rows. Hence,

$$A'' = A.$$

PROBLEMS

1. If

$$A = \begin{pmatrix} 2 & 1 \\ 3 & 4 \\ 5 & 6 \end{pmatrix};$$

construct A'. Construct A' if $A = (2, 1, 6, 9, 4)$.

2. If

$$A = \begin{pmatrix} 1 & 2 & x \\ y & 3 & 6 \\ 4 & z & 0 \end{pmatrix},$$

construct A'.

3. After transposition, what element does a_{61} become? a_{55}?
4. Prove that $A = B$ if and only if $A' = B'$.
5. Prove that if $A = B'$, then $A' = B$.
6. Two $n \times n$ matrices $A = (a_{ij})$ and $B = (b_{ij})$ are related by $b_{ij} = a_{i,n+1-j}$. Describe geometrically how B may be obtained from A.
7. Do the same with $b_{ij} = a_{n+1-j,n+1-i}$.
8. Show that $A''' = A'$. Can you formulate a general principle?

1.8 Who's Who in the World of Matrices

It is to be expected that some individual matrices and some families of matrices are more important than others. Let us meet a few of them. They receive special symbols.

THE ZERO MATRIX: This is a matrix whose elements are all zero. It is designated by 0.

$$0 = \begin{pmatrix} 0 & 0 & \cdots & 0 \\ 0 & 0 & \cdots & 0 \\ \cdot & \cdot & \cdots & \cdot \\ 0 & 0 & \cdots & 0 \end{pmatrix}.$$

Or again, $0 = (a_{ij})$ where $a_{ij} = 0$. As there are many such matrices, we should, strictly speaking, use a notation such as $0_{m\times n}$ that puts the order of the matrix into evidence. But this clumsy notation is employed only when utter clarity is necessary. A zero matrix should be distinguished from the number 0, printed in the same way. The context is usually sufficient to indicate whether the symbol is to mean a matrix or an ordinary number.

THE UNIT MATRIX: This is a square matrix with 1's on the principal diagonal and 0's elsewhere. It is designated by I. We have

$$I = \begin{pmatrix} 1 & 0 & 0 & \cdots & 0 \\ 0 & 1 & 0 & \cdots & 0 \\ 0 & 0 & 1 & \cdots & 0 \\ . & . & . & \cdots & . \\ 0 & 0 & 0 & & 1 \end{pmatrix},$$

or again, $I = (a_{ij})$ where

$$\begin{cases} a_{ij} = 0 & \text{if} \quad i \neq j \\ a_{ij} = 1 & \text{if} \quad i = j. \end{cases}$$

There is a unit matrix for each order, and when clarity is needed, the order is written as a subscript: I_n.

THE J MATRIX: This is a matrix with 1's everywhere:

$$J = \begin{pmatrix} 1 & 1 & 1 & \cdots & 1 \\ 1 & 1 & 1 & \cdots & 1 \\ . & . & . & & . \\ . & . & . & & . \\ 1 & 1 & 1 & \cdots & 1 \end{pmatrix}.$$

The matrix symbols 0, I, and J will *always* be used in this book to designate the matrices just defined.

We have already mentioned that the square matrices are very important in the theory. There are several kinds of square matrices that must be introduced.

THE DIAGONAL MATRICES: These are square matrices in which the elements that are not on the principal diagonal are all zero.

Examples:

$$\begin{pmatrix} 1 & 0 \\ 0 & -7 \end{pmatrix} \quad \text{or} \quad \begin{pmatrix} 4 & 0 & 0 \\ 0 & -5 & 0 \\ 0 & 0 & 0 \end{pmatrix}.$$

THE TRIANGULAR MATRICES: An *upper triangular* matrix is a square matrix all of whose nonzero elements are located on or above the principal diagonal. A *lower triangular matrix* is a square matrix all of whose nonzero elements are located on or below the principal diagonal. In other words, an upper triangular matrix has all zeros below its main diagonal, whereas a lower triangular matrix has all zeros above its main diagonal. For example,

$$\begin{pmatrix} 1 & 5 & 6 & 7 \\ 0 & 1 & 8 & 9 \\ 0 & 0 & 1 & 4 \\ 0 & 0 & 0 & -5 \end{pmatrix}$$

is upper triangular.

The matrix

$$\begin{pmatrix} 1 & 0 & 0 \\ 6 & -5 & 0 \\ 0 & 4 & 1 \end{pmatrix}$$

is lower triangular.

THE SYMMETRIC MATRICES: These are square matrices that are unchanged by transposition. Geometrically speaking, they are "symmetric" about the principal diagonal.

Examples:

$$\begin{pmatrix} 1 & 2 \\ 2 & 0 \end{pmatrix}, \quad \begin{pmatrix} 1 & 2 & 3 \\ 2 & 5 & 4 \\ 3 & 4 & 7 \end{pmatrix}.$$

If A is a symmetric matrix, then $a_{ij} = a_{ji}$. Hence, the condition for symmetry is that

$$A = A'.$$

THE PERMUTATION MATRICES: These are the square matrices associated with permutations as explained in Example 5 of Section 1.5. An alternate definition is that a permutation matrix is a square matrix whose elements are either zero or one and which has precisely a single 1 in each row and in each column. There are $n!$ different permutation matrices of order n.

PROBLEMS

1. Show that $I' = I$, $J' = J$, $0' = 0$. 0 and J are square matrices.
2. Can the equation $\begin{pmatrix} x - y & y - z \\ z - w & w - x \end{pmatrix} = I$ be solved for x, y, z, and w?

3. If D is a diagonal matrix, prove that $D' = D$.
4. Prove that the Pascal matrix (Problem 10, Page 8) is symmetric.
5. If the multiplication table is a symmetric matrix, what is the point in printing the redundant portion?
6. If $a_{ij} = i^2 + j^2$, show that $A = (a_{ij})$ is symmetric. What about $a_{ij} = (i - j)^2$ or $a_{ij} = i^3 - j^3$?
7. If A is a symmetric matrix of order $n \times n$, prove it can have as many as $\frac{1}{2}n(n + 1)$ different elements in it.
8. Show that if P is a permutation matrix, then P' is also a permutation matrix. Contrast the corresponding permutations.
9. A certain permutation matrix is symmetric. What does this mean about the corresponding permutation?
10. How many distinct $m \times n$ matrices are there whose elements are either zero or one?
11. If some (or all or none) of the 1's in a permutation matrix are changed to -1's, the resulting matrix is called a *pseudo-permutation matrix.* Find a formula for the number of pseudo-permutation matrices of order n.
12. Describe the graphs whose incidence matrices are permutation matrices.

CHAPTER 2

The Arithmetic of Matrices, Part I

The characters in our play have now been introduced. The play itself begins when the characters interact. Ordinary numbers interact with one another in arithmetic, and arithmetic stresses the four fundamental processes of addition, subtraction, multiplication, and division. We are about to introduce corresponding processes for matrices; in this chapter we shall study matrix addition and subtraction and we shall learn how and under what circumstances matrix multiplication is possible. The operation of division is known in matrix language as *inversion* and is sufficiently complicated and important to warrant a chapter of its own. Matrix inversion will be treated in Chapter 3.

If the theory of matrices consisted solely of keeping track of what number is in what position of a rectangular arrangement, then it would really be only data processing, and its proponents would be merely pigeonhole fanciers. What gives life to this clay is the possibility of doing arithmetic; and from there the subject takes off in numerous directions with astonishing vitality.

2.1 Adding Matrices

Two matrices will be added to one another by adding their corresponding elements. For example,

$$\begin{pmatrix} 2 & 1 & -7 \\ 4 & 1 & 9 \end{pmatrix} + \begin{pmatrix} 2 & 1 & 6 \\ 0 & -1 & 4 \end{pmatrix} = \begin{pmatrix} 4 & 2 & -1 \\ 4 & 0 & 13 \end{pmatrix},$$

or

$$(6 \quad 3 \quad x) + (1 \quad 2 \quad 3x) = (7 \quad 5 \quad 4x).$$

In order to carry out this process, the matrices to be added must have corresponding elements, and this implies that the matrices must have the same order. Two matrices that have the same order are *conformable* with respect to addition; two matrices with different orders are not conformable with respect to addition, and the process of addition will be considered to be meaningless for them.

Definition: *Two* $m \times n$ *matrices* $A = (a_{ij})$ *and* $B = (b_{ij})$ *are added by adding corresponding elements. The expression* $A + B$ *will designate the* $m \times n$ *matrix whose elements are* $a_{ij} + b_{ij}$. *Once again,*

$$(a_{ij}) + (b_{ij}) = (a_{ij} + b_{ij}).$$

What is behind this definition? We can point to several things. In Example 2 of Chapter 1, Section 5, there are two tables. We have already observed that if these two tables are added element by element, the resulting table is a meaningful one. This is not an isolated instance. Such a process of addition is frequently meaningful.

Element by element addition is also common in algebra. If one has

$$z = 2x + 3y$$

and

$$w = 4x - 2y,$$

then

$$z + w = (2 + 4)x + (3 - 2)y.$$

The expressions are added by adding the corresponding coefficients.

Two matrices, when added, will be joined by a plus sign. Even though matrix addition is conceptually different from ordinary addition, the plus sign joining matrices behaves quite conventionally. This is brought out by the three theorems that follow.

Theorem: *Matrix addition is commutative. That is, for any two matrices* A *and* B *conformable for addition,*

$$A + B = B + A.$$

PROOF: If $A = (a_{ij})$ and $B = (b_{ij})$, then by the definition of matrix addition, $A + B = (a_{ij} + b_{ij})$. But also, $B + A = (b_{ij} + a_{ij})$. Since ordinary addition is commutative, $b_{ij} + a_{ij} = a_{ij} + b_{ij}$. Hence $A + B = B + A$.

The proof boils down to this: matrix addition is commutative because ordinary addition is.

Theorem: *Matrix addition is associative. That is, for any three matrices* A, B, *and* C *that are conformable for addition,*

$$(A + B) + C = A + (B + C).$$

The parentheses in this equation refer to grouping in the addition process.

PROOF: If $A = (a_{ij})$, $B = (b_{ij})$, and $C = (c_{ij})$,* then the matrix $A + B$ has a general element $a_{ij} + b_{ij}$. This means that the matrix $(A + B) + C$ has a general element $(a_{ij} + b_{ij}) + c_{ij}$. In a similar fashion, the matrix $A + (B + C)$ has a general element $a_{ij} + (b_{ij} + c_{ij})$. By the associativity of ordinary addition, $(a_{ij} + b_{ij}) + c_{ij} = a_{ij} + (b_{ij} + c_{ij})$. Hence,

$$(A + B) + C = A + (B + C).$$

A consequence of these two theorems is that it is irrelevant how matrix sums are arranged. We have, $A + (B + C) = (A + B) + C$, and we can write simply $A + B + C$ for this common sum. Since $B + C = C + B$, we also have $A + (B + C) = A + (C + B) = (A + C) + B = A + C + B$. All other permutations are also possible:

$$\begin{aligned} & B + (A + C) = (B + A) + C \\ &= B + (C + A) = (B + C) + A \\ &= C + (A + B) = (C + A) + B \\ &= C + (B + A) = (C + B) + A \\ &= A + B + C. \end{aligned}$$

The reader should take notice that in the previous paragraphs, the parentheses "( )" were employed in several different senses: (a) as part of the name of a matrix, as in (a_{ij}), and (b) as a grouping symbol to indicate the order of the operations, for example, $(A + B) + C$.

The reader may well ask, why, if mathematics is the precise language it claims to be, do we put up with such ambiguities? One answer lies in the fact that mathematical manuscripts are prepared on typewriters that only have a small number of symbols. Hence symbols have to do double duty and even multiple duty. The switch from the double bars of an earlier generation to parentheses to indicate matrices undoubtedly reflects the wide use of the typewriter.

Theorem: *If* A *is an* $m \times n$ *matrix, and if* 0 *is the* $m \times n$ *zero matrix, then,*

$$A + 0 = 0 + A = A.$$

PROOF: To be supplied by the reader.

In the formulation of these theorems, we mention explicitly the fact that the relevant matrices are assumed to be conformable with respect to addition. To do this every time we write down a plus sign is obviously a great nuisance; in all further work, the tacit assumption is made that whenever an operation is written down, that operation can be carried out.

---

* Here the parentheses indicate matrices.

On the Role of Proof in Mathematics. As one proceeds through a mathematics curriculum from elementary courses to more advanced courses, the amount of time spent in the classroom and the amount of space devoted in textbooks to the proofs of theorems increases. Why should this be? Is the instructor or the author afraid that his mathematical statements have no validity until he has proved—or really, reproved—them? After all, if a statement has been proved once, then presumably it has been proved for all time. Pythagoras' theorem is no more true today than it was in Pythagoras' own day for all the countless numbers of school boys that have proved and reproved it. If we live in a house, we do not, as a rule, examine the boards and nails constantly. Why, then, should we do so in mathematics?

A number of reasons can be advanced for this practice.

1. A rigorous proof establishes the mathematical validity and respectability of a statement. It is like the pedigree of a thoroughbred horse or the authenticated papers of past ownership of a famous painting. When the horse or painting changes hands, the papers are brought out and inspected.
2. A proof may clarify a theorem and make it more comprehensible. It may do this by exhibiting the inner workings of the theorem. But not all proofs do it.
3. By going through the steps of a proof, we might see where certain hypotheses can be weakened or certain conclusions strengthened. In this way, we can arrive at generalizations of a theorem. Such generalizations will heighten our comprehension of the statement of the theorem.
4. A proof exhibits the tricks of the trade and enables the novice to develop new mathematics.
5. A proof is an argument that flows from hypotheses to the conclusion. Just as a theorem may exhibit certain aesthetic qualities—some theorems are pretty, others, less pretty—so also the manner of flow can exhibit aesthetic qualities. A certain proof may be pretty; other proofs (of the same theorem) may be less pretty.
6. Over the past several centuries a philosophy of mathematics has grown up which says that mathematics is the science of drawing necessary conclusions. This philosophy was promoted by the work of Bertrand Russell (1872–   ) who once wrote that "pure mathematics is the class of all propositions of the form p implies q." The letter p represents the hypotheses, and q the conclusion of a proposition and the total implication 'p implies q' is obtained by a chain of reasoning of a certain kind. This chain of reasoning is the "proof" of the proposition and hence is of crucial importance.

In recent years this philosophy has lost some strength. However, the study and the production of proofs remains central to the subject, as it has been, really, since the classic period of Greek mathematics. In recent years also, considerable effort has been spent in trying to program electronic computing machines to prove propositions. The results so far have been rather primitive; but it is interesting to contemplate what philosophy of mathematics we shall adopt if machines spew forth new theorems and their proofs the way a donut machine produces donuts.

PROBLEMS

1. If $A = \begin{pmatrix} 2 & 0 \\ 7 & -1 \end{pmatrix}$, $B = \begin{pmatrix} 1 & 1 \\ 1 & 0 \end{pmatrix}$, and $C = \begin{pmatrix} 0 & 1 \\ 1 & 1 \end{pmatrix}$, find $A + I$, $B + J$, $A + B + C$, $A + A + 0 + A$, $I + I + C$.

2. Solve the matrix equation

$$\begin{pmatrix} x^2 & x \\ y & y \end{pmatrix} + \begin{pmatrix} 0 & -x \\ -y & 0 \end{pmatrix} = I$$

for x and y.

3. If w_1, w_2, and w_3 are the three cube roots of 1, show that $(w_1, w_2, w_3) + (w_2, w_3, w_1) + (w_3, w_1, w_2) = 0$.

4. Show that $(A + B)'$, that is, the transpose of the sum of A and B equals $A' + B'$. Then show that the transpose of the sum of any number of matrices is equal to the sum of the transposes of the matrices.

5. Show that $(A' + B)' = A + B'$. Under what conditions does the expression $A' + B$ make sense?

6. Two matrices are symmetric. Is their sum necessarily symmetric?

7. Is the sum of two permutation matrices ever a permutation matrix?

8. Use the theorems of this section to prove in a formal way that

$$(A + I) + 0 + B = B + A + I.$$

9. Suppose that a United Nations publication contains the following table.

Where the Consumers' Dollar Went in 1964

	ENGLAND	IRELAND	TURKEY	U.S.A.
FOOD				
HOUSING				
CLOTHING				
OTHER				

We have not listed the entries in this table, but they are given in percentages of total income. Would it be meaningful to perform matrix addition on two such tables representing two consecutive years?

10. Is the sum of two triangular matrices triangular?

11. Give a formal proof of the fact that $A + 0 = 0 + A = A$.

12. There is a saying "If equals are added to equals, the results are equal." Is this true for matrix addition? Prove your claim.

13. For any square matrix A, the matrix $A + A'$ is symmetric. There are several ways of proving this. The first is to examine the general term of $A + A'$: if $A = (a_{ij})$, then $A' = (a_{ji})$ and hence $A + A' = (a_{ij} + a_{ji})$. Since the term in the i,jth position is $a_{ij} + a_{ji}$, the term in the j,ith position must be $a_{ji} + a_{ij}$, and this comes to the same thing. Hence $A + A'$ is symmetric.

The second method does not consider the elements, but makes use of established properties of the operation of transposition: ($'$). $A + A'$ is symmetric if and only if $(A + A')' = A + A'$. Now, by Problem 5 $(A + A')' = A' + A = A + A'$.

Generally, proofs that do not make use of matrix elements are considered to be more elegant and to the point than those that do.

14. Let $P_1, P_2 \ldots, P_6$ designate the six permutation matrices of order 3×3. Compute $P_1 + P_2 + P_3 + P_4 + P_5 + P_6$.

15. The parenthesis is a multiduty symbol in the theory of matrices. Such symbols have been met with before. For example, the bar is a triple-duty symbol. In "$5 - 2$" the bar is used to denote the *binary* operation of subtraction. In "-5" the bar is part of the symbol for a negative number. In "$-a$," the bar denotes the unary operation of taking the negative, that is, the additive inverse of a number.

Explain these three usages in somewhat more detail.

2.2 Subtracting Matrices

Once addition is here, can subtraction be far behind? Two matrices of the same order are subtracted by subtracting their corresponding elements.

Example:

$$\begin{pmatrix} 2 & -1 \\ 1 & 1 \end{pmatrix} - \begin{pmatrix} -2 & -1 \\ 0 & x \end{pmatrix} = \begin{pmatrix} 4 & 0 \\ 1 & 1 - x \end{pmatrix}.$$

Matrices that are conformable for addition are conformable for subtraction and vice versa.

Definition: *If* $\mathrm{A} = (\mathrm{a_{ij}})$ *is an* $\mathrm{m} \times \mathrm{n}$ *matrix, then its negative, designated by* $-\mathrm{A}$, *is the* $\mathrm{m} \times \mathrm{n}$ *matrix whose elements are* $-\mathrm{a_{ij}}$. *By the difference* $\mathrm{A} - \mathrm{B}$, *we shall mean the matrix* $\mathrm{A} + (-\mathrm{B})$, *that is to say, if* $\mathrm{A} = (\mathrm{a_{ij}})$, *and* $\mathrm{B} = (\mathrm{b_{ij}})$, *then* $\mathrm{A} - \mathrm{B} = (\mathrm{a_{ij}} - \mathrm{b_{ij}})$.

The following theorem sums up the behavior of subtraction, and of the minus sign.

Theorem:

$$-0 = 0. \tag{1}$$

For any matrix A,

$$\mathrm{A} - \mathrm{A} = \mathrm{A} + (-\mathrm{A}) = 0; \tag{2}$$

(3) $$-(-\mathrm{A}) = \mathrm{A}.$$

For any two matrices A *and* B *(that are conformable for addition),*

(4) $$-(\mathrm{A} + \mathrm{B}) = (-\mathrm{A}) + (-\mathrm{B}) = -\mathrm{A} - \mathrm{B}.$$

PROOF: Make use of the corresponding properties of ordinary numbers.

Thus we see that matrix expressions behave quite conventionally when it comes to addition and subtraction. A further instance of this is the following fact: if

$$X + A = B,$$

then

$$X = B - A,$$

and conversely. Thus, *in a matrix equation, a matrix can be shifted from one side of the equation to the other side provided its sign is changed.*

We give a formal proof of this fact. If $X + A = B$, then by the definition of equality, $X + A$ and B are merely two different names for the same matrix. Hence, we may add the matrix $-A$ to $X + A$ and to B, and obtain the same result. That is,

$$(X + A) + (-A) = B + (-A).$$

By the associativity of addition

$$\begin{aligned}(X + A) + (-A) &= X + (A + (-A)) \\ &= X + 0 \\ &= X.\end{aligned}$$

But, by the definition of subtraction,

$$B + (-A) = B - A.$$

Hence,

$$X = B - A.$$

The converse is proved similarly.

PROBLEMS

1. Simplify

$$\begin{pmatrix} x - y & y - z & z - w \\ w - x & x - y & y - z \end{pmatrix} - \begin{pmatrix} x - w & y - x & z - y \\ y - x & z - y & w - z \end{pmatrix}.$$

2. Show that $-(A - B) = -A + B$, and that $(A - B) + (B - C) + (C - A) = 0$.
3. If $X + J = I$, find X explicitly. Work with matrices of order 4.
4. Is it true that $(A - B)' = A' - B'$ is an identity?

5. If A and B are symmetric, is $A - B$ symmetric?
6. Is there any distinction between $(-A)'$ and $-(A')$?
7. Under what circumstances does the expression $A' - B$ make sense? Simplify the expression $-(A' - B)'$.
8. Two $m \times n$ matrices are added or subtracted. How many ordinary additions or subtractions must be performed in the process?

Questions relating to the number of ordinary arithmetic operations involved in matrix arithmetic are important in planning high speed computer calculations.

9. A breakdown of the votes in the 1963 elections of a certain country has been tabulated as follows:

PARTY	DISTRICT I	DISTRICT II	DISTRICT III	DISTRICT IV
RIGHT	9,072	6,298	2,005	8,395
RIGHT CENTER	11,254	7,204	9,873	10,307
CENTER	30,173	8,911	6,004	16,663
LEFT CENTER	28,144	10,983	12,845	34,187
LEFT	20,001	4,082	6,092	18,291

Interpret row sums, column sums, and the difference of two such matrices for two successive elections.

10. Construct a six point graph whose incidence matrix is $J - I$.

2.3 Scalar Multiplication

In this section we begin the study of the multiplication of matrices. Whereas matrix addition and subtraction are rather similar to the ordinary processes, multiplication exhibits a number of differences. In the first place, there are two kinds of multiplication: the multiplication of a matrix by a constant, and the multiplication of a matrix by another matrix. The former is the simple one, and we begin with it.

Once the addition of matrices has been defined, it is only natural that we write down matrix expressions such as $A + A$ or $A + A + A + A$. Following the precedent set by algebra, we are tempted to denote the first sum by $2A$ and the second sum by $4A$. Let us see what this would mean as far as the matrix elements are concerned. If $A = (a_{ij})$, then $A + A = (a_{ij}) + (a_{ij}) = (2a_{ij})$. Thus, if we designate $A + A$ by $2A$, we shall have $2A = (2a_{ij})$. In a similar way, $4A = A + A + A + A = (4a_{ij})$.

Consider, next, this argument: if the matrix equation $X + X = B$ were solved for X, we should like to be in a position to write $2X = B$, and then $X = \frac{1}{2}B$. Now the examination of the matrix equation in terms of the elements leads to $(x_{ij}) + (x_{ij}) = (b_{ij})$, or, $(2x_{ij}) = (b_{ij})$. Hence, $x_{ij} = \frac{1}{2}b_{ij}$. This would imply that $\frac{1}{2}B = (\frac{1}{2}b_{ij})$.

Considerations and desires of this sort lead us to the conclusion that it would be convenient for us to define multiplication of a matrix A by an ordinary number c and have it equal the matrix that results by multiplying all the elements of A by c. This is precisely what we shall do.

To contrast matrices with ordinary numbers, the ordinary numbers are often called *scalars*. Scalars are generally denoted by small letters and matrices by capital letters. The type of multiplication just described is called *scalar* multiplication.

Definition: *If* $\mathrm{A} = (\mathrm{a_{ij}})$ *is an* $\mathrm{m} \times \mathrm{n}$ *matrix, then* cA *will designate the scalar product of* A *by* c. *It is an* $\mathrm{m} \times \mathrm{n}$ *matrix whose elements are* $\mathrm{ca_{ij}}$. *In other words,*

$$\mathrm{cA} = (\mathrm{ca_{ij}}).$$

Examples:

$$4\begin{pmatrix} 0 & 1 \\ -\frac{1}{2} & 2 \\ -3 & x \end{pmatrix} = \begin{pmatrix} 0 & 4 \\ -2 & 8 \\ -12 & 4x \end{pmatrix}$$

$$-2(-2, 1, 0, 4) = (4, -2, 0, -8)$$

$$x\begin{pmatrix} 1 & 0 \\ 0 & 1 \end{pmatrix} + y\begin{pmatrix} 0 & 1 \\ 1 & 0 \end{pmatrix} = \begin{pmatrix} x & y \\ y & x \end{pmatrix}.$$

Further motivation for this definition can be found in the fact that it is often useful to multiply each element of a matrix by a fixed number. Consider Example 4 on page 10. If we wanted to convert the information contained in this matrix from miles to kilometers, we would have to multiply each element by 1.609. This transformation is equivalent to a change in scale, and this kind of change is actually the origin of the word *scalar*.

Scalar multiplication obeys a number of laws, and these are summed up in the theorem that follows.

Theorem: *Let* A *and* B *be two* $\mathrm{m} \times \mathrm{n}$ *matrices, and let* a *and* b *be ordinary numbers (scalars). Then,*

$$\mathrm{a(bA)} = \mathrm{(ab)A} \tag{1}$$

$$\mathrm{(a + b)A} = \mathrm{aA} + \mathrm{bA} \tag{2}$$

$$\mathrm{a(A + B)} = \mathrm{aA} + \mathrm{aB} \tag{3}$$

$$\mathrm{(1)A} = \mathrm{A} \tag{4}$$

$$\mathrm{(-1)A} = -\mathrm{A} \tag{5}$$

$$\mathrm{a0} = 0 \tag{6}$$

$$\mathrm{0A} = 0. \tag{7}$$

Before giving some examples to illustrate the workings of this theorem, some preliminary comments are in order. The parentheses in Equations (1)–(5) are used as grouping symbols to make clear the order of operations on various scalars and matrices. Thus, in Equation (1) bA is the scalar product of A *by* b, and hence $a(bA)$ is the scalar product of bA by a. On the other side of the equation, $(ab)A$ is the scalar product of A by ab. This is, conceptually, quite a different thing, and so the identity of the two is something to prove.

In Equations (6) and (7) the symbol "0" is used in two different senses. In Equation (6) it designates a zero matrix. In the left-hand part of Equation (7) it designates the zero scalar, whereas on the right-hand side it designates a zero matrix. To be consistent, the zero scalar should be written with a small letter, but this causes typographical difficulties. No mathematical difficulties should be encountered as a result of this lapse.

The following examples elucidate these laws.

(a) $2(4A) = 8A$

(b) $7A - 4A = (7 - 4)A = 3A$

(c) $5(A + A - B) = 5(2A - B) = 10A - 5B$

(d) $2(A - B) + 4(\frac{1}{2}B - C) = 2A - 2B + 2B - 4C =$
$2A + 0 - 4C = 2(A - 2C)$.

It should be apparent that these simplifications have been carried out as in ordinary algebra.

(e) Find a 3×3 matrix X such that $-4(X - I) = X + J$.

We have $-4X + 4I = X + J$.

Hence, $-5X = -4I + J$.

Therefore, $X = \frac{4}{5}I - \frac{1}{5}J =$

$$\begin{pmatrix} 3/5 & -1/5 & -1/5 \\ -1/5 & 3/5 & -1/5 \\ -1/5 & -1/5 & 3/5 \end{pmatrix}.$$

The statements (1)–(7) in the above theorem can be established by examining the individual elements of the matrices on the two sides of the equations. We shall do this for Statement (1). The formal proof of the remainder of the theorem will be posed as a problem.

Suppose that $A = (a_{ij})$. Then, by the definition of the scalar product, $bA = (ba_{ij})$. Once again, $a(bA) = (aba_{ij})$. On the other hand, $(ab)A = ((ab)a_{ij}) = (aba_{ij})$. Therefore, $a(bA) = (ab)A$.

PROBLEMS

1. If $A = \begin{pmatrix} 2 & 0 & 2 \\ -1 & 1 & 1 \end{pmatrix}$ and $B = \begin{pmatrix} 0 & 1 & 1 \\ -1 & 1 & -1 \end{pmatrix}$, compute the matrices $3A + 2B$, $2A - 3B$.

2. Compute $2I + J$ for 3×3 matrices.

3. Suppose that A, B, C are 4×4 matrices while a, b, c are ordinary numbers. Take into consideration all the matrix operations that have been defined up to this point and determine which of the following expressions make sense and which do not.

(a) $c(b(aA))$ (b) $(a + c)(aA + bB)$
(c) $c(a + A)$ (d) $(a + b + c)(A + B + C)$
(e) $c(b(A'))'$ (f) $cA + cb$.

4. Determine X if $2(X + B - A) = 3(X - \frac{2}{3}A)$.

5. Determine X and Y if the two conditions

$$X + Y = \begin{pmatrix} 1 & 1 \\ 2 & 2 \end{pmatrix} \quad \text{and} \quad X - Y = \begin{pmatrix} 2 & 2 \\ 1 & 1 \end{pmatrix}$$

hold simultaneously.

6. X and Y are 3×3 matrices to be determined explicitly from the simultaneous conditions $X + 2Y = I$, $2X - Y = 0$.

7. A is a matrix and a is a scalar. Prove that $(aA)' = aA'$. Prove, similarly, that $(aA + bB)' = aA' + bB'$.

8. Simplify the expression $[-3(A' - 2B)]'$.

9. Prove that if $aA = 0$ and if $a \neq 0$, then $A = 0$.

10. If $aA = bA$, does it necessarily follow that $a = b$?

11. Prove parts (2)–(6) of the theorem of this section.

12. k and λ are scalars. Describe the elements of the matrix $kI + \lambda(J - I)$.

13. Let A be a square matrix. Define a matrix A_t, by means of the formula

$$A_t = tA + (1 - t)A'.$$

Compute A_t explicitly if $A = \begin{pmatrix} 1 & 2 \\ 3 & 4 \end{pmatrix}$. Show that, in general, $A_0 = A'$, $A_1 = A$, and that $A_{\frac{1}{2}}$ is symmetric.

14. If $A = -A'$, the matrix A is called *skew-symmetric*. Prove that if B is any square matrix, the matrix $\frac{1}{2}(B - B')$ is skew-symmetric.

15. An $m \times n$ matrix is to be multiplied by a scalar. How many ordinary multiplications must be performed?

2.4 Matrix Multiplication

It will be recalled that a *row vector* is a matrix with one row and a column vector is a matrix with one column. As a preliminary step toward the definition of matrix multiplication, it is convenient to introduce the notion of the *inner product* of two vectors. This notion is attributed to the American scientist Josiah Willard Gibbs (1839–1903), and is of utility both in matrix multiplication as well as in the study of linear algebra that follows in the later chapters. The arithmetic aspect of the inner product is stressed here, but in a later chapter, we shall discover a very striking geometrical interpretation.

Take two vectors (row vectors or column vectors or one of each) that have the same number of elements. The inner product of these vectors is defined as the sum of the products of the corresponding elements. If the vectors are designated by A and B, the inner product is designated by $A \bullet B$. *The inner product of two vectors is a number.*

Here is a formal definition of the inner product.

Definition: *Let* A *and* B *be* $1 \times n$ *or* $n \times 1$ *matrices.* A *has elements* $a_1, a_2, \ldots, a_n$, *and* B *has elements* $b_1, b_2, \ldots, b_n$. *The inner product of* A *and* B *is given by the formula*

$$A \bullet B = a_1b_1 + a_2b_2 + \cdots + a_nb_n.$$

Examples: The inner product of (1 2 3) and (4 5 6) is $(1 \times 4) + (2 \times 5) + (3 \times 6) = 32$. The inner product of

$$(1\ 2\ 3) \text{ and } \begin{pmatrix} a \\ b \\ c \end{pmatrix} \text{ is } a + 2b + 3c.$$

If you are familiar with how the sigma notation for sums works, you will recognize that this formula can be abbreviated somewhat by writing

$$A \bullet B = \sum_{k=1}^{n} a_kb_k.$$

PROBLEMS

1. Compute the inner products of $(-1\ 2\ 1)$ and $\begin{pmatrix} 4 \\ 1 \\ 3 \end{pmatrix}$. Of $(0\ x\ y)$ and $(x\ x\ 3)$.

Of $(x\ y\ z)$ and $\begin{pmatrix} x \\ y \\ z \end{pmatrix}$.

2. If $A = (1\ 1\ 1)$, $B = (3\ 1\ 4)$, $C = (0\ 1\ 2)$, compute the quantities $A \bullet A$, $A \bullet B$, $A \bullet C$, $(A - B) \bullet (A + B)$, $(2A) \bullet (3B)$, $A \bullet (B + C)$, $(A + B) \bullet C$, $(A - B) \bullet (C - B)$, $(A + 2B + C) \bullet (A + B + 2C)$.

3. If A and B are both 1×1 vectors, show that the inner product reduces to an ordinary product.

4. A and B are $1 \times n$ vectors. How many ordinary multiplications and how many ordinary additions are necessary to compute the quantity $A \bullet B$?

Inner products of vectors are sums of ordinary products of numbers. Josiah Willard Gibbs certainly did not invent sums of products. Why all the fuss? Why give such an arithmetic combination a special name? The answer lies in the fact that these sums have interesting algebraic properties and that they play a unifying role in various theories in algebra, geometry, and mathematical physics. Even in numerical analysis, which is the theory of computation, the notion of an inner product is a useful one.

The reader who has access to a desk calculator of the capabilities of, say, the Marchant "Figuremaster," will find that the computation of inner products is a relatively easy matter. All one needs to do is to carry out the multiplications and the additions take care of themselves automatically. In the language of business, inner products are known as "cumulative multiplications" and occur in invoices and inventories (Figure 2.1). Suppose that a clerk must compute

75.5 yds. at $1.25	$ 94.38
$48\frac{1}{2}$ doz. at $6.21	301.19
98 cases at $5.35	524.30
	$919.87.

This is done by the following operations (ignoring questions of decimals). Enter 75.5 on the keyboard and 1,2,5 on the multiplier. Clear the keyboard and upper dials. Enter 48.50 on the keyboard and 6,2,1 on the multiplier. Clear the keyboard and upper dials. Enter 98 on the keyboard and 5,3,5 on the multiplier. The total 919.87 is now read off the middle dials.

In mathematics, and even in business, some of the products may be negative, and this is handled on the machine by depressing a special negative multiplication key.

J. J. Smith & Company
116 Rialto Street N.W.
Washington 31, D.C.

SOLD TO P. J. Davis
Chevy Chase
Maryland

Quantity	*Item*	*Unit Price*	
3	Shirts	3.98	11.94
2	Ties	3.00	6.00
2	Socks	1.50	3.00
6	T-Shirts	1.50	9.00
		TOTAL	29.94

FIGURE 2.1 *Inner Products in a Department Store*

We are now ready to define the multiplication of one matrix by another. As in the case of matrix addition and subtraction, matrix multiplication is defined only when the multiplier and the multiplicand are conformable, but conformability for multiplication differs from that of addition or subtraction. *Two matrices are conformable for multiplication when the number of columns of the first factor equals the number of rows of the second factor.* Thus, for example, the matrices $\begin{pmatrix} x & x & x \\ x & x & x \end{pmatrix}$ and $\begin{pmatrix} x & x \\ x & x \\ x & x \end{pmatrix}$ are conformable as are $\begin{pmatrix} x & x \\ x & x \end{pmatrix}$ and $\begin{pmatrix} x & x \\ x & x \end{pmatrix}$, or $(x\ x\ x\ x\ x)$ and $\begin{pmatrix} x \\ x \\ x \\ x \\ x \end{pmatrix}$.

(We have entered dummy x's for elements: the shape is all that matters.) The orders of two matrices A and B that are conformable for multiplication can be written as $m \times n$ and $n \times p$ respectively.

Designate the m rows of A by $A_1, A_2, \ldots, A_m$. (Consider them as row vectors.) Designate the p columns of B by $B_1, B_2, \ldots, B_p$. (Consider them as column vectors.) These vectors all have n elements (because the number of columns of A is n and the number of rows of B is also n). For each integer i between 1 and m, inclusive, and for each integer j between 1 and p, inclusive, the inner product $A_i \bullet B_j$ can therefore be formed. This number will be the element c_{ij} in the i, jth position of the product $C = AB$.

Definition: *If* A *is an* m $\times$ n *matrix with rows* $A_1, A_2, \ldots, A_m$, *and* B *is an* n $\times$ p *matrix with columns* $B_1, B_2, \ldots, B_p$, *then the product* AB *is an* m $\times$ p *matrix* C *whose elements* c_{ij} *are given by the formula*

$$c_{ij} = A_i \bullet B_j.$$

We may also write

$$C = AB = \begin{pmatrix} A_1 \bullet B_1 & A_1 \bullet B_2 & \cdots & A_1 \bullet B_p \\ A_2 \bullet B_1 & A_2 \bullet B_2 & \cdots & A_2 \bullet B_p \\ \cdot & \cdot & & \cdot \\ A_m \bullet B_1 & A_m \bullet B_2 & \cdots & A_m \bullet B_p \end{pmatrix}.$$

This definition, which is of fundamental importance to the theory of matrices, is illustrated by the following example.

If $A = \begin{pmatrix} 3 & 1 & 2 \\ -1 & 1 & 0 \end{pmatrix}$ and $B = \begin{pmatrix} 4 & 6 \\ 5 & 7 \\ 8 & 9 \end{pmatrix}$, then A is a 2×3 matrix and B

is a 3×2 matrix. These two matrices are conformable for multiplication, and their product AB will be a 2×2 matrix. Now, $A_1 = (3\ 1\ 2)$ and $A_2 = (-1\ 1\ 0)$. Moreover, $B_1 = \begin{pmatrix} 4 \\ 5 \\ 8 \end{pmatrix}$ and $B_2 = \begin{pmatrix} 6 \\ 7 \\ 9 \end{pmatrix}$. The inner products that are elements of the matrix product AB are as follows:

$$\begin{aligned}
A_1 \bullet B_1 &= (3 \times 4) + (1 \times 5) + (2 \times 8) = 33; \\
A_1 \bullet B_2 &= (3 \times 6) + (1 \times 7) + (2 \times 9) = 43; \\
A_2 \bullet B_1 &= (-1 \times 4) + (1 \times 5) + (0 \times 8) = 1; \\
A_2 \bullet B_2 &= (-1 \times 6) + (1 \times 7) + (0 \times 9) = 1.
\end{aligned}$$

Hence we write

$$\begin{pmatrix} 3 & 1 & 2 \\ -1 & 1 & 0 \end{pmatrix} \begin{pmatrix} 4 & 6 \\ 5 & 7 \\ 8 & 9 \end{pmatrix} = \begin{pmatrix} 33 & 43 \\ 1 & 1 \end{pmatrix}.$$

Verify the following matrix multiplication:

$$\begin{pmatrix} -1 & 1 \\ 1 & 2 \end{pmatrix} \begin{pmatrix} y & 0 \\ -1 & 1 \end{pmatrix} = \begin{pmatrix} -y-1 & 1 \\ y-2 & 2 \end{pmatrix}.$$

Matrix multiplication can be carried out by a "two finger scheme" that the author finds useful when the orders of the matrices are not too large. *The element in the* i,j*th position in the final product* AB *is the inner product of the* i*th row of* A *by the* j*th column of* B. This is depicted in Figure 2.2.

Take the left index finger and place it on the 1st element of the ith row

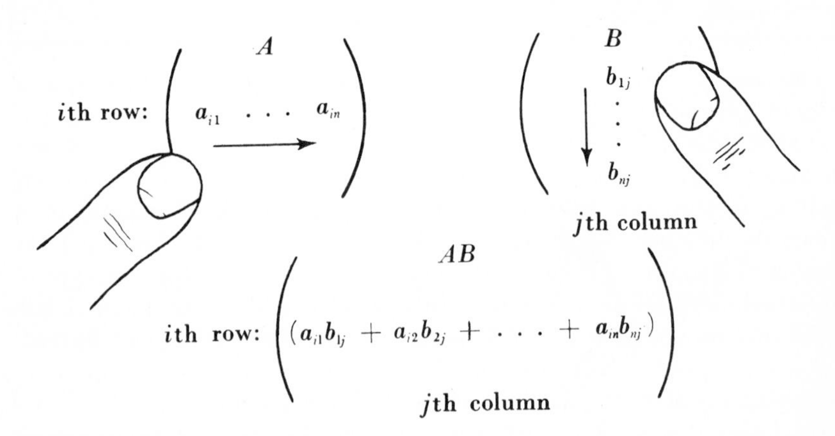

FIGURE 2.2 *Matrix Multiplication as a Two Finger Exercise*

of A. Take the right index finger and place it on the 1st element of the jth column of B. Move the left index finger across the row, element by element, and simultaneously, move the right index finger down the column. The number of elements will match because of the conformability condition for multiplication. (If they do not match, the product is not defined.) As each finger comes to rest on its respective number, multiply the numbers, and keep a running sum of the numbers in your head. The final sum will be the i,jth element of the product AB.

It is also important for the student to become familiar with the various combinations of matrix orders for which multiplication is possible. These are summed up in the following table, and the entries should be verified.

Conformability Conditions for Matrix Multiplication

TYPE	ORDER OF FIRST FACTOR	ORDER OF SECOND FACTOR	ORDER OF PRODUCT
Rectangle by rectangle	$m \times n$	$n \times p$	$m \times p$
Square by square	$n \times n$	$n \times n$	Square: $n \times n$
Row by rectangle	$1 \times n$	$n \times p$	Row: $1 \times p$
Rectangle by column	$m \times n$	$n \times 1$	Column: $m \times 1$
Row by column	$1 \times n$	$n \times 1$	1×1

The second through the fifth lines of this table are, of course, special cases of the first line.

It should be observed carefully that the conformability of two matrices for multiplication depends upon the order in which the factors are taken. That is, the product AB can be formed if the number of columns of A equals the number of rows of B. The product BA can be formed if the number of columns of B equals the number of rows of A. But one type of conformability does not guarantee the other type. For example if A is a 3×2 matrix, and B is a 2×7 matrix, the product AB can be formed, but not the product BA. In this respect, the multiplication of matrices differs sharply from the multiplication of ordinary numbers.

In closing this section, a word is in order about the notation used for matrix products. The most common notation is to place the matrices to be multiplied next to one another without any symbols intervening. This is illustrated by AB, CD, or $\begin{pmatrix} 1 & 1 \\ 1 & 1 \end{pmatrix}\begin{pmatrix} 2 & 0 \\ 4 & 1 \end{pmatrix}$. Parentheses are employed as needed for grouping. Thus, $A(B + C)$ indicates the product of A by the sum of B and C. The expression $A(B + C)'$ would indicate the product of A by the transpose of the sum of B and C.

PROBLEMS

1. If $A = \begin{pmatrix} 1 & 2 \\ 2 & -1 \end{pmatrix}$, and $B = \begin{pmatrix} 4 & -1 \\ 1 & 0 \end{pmatrix}$, write out in detail, following the example of the text, the vectors A_1, A_2, B_1, B_2, the four inner products, and the matrix product AB.

2. Perform the indicated multiplications.

$$\begin{pmatrix} 1 & 3 \\ 3 & 1 \end{pmatrix}\begin{pmatrix} 1 & 4 \\ 4 & 1 \end{pmatrix}, \quad (2 \quad 0 \quad 5)\begin{pmatrix} 9 \\ -1 \\ 3 \end{pmatrix}, \quad \begin{pmatrix} 1 & 4 & 0 \\ 1 & -3 & 1 \end{pmatrix}\begin{pmatrix} 1 & -1 \\ -1 & 1 \\ 5 & 0 \end{pmatrix},$$

$$\begin{pmatrix} 1 & -1 \\ -1 & 1 \end{pmatrix}\begin{pmatrix} -1 & 1 \\ 1 & -1 \end{pmatrix}, \quad (1 \quad 2 \quad 3 \quad 4)\begin{pmatrix} 4 \\ 2 \\ 3 \\ 1 \end{pmatrix},$$

$$(1 \quad -1)\begin{pmatrix} 2 & 1 & 2 \\ 2 & 1 & 3 \end{pmatrix}, \quad (2 \quad 0)\begin{pmatrix} -1 & 6 & 1 \\ 1 & 0 & 4 \end{pmatrix}.$$

3. Find the products:

$$\begin{pmatrix} 1 & 1 & 1 \\ 0 & 1 & 1 \\ 2 & 1 & 1 \end{pmatrix}\begin{pmatrix} 1 & -1 & 1 \\ 2 & 0 & 2 \\ 3 & -1 & 1 \end{pmatrix}, \quad \begin{pmatrix} 1 & 1 & 1 \\ 1 & 1 & 1 \\ 1 & 1 & 1 \end{pmatrix}\begin{pmatrix} 1 & 1 & 1 \\ 1 & 1 & 1 \\ 1 & 1 & 1 \end{pmatrix},$$

$$\begin{pmatrix} 1 & 0 & 0 \\ 0 & 1 & 0 \\ 0 & 0 & 0 \end{pmatrix}\begin{pmatrix} 7 & 3 & 2 \\ 2 & 1 & 4 \\ 1 & 0 & 1 \end{pmatrix}, \quad \begin{pmatrix} 1 & 0 & 0 \\ 0 & 0 & 0 \\ 0 & 0 & 0 \end{pmatrix}\begin{pmatrix} 7 & 3 & 2 \\ 2 & 1 & 4 \\ 1 & 0 & 1 \end{pmatrix},$$

$$\begin{pmatrix} 1 & 2 & 3 \\ 0 & 1 & 2 \\ 0 & 0 & 1 \end{pmatrix}\begin{pmatrix} 1 & -2 & 1 \\ 0 & 1 & -2 \\ 0 & 0 & 1 \end{pmatrix}, \quad \begin{pmatrix} 1 & 1 & 1 \\ 1 & 2 & 3 \\ 1 & -1 & 1 \end{pmatrix}\begin{pmatrix} 1 & 1 & 1 \\ 1 & 2 & 3 \\ 1 & -1 & 1 \end{pmatrix},$$

$$\begin{pmatrix} 6 & 3 & 1 \\ 4 & 8 & 9 \\ -1 & 7 & 5 \end{pmatrix}\begin{pmatrix} 1 & 0 & 0 \\ 0 & 1 & 0 \\ 0 & 0 & 1 \end{pmatrix}.$$

4. Multiply:

$$\begin{pmatrix} 1 & 6 & 1 \\ 0 & 1 & 2 \\ 0 & 0 & 1 \end{pmatrix}\begin{pmatrix} x \\ y \\ z \end{pmatrix}, \quad (1 \;\; 4 \;\; 3 \;\; 2)\begin{pmatrix} x \\ y \\ z \\ w \end{pmatrix}, \quad (1 \;\; 4 \;\; 3 \;\; 2)\begin{pmatrix} 1 \\ -9 \\ 3 \\ -2 \end{pmatrix},$$

$$(x \;\; y \;\; z)\begin{pmatrix} x \\ y \\ z \end{pmatrix}.$$

5. Multiply:

$$\begin{pmatrix} x & y \\ y & x \end{pmatrix}\begin{pmatrix} y & -x \\ -x & y \end{pmatrix}, \quad \begin{pmatrix} a & b \\ c & d \end{pmatrix}\begin{pmatrix} x & y \\ z & w \end{pmatrix}, \quad \begin{pmatrix} 1 & 0 & 0 \\ 0 & 4 & 0 \\ 0 & 0 & 5 \end{pmatrix}\begin{pmatrix} a \\ b \\ c \end{pmatrix},$$

$$\begin{pmatrix} a & b \\ -b & a \end{pmatrix}\begin{pmatrix} p & q \\ -q & p \end{pmatrix}.$$

6. Compute JJ and $(JJ)J$. Here J is assumed to be 5×5.

7. If A is a 3×2 matrix, for which of the following orders of B can the product AB be formed: 2×2, 2×1, 1×2, 3×4, 3×2.

8. If both AB and BA can be formed, what can be said about the orders of A and B?

9. Form the product $\begin{pmatrix} 1, 1+i \\ 1-i, 2 \end{pmatrix}\begin{pmatrix} 1, 1-i \\ 1+i, 2 \end{pmatrix}$ where $i = \sqrt{-1}$.

10. Prove that the product of two upper triangular matrices is also upper triangular.

11. Is the product of two symmetric matrices necessarily symmetric?

12. Under what order conditions can the product AA' be formed?

13. A is an $m \times n$ and B is an $n \times p$ matrix. Show that in order to compute the product AB, we need to perform $m \times n \times p$ ordinary multiplications and $m \times (n-1) \times p$ ordinary additions.

14. Write the Pascal triangle in the form of a lower triangular matrix:

$$T = \begin{pmatrix} 1 & 0 & 0 & 0 & 0 & 0 \cdots \\ 1 & 1 & 0 & 0 & 0 & 0 \\ 1 & 2 & 1 & 0 & 0 & 0 \\ 1 & 3 & 3 & 1 & 0 & 0 \\ 1 & 4 & 6 & 4 & 1 & 0 \\ \vdots & & & & & \end{pmatrix}.$$

Compute TT'. Do you recognize the product?

15. B is a diagonal matrix. Contrast A and AB. Contrast A and BA. A is a given square matrix.

2.5 Why and Wherefore

The definition of matrix multiplication was first given by the English mathematician Arthur Cayley (1821–1895). It is important to understand what is behind this unusual and somewhat complicated definition. It is natural, for instance, to wonder why multiplication was not defined in the simple way that addition was, by saying that the product of two matrices of the same order is equal to the matrix composed of the products of the corresponding elements. If this were done, it is not difficult to see that matrix arithmetic would be equivalent to ordinary arithmetic, with the sole exception that it would be ordinary arithmetic done in rectangular batches. Nothing new would be added. Each element would be substantially independent; there would be no interlinking of the various elements to bind the array into a whole, new entity.

But why the complicated rule for conformability? Why the long inner product computations necessary to arrive at the product matrix? There are a number of reasons that can be given, but the primary one is this: matrix multiplication fulfills the need for providing a simple mechanism for changing variables. Suppose, for example, that

$$\begin{cases} y_1 = a_{11}x_1 + a_{12}x_2 + a_{13}x_3 \\ y_2 = a_{21}x_1 + a_{22}x_2 + a_{23}x_3. \end{cases}$$

Suppose, further, that

$$\begin{cases} z_1 = b_{11}y_1 + b_{12}y_2 \\ z_2 = b_{21}y_1 + b_{22}y_2. \end{cases}$$

In these equations, the x's and the y's are to be considered as unknowns, or variables, while the a's and the b's are constants. The x's are related to the y's by the first set of equations, and the y's are related to the z's by the second set of equations. How are the x's related to the z's? To answer this, we must substitute the values of the y's (given by the first set of equations) into the second set of equations, and then simplify the resulting expressions:

$$\begin{cases} z_1 = b_{11}(a_{11}x_1 + a_{12}x_2 + a_{13}x_3) + b_{12}(a_{21}x_1 + a_{22}x_2 + a_{23}x_3) \\ z_2 = b_{21}(a_{11}x_1 + a_{12}x_2 + a_{13}x_3) + b_{22}(a_{21}x_1 + a_{22}x_2 + a_{23}x_3). \end{cases}$$

By multiplying these expressions out and then collecting the coefficients of the x's, we obtain

$$\begin{cases} z_1 = (b_{11}a_{11} + b_{12}a_{21})x_1 + (b_{11}a_{12} + b_{12}a_{22})x_2 + (b_{11}a_{13} + b_{12}a_{23})x_3 \\ z_2 = (b_{21}a_{11} + b_{22}a_{21})x_1 + (b_{21}a_{12} + b_{22}a_{22})x_2 + (b_{21}a_{13} + b_{22}a_{23})x_3. \end{cases}$$

Now observe that the coefficients of x_1, x_2, and x_3 are precisely the elements of the matrix product:

$$\begin{pmatrix} b_{11} & b_{12} \\ b_{21} & b_{22} \end{pmatrix} \begin{pmatrix} a_{11} & a_{12} & a_{13} \\ a_{21} & a_{22} & a_{23} \end{pmatrix}.$$

Not only this, but they are located in the proper positions.

The conformability conditions for multiplication—in this case 2×2 is conformable with 2×3—means that there is the same number of intermediate variables (the y's) in both sets of equations so that the transformation from the x's to the y's and then from the y's to the z's can be carried out.

Matrix multiplication therefore provides a quick and easy rule of thumb for carrying out changes of variable, and this type of transformation is common throughout the length and breadth of mathematics.

Example 1:

$$\text{If } \begin{cases} y_1 = 3x_1 + 4x_2 + 5x_3 \\ y_2 = x_1 + x_2 + x_3, \end{cases}$$

$$\text{and } \begin{cases} z_1 = y_1 - y_2 \\ z_2 = y_1 + y_2, \end{cases}$$

express the z's directly in terms of the x's. Solution using matrices: From the product

$$\begin{pmatrix} 1 & -1 \\ 1 & 1 \end{pmatrix} \begin{pmatrix} 3 & 4 & 5 \\ 1 & 1 & 1 \end{pmatrix} = \begin{pmatrix} 2 & 3 & 4 \\ 4 & 5 & 6 \end{pmatrix}.$$

Hence,

$$\begin{cases} z_1 = 2x_1 + 3x_2 + 4x_3 \\ z_2 = 4x_1 + 5x_2 + 6x_3. \end{cases}$$

Example 2:

$$\text{If } \begin{cases} y_1 = x_1 + x_3 + x_4 \\ y_2 = x_2 + x_3 + x_4 \\ y_3 = x_1 + x_2 + x_4, \end{cases}$$

$$\text{and } \begin{cases} z_1 = 3y_1 + 2y_2 \\ z_2 = y_1 - y_2 + y_3, \end{cases}$$

find the z's directly in terms of the x's using matrix multiplication. Here one must observe certain precautions. There are four x's and three y's, and in forming the coefficient matrices, we must insert zeros wherever a particular letter is missing. Thus, rewrite these equations as

$$\begin{cases} y_1 = x_1 + 0x_2 + x_3 + x_4 \\ y_2 = 0x_1 + x_2 + x_3 + x_4 \\ y_3 = x_1 + x_2 + 0x_3 + x_4, \end{cases}$$

$$\text{and } \begin{cases} z_1 = 3y_1 + 2y_2 + 0y_3 \\ z_2 = y_1 - y_2 + y_3. \end{cases}$$

The appropriate matrix product is then

$$\begin{pmatrix} 3 & 2 & 0 \\ 1 & -1 & 1 \end{pmatrix} \begin{pmatrix} 1 & 0 & 1 & 1 \\ 0 & 1 & 1 & 1 \\ 1 & 1 & 0 & 1 \end{pmatrix} = \begin{pmatrix} 3 & 2 & 5 & 5 \\ 2 & 0 & 0 & 1 \end{pmatrix}.$$

Hence,

$$\begin{cases} z_1 = 3x_1 + 2x_2 + 5x_3 + 5x_4 \\ z_2 = 2x_1 \qquad\qquad\qquad + x_4. \end{cases}$$

Changes of variable are known as *transformations*, and consequently, the study of matrix algebra is equivalent to the study of the algebra of transformations.

PROBLEMS

Carry out the following changes of variable, or transformations, by using matrix multiplication.

1. $\begin{cases} w = 3x + 2y \\ v = x - y \end{cases} \qquad \begin{cases} p = w + v \\ q = 7w + v \end{cases}$

   Find p and q in terms of x and y.

2. $\begin{cases} p = w - v \\ q = 3w + 4v \end{cases} \qquad \begin{cases} w = x + y \\ v = 2x - y \end{cases}$

   Find p and q in terms of x and y.

3. $\begin{cases} m = x + 3y \\ n = 2x + y \end{cases} \qquad \begin{cases} w = 4m + n \\ v = 2m - 3n \end{cases}$

   Find w and v in terms of x and y.

4. $\begin{cases} a = 2s + t \\ b = s - 2t \end{cases} \qquad \begin{cases} x = a + 2b \\ y = 2a + 4b \end{cases}$

   Find x and y in terms of s and t.

5. $\begin{cases} w = x + y + z \\ u = x \qquad + z \\ v = -x - y + z \end{cases} \qquad \begin{cases} p = 3w + 4u + v \\ q = 4w + 3u + v \\ r = w - u - v \end{cases}$

   Find p, q, and r in terms of x, y, z.

6. $\begin{cases} p = w + u + v \\ q = \qquad u + v \\ r = \qquad\qquad v \end{cases} \qquad \begin{cases} w = x + y + z \\ u = \qquad y + z \\ v = \qquad\qquad z \end{cases}$

   Find p, q, and r in terms of x, y, and z.

7. $\begin{cases} p = w + u \\ q = \qquad u + v \\ r = w \qquad + v \end{cases} \qquad \begin{cases} w = x + y \\ u = \qquad y + z \\ v = x \qquad + z \end{cases}$

Find p, q, and r in terms of x, y, and z.

8. $\begin{cases} a = x + 2y \\ b = x + y + z \\ c = -x + y + z \end{cases}$ $\begin{cases} w = a + 2b \\ u = a + b + c \\ v = a - b + 2c \end{cases}$

Find w, u, v in terms of x, y, z.

9. If $\begin{cases} w = y \\ v = x \end{cases}$ and $\begin{cases} p = v \\ q = w \end{cases}$

Find p and q in terms of x and y. Use matrix multiplication.

10. If $\begin{cases} x_1 = y_2 \\ x_2 = y_1 \\ x_3 = y_3 \end{cases}$ and $\begin{cases} y_1 = z_2 \\ y_2 = z_3 \\ y_3 = z_1 \end{cases}$

Find x_1, x_2, x_3 in terms of z_1, z_2, z_3. Use matrix multiplication.

11. If $\begin{cases} x_1 = y_2 \\ x_2 = y_3 \\ x_3 = y_1 \\ x_4 = y_4 \end{cases}$ and $\begin{cases} y_1 = z_3 \\ y_2 = z_1 \\ y_3 = z_4 \\ y_4 = z_2 \end{cases}$

Find the z's in terms of the x's. Use matrix multiplication.

12. If $\begin{cases} w = -x + y \\ v = x + y \end{cases}$ and $\begin{cases} p = -\frac{1}{2}w + \frac{1}{2}v \\ q = \frac{1}{2}w + \frac{1}{2}v \end{cases}$

Find p and q in terms of x and y. Also find x and y in terms of p and q.

13. In Problem 1, find x and y in terms of p and q.

2.6 Multiplication Has Its Rules

We shall state the worst at the very beginning, and then everything that follows will come as a pleasant relief. *Matrix multiplication is not commutative.* This is to say, the product AB is *not necessarily* equal to the product BA. We have already observed that if the product AB is defined, the product BA is not necessarily defined. This fact, by itself, should alert us that something is strange. But even if the product BA is defined, it may not be the same as AB.

For example, if

$$A = \begin{pmatrix} 1 & 1 \\ 0 & 1 \end{pmatrix} \quad \text{and} \quad B = \begin{pmatrix} 1 & 1 \\ 1 & 0 \end{pmatrix}, \quad \text{then}$$

$$AB = \begin{pmatrix} 2 & 1 \\ 1 & 0 \end{pmatrix} \quad \text{while} \quad BA = \begin{pmatrix} 1 & 2 \\ 1 & 1 \end{pmatrix}.$$

Therefore,

$$AB \neq BA.$$

This unfamiliar situation means that in talking about products, it does not suffice to say simply "Multiply A by B," for if we mean AB it is one thing, but if we mean BA, it may be another. There are two types of matrix multiplication: in the product AB, B is said to be *premultiplied* by A or to be *multiplied by* A *on the left*, while in the product BA, B is said to be *postmultiplied* by A or to be *multiplied by* A *on the right.*

Although AB and BA are not necessarily the same, they may be the same from time to time. For example,

$$\text{if} \quad A = \begin{pmatrix} 1 & 2 \\ -2 & 0 \end{pmatrix} \quad \text{and} \quad B = \begin{pmatrix} -3 & 2 \\ -2 & -4 \end{pmatrix},$$

then we can compute

$$AB = \begin{pmatrix} -7 & -6 \\ 6 & -4 \end{pmatrix} \quad \text{and} \quad BA = \begin{pmatrix} -7 & -6 \\ 6 & -4 \end{pmatrix}.$$

Two matrices A and B for which $AB = BA$ are said to *commute with one another*.

PROBLEMS

1. Do the matrices

$$\begin{pmatrix} 1 & 2 & 1 \\ 2 & 1 & 1 \\ 2 & -1 & 1 \end{pmatrix} \quad \text{and} \quad \begin{pmatrix} 1 & 1 & 1 \\ 1 & -1 & 1 \\ -1 & 1 & 1 \end{pmatrix} \quad \text{commute?}$$

2. Do the matrices $\begin{pmatrix} a & b \\ c & a \end{pmatrix}$ and $\begin{pmatrix} b & a \\ a & c \end{pmatrix}$, or $\begin{pmatrix} 1 & a \\ a & 1 \end{pmatrix}$ and $\begin{pmatrix} 1 + a^2 & 2a \\ 2a & 1 + a^2 \end{pmatrix}$ commute?

3. Do the matrices J and $I - J$, of order 3×3, commute?

4. Show that any two diagonal matrices of the same order commute with one another.

5. Multiply $\begin{pmatrix} 3 & 1 \\ 2 & 6 \end{pmatrix}$ on the right by $\begin{pmatrix} -1 & 1 \\ 2 & 0 \end{pmatrix}$. Multiply it on the left by the same matrix.

6. If the matrix $\begin{pmatrix} 1 & 2 \\ 3 & 0 \end{pmatrix}$ commutes with the matrix $\begin{pmatrix} a & b \\ c & d \end{pmatrix}$, what must be the relationship among the quantities a, b, c, and d?

7. Explain what multiplying a square matrix A on the right by J does. What about multiplication on the left?

8. What can you say about the elements of a 2×2 matrix that commutes with J?

Although matrix multiplication is not commutative, it is *associative and distributive*. Associativity means that

$$(AB)C = A(BC).$$

It has the important consequence that in forming products, attention need not be paid to the order in which the partial products are formed.

For example, in evaluating $ABCD$, we may form the products AB and CD and then $(AB)(CD)$. Or, we may form AB, then $(AB)C$, and finally $((AB)C)D$. Or, we may proceed with any grouping we like and have the assurance that all the answers will be the same.

There are two distributive laws since there are effectively two kinds of multiplication, multiplication on the left and multiplication on the right;

$$A(B + C) = AB + AC$$
$$(A + B)C = AC + BC.$$

In each of the last three equations, proper attention must be paid to the conformability of the matrices with respect to the indicated operations. Thus, in the associative law, AB can be formed if A is an $m \times n$ matrix and B is an $n \times p$ matrix. The product AB is then an $m \times p$ matrix. Therefore, the product $(AB)C$ can be formed if C is a $p \times q$ matrix, and the product will be an $m \times q$ matrix. But notice that under these conditions, BC can be formed and will be an $n \times q$ matrix. Hence $A(BC)$ can be formed and will be an $m \times q$ matrix. Thus, $(AB)C$ and $A(BC)$ have the same order.

Here is a numerical example that exhibits the workings of the associative law:

$$\text{If} \quad A = \begin{pmatrix} 1 & 2 \\ 3 & 4 \end{pmatrix}, \quad B = \begin{pmatrix} 1 & 0 \\ 2 & 3 \end{pmatrix}, \quad \text{and} \quad C = \begin{pmatrix} 1 & -1 \\ 0 & 1 \end{pmatrix};$$

$$\text{then} \quad AB = \begin{pmatrix} 5 & 6 \\ 11 & 12 \end{pmatrix} \quad \text{and hence} \quad (AB)C = \begin{pmatrix} 5 & 1 \\ 11 & 1 \end{pmatrix}.$$

On the other hand, $BC = \begin{pmatrix} 1 & -1 \\ 2 & 1 \end{pmatrix}$ and $A(BC) = \begin{pmatrix} 5 & 1 \\ 11 & 1 \end{pmatrix}$, as before.

We formulate a theorem that sums up various properties of matrix multiplication.

Theorem: *If* A,B, *and* C, *are matrices; if* I *is the unit matrix and* 0 *is the zero matrix, then, with proper attention paid to conformability, we have*

$(AB)C = A(BC)$	the associative law;
$(A + B)C = AC + BC$ $A(B + C) = AB + AC$	the distributive laws;
$0A = A0 = 0$	multiplication by zero;
$AI = IA = A$	multiplication by the unit.

Although these laws are familiar enough when applied to ordinary numbers, the rule of the formation of matrix products is sufficiently complicated so that these laws are by no means self-evident for matrices. They require proof; the failure of the commutative law should convince one of this.

In each instance, a proof can be given by exhibiting explicitly the matrix elements on the left side of the equation and on the right side of the equation and showing that the elements are identical. We shall carry out the proof supposing that the matrices are 2×2. The general case is no different in principle.

Let $$A = \begin{pmatrix} a_{11} & a_{12} \\ a_{21} & a_{22} \end{pmatrix}, \qquad B = \begin{pmatrix} b_{11} & b_{12} \\ b_{21} & b_{22} \end{pmatrix}, \qquad C = \begin{pmatrix} c_{11} & c_{12} \\ c_{21} & c_{22} \end{pmatrix}.$$

Then,

$$AB = \begin{pmatrix} a_{11}b_{11} + a_{12}b_{21}, & a_{11}b_{12} + a_{12}b_{22} \\ a_{21}b_{11} + a_{22}b_{21}, & a_{21}b_{12} + a_{22}b_{22} \end{pmatrix}.$$

Therefore,

$$(AB)C = \begin{pmatrix} (a_{11}b_{11} + a_{12}b_{21})c_{11} + (a_{11}b_{12} + a_{12}b_{22})c_{21}, & (a_{11}b_{11} + a_{12}b_{21})c_{12} + (a_{11}b_{12} + a_{12}b_{22})c_{22} \\ (a_{21}b_{11} + a_{22}b_{21})c_{11} + (a_{21}b_{12} + a_{22}b_{22})c_{21}, & (a_{21}b_{11} + a_{22}b_{21})c_{12} + (a_{21}b_{12} + a_{22}b_{22})c_{22} \end{pmatrix}.$$

On the other hand,

$$BC = \begin{pmatrix} b_{11}c_{11} + b_{12}c_{21}, & b_{11}c_{12} + b_{12}c_{22} \\ b_{21}c_{11} + b_{22}c_{21}, & b_{21}c_{12} + b_{22}c_{22} \end{pmatrix}.$$

And therefore,

$$A(BC) = \begin{pmatrix} a_{11}(b_{11}c_{11} + b_{12}c_{21}) + a_{12}(b_{21}c_{11} + b_{22}c_{21}), & a_{11}(b_{11}c_{12} + b_{12}c_{22}) + a_{12}(b_{21}c_{12} + b_{22}c_{22}) \\ a_{21}(b_{11}c_{11} + b_{12}c_{21}) + a_{22}(b_{21}c_{11} + b_{22}c_{21}), & a_{21}(b_{11}c_{12} + b_{12}c_{22}) + a_{22}(b_{21}c_{12} + b_{22}c_{22}) \end{pmatrix}.$$

Now it takes but a moment to expand the parentheses above, and to verify that the matrices $A(BC)$ and $(AB)C$ are identical, element by element. We can therefore write

$$A(BC) = (AB)C.$$

The proof of the first distributive law is carried out in the following way.

$$A + B = \begin{pmatrix} a_{11} + b_{11} & a_{12} + b_{12} \\ a_{21} + b_{21} & a_{22} + b_{22} \end{pmatrix},$$

and hence

$$(A + B)C = \begin{pmatrix} (a_{11} + b_{11})c_{11} + (a_{12} + b_{12})c_{21}, & (a_{11} + b_{11})c_{12} + (a_{12} + b_{12})c_{22} \\ (a_{21} + b_{21})c_{11} + (a_{22} + b_{22})c_{21}, & (a_{21} + b_{21})c_{12} + (a_{22} + b_{22})c_{22} \end{pmatrix}.$$

However,

$$AC = \begin{pmatrix} a_{11}c_{11} + a_{12}c_{21} & a_{11}c_{12} + a_{12}c_{22} \\ a_{21}c_{11} + a_{22}c_{21} & a_{21}c_{12} + a_{22}c_{22} \end{pmatrix} \quad \text{and}$$

$$BC = \begin{pmatrix} b_{11}c_{11} + b_{12}c_{21} & b_{11}c_{12} + b_{12}c_{22} \\ b_{21}c_{11} + b_{22}c_{21} & b_{21}c_{12} + b_{22}c_{22} \end{pmatrix}.$$

Add the last two matrices together, and compare them element by element with the matrix immediately above them. We find that

$$(A + B)C = AC + BC.$$

The second distributive law is proved in a similar fashion. The proof of the law of multiplication by the zero matrix is utterly trivial. The law of multiplication by the unit matrix has somewhat more meat to it. The reader should convince himself of the truth of the following product.

$$\begin{pmatrix} 1 & 0 & \cdots & 0 \\ 0 & 1 & \cdots & 0 \\ \cdot & \cdot & \cdots & \cdot \\ 0 & 0 & \cdots & 1 \end{pmatrix} \begin{pmatrix} a_{11} & a_{12} & \cdots & a_{1n} \\ a_{21} & a_{22} & \cdots & a_{2n} \\ \cdot & \cdot & \cdots & \cdot \\ a_{n1} & a_{n2} & \cdots & a_{nn} \end{pmatrix} = \begin{pmatrix} a_{11} & a_{12} & \cdots & a_{1n} \\ a_{21} & a_{22} & \cdots & a_{2n} \\ \cdot & \cdot & \cdots & \cdot \\ a_{n1} & a_{n2} & \cdots & a_{nn} \end{pmatrix}.$$

He should also find the result of multiplication on the right-hand side by I, and thus verify the fact that multiplication on either side by the unit matrix I leaves the multiplicand unchanged. In this respect, the unit matrix I behaves like the ordinary number 1.

The distributive law holds for any number of summands. For example,

$$(A + B + C + D)E = AE + BE + CE + DE$$

or

$$A(B + C + D + E) = AB + AC + AD + AE,$$

and this can be demonstrated by repeated application of the simple distributive law. For example,

$(A + B + C + D)E = ((A + B) + (C + D))E$ (by the associative law of addition);

$((A + B) + (C + D))E = (A + B)E + (C + D)E$ (by the distributive law);

$(A + B)E + (C + D)E = AE + BE + CE + DE$ (again, by the distributive law).

Scalar multiplication relates itself to matrix multiplication in an obvious way. The rules are contained in the following theorem.

Theorem: *If* c *is a scalar (an ordinary number) and if* A *and* B *are conformable for matrix multiplication, then*

$$c(AB) = (cA)B = A(cB).$$

This theorem tells us that a scalar multiplier may be moved freely throughout the factors in a matrix product. We can, for instance, write $6AB$ or $A6B$ without being concerned about the order in which the multiplication is carried out. The last expression "looks" peculiar and would usually be written as $A(6B)$.

PROOF: Let A be an $m \times n$ matrix with elements a_{ij}, and B be an $n \times p$ matrix with elements b_{ij}. By the definition of scalar multiplication, the elements of cA are ca_{ij}, and the elements of cB are cb_{ij}. By the definition of matrix multiplication, the i,jth element of AB is $a_{i1}b_{1j} + a_{i2}b_{2j} + \cdots + a_{in}b_{nj}$. Hence the i,jth element of $c(AB)$ is $c(a_{i1}b_{1j} + a_{i2}b_{2j} + \cdots + a_{in}b_{nj})$. On the other hand, the i,jth element of $(cA)B$ is $ca_{i1}b_{1j} + ca_{i2}b_{2j} + \cdots + ca_{in}b_{nj}$, while the i,jth element of $A(cB)$ is $a_{i1}cb_{1j} + a_{i2}cb_{2j} + \cdots + a_{in}cb_{nj}$. The number c factors out of these last two expressions, and so the i,jth elements of $c(AB)$, $(cA)B$, and $A(cB)$ are equal. The three matrix products must also be equal to one another.

Corollary: *If* a *and* b *are scalars and if* A *and* B *are conformable for matrix multiplication, then*

$$(aA)(bB) = ab\,(AB).$$

PROOF:

$$(aA)(bB) = a(A(bB))$$

$$= a(b(AB)) = (ab)(AB).$$

These steps are validated by using the theorem just proved and using part (1) of the theorem on page 30.

PROBLEMS

1. Discuss the respective orders of A, B, and C that make the two distributive laws meaningful.
2. Verify the two distributive laws numerically with the selection

$$A = \begin{pmatrix} 1 & 2 \\ 3 & 4 \end{pmatrix}, \quad B = \begin{pmatrix} 1 & 0 \\ 2 & 3 \end{pmatrix}, \quad C = \begin{pmatrix} 1 & -1 \\ 0 & 1 \end{pmatrix}.$$

Verify the laws with the selection

$$A = \begin{pmatrix} 1 & -1 \\ 2 & 0 \end{pmatrix}, \quad B = \begin{pmatrix} 0 & 4 \\ 1 & 2 \end{pmatrix}, \quad C = \begin{pmatrix} 1 & 1 \\ 1 & 1 \end{pmatrix}.$$

3. Use the first set of matrices in Problem 2 and verify directly that $6(AB) = (6A)B = A(6B)$.

4. Verify the associative law with both sets of matrices in Problem 2.

5. In how many different ways can one arrive at the product $ABCDE$? For example, $(A(BC))(DE)$ is one such way.

6. Prove that $A(B + C)D = ABD + ACD$.

7. Is $AABB$ necessarily equal to $ABAB$?

8. Show that if the matrices A, B, and C commute with one another then $A(B - C) + B(C - A) + C(A - B) = 0$.

9. Suppose that A is an $m \times n$ matrix, B is $n \times p$, and C is $p \times q$. To compute the product $(AB)C$ in the order indicated requires $mnp + mpq$ ordinary multiplications and $m(n - 1)p + m(p - 1)q$ additions. Verify this.

10. On the other hand, show that to compute it in the order $A(BC)$ requires $npq + mnq$ multiplications and $n(p - 1)q + m(n - 1)q$ additions.

11. Compare the relative amounts of work involved in computing $A(BC)$ and $(AB)C$ when $m = 1$, $n = 4$, $p = 2$, $q = 5$.

12. Compare the amount of arithmetic necessary to compute $A(B + C)$ with the amount necessary to compute $AB + AC$.

13. Find the mode of grouping the product

$$\begin{pmatrix} 1 \\ 2 \\ 3 \end{pmatrix} (3 \quad 2 \quad 1) \begin{pmatrix} 1 \\ -1 \\ -4 \end{pmatrix} (3 \quad 1 \quad 5)$$

that requires the fewest ordinary multiplications.

14. Let the notation $S(A)$ mean the sum of all the elements in the matrix A. Prove that $S(A + B) = S(A) + S(B)$. If c is a scalar, prove that $S(cA) = cS(A)$. Designate the sum of the elements of the ith column of A by α_i and the sum of the elements of the jth row of B by β_j. Prove that $S(AB) = \alpha_1\beta_1 + \alpha_2\beta_2 + \cdots + \alpha_n\beta_n$.

2.7 Matrix Powers and Polynomials

If A is a square matrix, we can form the product AA. It is natural to abbreviate AA by A^2. It would be natural to abbreviate AAA by A^3. Since matrix multiplication is associative, it makes no difference how AAA has been computed: $AAA = A(AA) = (AA)A = (A^2)A$. The common value of these products will be denoted by A^3. If four A's are multiplied together, we have, by the associative law, $(AAA)A = (A^3)A = ((A^2)A)A = (A^2)(A^2) = A(A(A^2)) = A(A^3)$. The common value of these products is designated by A^4.

Example 1: If $A = \begin{pmatrix} 1 & 2 \\ 3 & 4 \end{pmatrix}$, then $A^2 = \begin{pmatrix} 1 & 2 \\ 3 & 4 \end{pmatrix}\begin{pmatrix} 1 & 2 \\ 3 & 4 \end{pmatrix} = \begin{pmatrix} 7 & 10 \\ 15 & 22 \end{pmatrix}$ and

$A^3 = (A^2)A = \begin{pmatrix} 7 & 10 \\ 15 & 22 \end{pmatrix}\begin{pmatrix} 1 & 2 \\ 3 & 4 \end{pmatrix} = \begin{pmatrix} 37 & 54 \\ 81 & 118 \end{pmatrix}$.

Example 2: $(0)(0) = 0^2 = 0$.

Example 3: $II = I^2 = I$. $\quad I^3 = I^2 I = I$.

Example 4: By using the distributive law, we find that $(A + B)^2 = (A + B)(A + B) = A(A + B) + B(A + B) = AA + AB + BA + BB = A^2 + AB + BA + B^2$.

This differs from the usual formula of algebra inasmuch as AB may not be the same thing as BA. If, however, A and B commute, we can write

$$(A + B)^2 = A^2 + 2AB + B^2.$$

Definition: *If* m *is a positive integer,* A^m *is defined as the product of* m A*'s:* $A^m = AAA \cdots A$. *(By the associative law of multiplication the grouping of the factors is immaterial.) If* $A \neq 0$, *the zeroth power of* A, A^0, *is defined as* I.

The matrix expression 0^0 is not defined. The "usual" Law of Exponents holds for matrix powers.

Theorem: *If* m *and* n *are positive or zero integers, and if* A *is a square matrix, then (with the exception of any case in which* 0^0 *appears),*

$$(A^m)(A^n) = (A^n)(A^m) = A^{m+n} \tag{1}$$
$$(A^m)^n = (A^n)^m = A^{mn} \tag{2}$$
$$I^m = I \tag{3}$$
$$0^m = 0. \tag{4}$$

PROOF: Statements (3) and (4) should be obvious in view of Examples (2) and (3).

$(A^m)(A^n)$ designates m A's followed by n A's. By the associative law, the grouping of the factors is immaterial and so this equals the product of $m + n$ A's which is A^{m+n}. If m is 0, then $A^m = I$. Hence $(A^m)(A^n) = IA^n = A^n = A^{m+n}$. A similar argument covers the case in which $n = 0$.

$(A^m)^n$ designates the product of n blocks of m A's. $(A^n)^m$ designates m blocks of n A's. In either case, we obtain the product of mn A's. Therefore, $(A^m)^n = (A^n)^m = A^{mn}$. If $m = 0$, $A^0 = I$. Hence $(A^m)^n = (I)^n = I = A^0 = A^{mn}$. Similarly, for $n = 0$.

This covers the Law of Exponents as far as non-negative integer powers are concerned. Negative powers will be taken up after the notion of matrix inversion has been introduced.

Note that the first law of exponents (1) implies that different powers of the same matrix commute with one another.

PROBLEMS

1. Set $A = \begin{pmatrix} 1 & -1 \\ 1 & 2 \end{pmatrix}$. Compute A^2, A^3, and A^4. Show directly that $A(A^3) = (A^3)A$.

2. Multiply $AABB$ by $BABA$ on the right and express the product in the neatest form. Multiply it on the left.

3. If

$$A = \begin{pmatrix} 0 & 1 & 1 \\ 0 & 0 & 1 \\ 0 & 0 & 0 \end{pmatrix},$$

compute A^2, A^3, and A^4.

4. If $A = \begin{pmatrix} 1 & 1 \\ 0 & 1 \end{pmatrix}$, find a formula for the elements of A^n.

5. The matrix J has order $n \times n$. Find a formula for the elements of J^m. (Recall that all the elements of J are 1).

6. Compute $(J - I)^2$ in two different ways. Use 4×4 matrices.

7. D is a diagonal matrix. Describe the elements of D^n.

8. If $A = \begin{pmatrix} \cos\theta & \sin\theta \\ -\sin\theta & \cos\theta \end{pmatrix}$, prove that $A^2 = \begin{pmatrix} \cos 2\theta & \sin 2\theta \\ -\sin 2\theta & \cos 2\theta \end{pmatrix}$.

9. Prove that $A^3 = \begin{pmatrix} \cos 3\theta & \sin 3\theta \\ -\sin 3\theta & \cos 3\theta \end{pmatrix}$. What do you suppose is the general result?

10. If

$$H = \begin{pmatrix} 1 & 0 & 0 & \cdots & 0 \\ 0 & 0 & 0 & \cdots & 0 \\ \cdot & \cdot & \cdot & \cdots & \cdot \\ 0 & 0 & 0 & \cdots & 0 \end{pmatrix},$$

prove that $H^2 = H$. Compute H^{1000}.

11. If $AB = BA$, show that $A^2B = BA^2$.

12. If $AB = BA$, show that $A^mB^n = B^nA^m$ where m and n are any positive integers.

13. A is a square matrix of order n. How many ordinary multiplications are necessary to compute A^p by means of successive matrix multiplications?

14. A is a square matrix of order n. Compare the number of ordinary multiplications necessary to compute A^8: (1) By means of successive matrix multiplications. (2) By means of $A^8 = ((A^2)^2)^2$.

15. If

$$M = \begin{pmatrix} 1 & a & b & c \\ a^{-1} & 1 & a^{-1}b & a^{-1}c \\ b^{-1} & ab^{-1} & 1 & b^{-1}c \\ c^{-1} & ac^{-1} & bc^{-1} & 1 \end{pmatrix},$$

prove that $M^2 = 4M$. Hence, prove that $M^n = 4^{n-1}M$.

A polynomial of degree n in a variable x is an expression of the form $a_0x^n + a_1x^{n-1} + \cdots + a_{n-1}x + a_n$. The letters $a_0, a_1, \ldots, a_n$ represent certain constants. The expressions $5x^2 + 2x + 1$ and $-21x^6 - 14x^4 + 6x^3 + x$ are examples of polynomials in x. Now that we have seen how to form matrix powers, it is a simple matter to form matrix polynomials. If A is a square matrix, the expression $5A^2 + 2A + I$ and $-21A^6 - 14A^4 + 6A^3 + A$ are polynomials in the matrix A or, briefly, matrix polynomials.

Note that an expression such as $5A^2 + 2A + 1$ would be meaningless, since we cannot add constants to matrices. For this reason, the "constant term" in a matrix polynomial is taken to be a multiple of I. This coincides with the usage for ordinary polynomials, for $5x^2 + 2x + 1$ is the same as $5x^2 + 2x + 1\,x^0$ and $5A^2 + 2A + I$ is the same as $5A^2 + 2A + A^0$.

Definition: *A matrix polynomial in a square matrix* A *is an expression of the form*

$$a_0A^n + a_1A^{n-1} + \cdots + a_{n-1}A + a_nI$$

where $a_0, a_1, \ldots, a_n$ *are constants.*

Example 1: If $A = \begin{pmatrix} 1 & 5 \\ -1 & 2 \end{pmatrix}$, then $A^2 = \begin{pmatrix} -4 & 15 \\ -3 & -1 \end{pmatrix}$, and hence

$$5A^2 + 2A + I = \begin{pmatrix} -17 & 85 \\ -17 & 0 \end{pmatrix}.$$

Example 2: The matrix $A = \begin{pmatrix} 1 & 1 \\ -1 & 1 \end{pmatrix}$ satisfies the quadratic matrix equation $A^2 - 2A + 2I = 0$. For, we may compute $A^2 = \begin{pmatrix} 0 & 2 \\ -2 & 0 \end{pmatrix}$ and $-2A = \begin{pmatrix} -2 & -2 \\ 2 & -2 \end{pmatrix}$. Hence, $A^2 - 2A + 2I = \begin{pmatrix} 0 & 0 \\ 0 & 0 \end{pmatrix}$.

Polynomials in the *same* square matrix, A, can be added, subtracted, and multiplied one by the other in accordance with the "usual" rules of algebra. For example, compare and justify the sums

$$\begin{array}{r} 5x^2 - 3x + 1 \\ x^2 + 2x + 2 \\ \hline 6x^2 - x + 3 \end{array} \qquad \begin{array}{r} 5A^2 - 3A + I \\ A^2 + 2A + 2I \\ \hline 6A^2 - A + 3I \end{array}.$$

Compare and justify the products (formed by using the distributive law)

$$\begin{array}{rrrr} x^2 & + x & + 2 & \\ x & - 1 & & \\ \hline x^3 + x^2 & + 2x & & \\ - x^2 & - x & - 2 & \\ \hline x^3 & + x & - 2 & \end{array} \qquad \begin{array}{rrrr} A^2 & + A & + 2I & \\ A & - I & & \\ \hline A^3 + A^2 & + 2A & & \\ - A^2 & - A & - 2I & \\ \hline A^3 & + A & - 2I & \end{array}.$$

The matrix algebra mimics the conventional algebra exactly. This means that if one has a polynomial identity in the variable x, a true matrix identity will result if a square matrix A is written in place of x. (Constant terms are to be replaced by appropriate multiples of I.)

A special instance of this is that *polynomials in the same matrix* A *always commute.* For example,

$$(2x + 1)(3x + 1) = (3x + 1)(2x + 1)$$

is an ordinary algebraic identity. Hence,

$$(2A + I)(3A + I) = (3A + I)(2A + I),$$

which expresses the commutativity of the matrices $2A + I$ and $3A + I$, is a matrix identity. This may be verified by multiplying out:

$$(2A + I)(3A + I) = (2A)(3A) + (2A)I + I(3A) + I(I).$$

Simplifying, this becomes $6A^2 + 2A + 3A + I$ or $6A^2 + 5A + I$. On the other hand, $(3A + I)(2A + I) = (3A)(2A) + (3A)I + I(2A) + I(I)$. Simplifying, this becomes $6A^2 + 3A + 2A + I$ or $6A^2 + 5A + I$—the same final answer.

On the other hand, the manipulation of polynomials in *several different* matrices may not necessarily follow the usual rules of algebra. See, for instance, Example 4, page 50.

PROBLEMS

1. Show that the matrix $A = \begin{pmatrix} 1 & 2 \\ 3 & 4 \end{pmatrix}$ satisfies the equation $A^2 - 5A - 2I = 0$.

2. Show that the matrix A of Problem 1 also satisfies the equation

$$A^3 - 27A - 10I = 0.$$

3. If

$$B = \begin{pmatrix} 1 & 1 & 1 \\ 1 & -1 & 1 \\ -1 & 1 & 1 \end{pmatrix},$$

compute $B^3 + B$. Compute $2B^2 + I$. Show directly that $B^3 + B$ and $2B^2 + I$ commute.

4. Let $A = \begin{pmatrix} 3 & -2 \\ 1 & 1 \end{pmatrix}$. Compute $3A^2 - 9A + 6I$. Compute $3(A - I)(A - 2I)$. Do the two results agree?

5. Let $A = \begin{pmatrix} a & b \\ c & -a \end{pmatrix}$ and suppose that the elements are related by the equation $a^2 + bc = 1$. Prove that $A^2 = I$. Hence conclude that the matrix I has infinitely many square roots. How does this situation compare with ordinary algebra?

6. Suppose that $p(x)$, $q(x)$, and $r(x)$ are three polynomials for which $p(x)q(x) = r(x)$, for all values of x. For example, $p(x) = 1 - x^2$, $q(x) = 1 + x^2$, $r(x) = 1 - x^4$. By $p(A)$, $q(A)$, $r(A)$ we will mean the corresponding matrix polynomials of the square matrix A. For example, $p(A) = I - A^2$, $q(A) = I + A^2$, $r(A) = I - A^4$. Does it always follow that $(p(A))(q(A)) = r(A)$?

7. If the numbers p, q, and r satisfy the equation $p^2 + q^2 + r^2 = 1$, show that the matrix

$$A = \begin{pmatrix} 0 & r & q \\ -r & 0 & p \\ -q & -p & 0 \end{pmatrix}$$

satisfies the equation $A^3 + A = 0$.

8. Suppose a matrix A satisfies the equation $A^2 - 2A + I = 0$. Show that $A^3 = 3A - 2I$ and $A^4 = 4A - 3I$.

9. Prove that $A^3 + 6A^2 + 7A + I = A(A(A + 6I) + 7I) + I$.

2.8 The Transpose of a Product

Suppose that A is an $m \times n$ matrix with elements a_{ij} and B is an $n \times p$ matrix with elements b_{ij}. Then, by the definition of matrix multiplication, AB is an $m \times p$ matrix whose element c_{ij} in the ith row and jth column, is given by

$$c_{ij} = a_{i1}b_{1j} + a_{i2}b_{2j} + \cdots + a_{in}b_{nj}.$$

The transpose of AB, designated by $(AB)'$, is obtained from AB by interchanging rows and columns. This is accomplished by switching the place of the i and the j; that is to say, the element in the ith and jth column of $(AB)'$ is

$$a_{j1}b_{1i} + a_{j2}b_{2i} + \cdots + a_{jn}b_{ni}.$$

This can be written as

$$b_{1i}a_{j1} + b_{2i}a_{j2} + \cdots + b_{ni}a_{jn}.$$

Now,

$$\begin{pmatrix} b_{1i} \\ b_{2i} \\ \cdot \\ \cdot \\ \cdot \\ b_{ni} \end{pmatrix}$$

is the ith column of B, and $(a_{j1}\, a_{j2} \cdots a_{jn})$ is the jth row of A. This means that $(b_{1i}\, b_{2i} \cdots b_{ni})$ is the ith row of B' and

$$\begin{pmatrix} a_{j1} \\ a_{j2} \\ \cdot \\ \cdot \\ \cdot \\ a_{jn} \end{pmatrix}$$

is the jth column of A$'$. The matrix product $B'A'$ has, therefore, as an element in its ith row and jth column

$$b_{1i}a_{j1} + b_{2i}a_{j2} + \cdots + b_{ni}a_{jn}.$$

If we compare this expression with the one derived above, we conclude that

$$(AB)' = B'A'.$$

Notice, once again, that the product $B'A'$ can be defined; for B' is a $p \times n$ matrix while A' is an $n \times m$ matrix. They are therefore conformable for multiplication in the given order.

We formulate this as a theorem.

Theorem: *If* A *and* B *are conformable for multiplication, then*

$$(\mathrm{AB})' = \mathrm{B}'\mathrm{A}'.$$

This rule can be extended to more than two factors. Suppose we have to deal with $(ABC)'$. By the associative property of multiplication,

$$(ABC)' = (A(BC))'.$$

Apply the theorem,

$$(A(BC))' = (BC)'A'.$$

Apply the theorem once again.

$$(BC)'A' = (C'B')A' = C'B'A'.$$

Therefore,

$$(ABC)' = C'B'A'.$$

The same trick will work with any number of factors and we shall state the result as a corollary.

Corollary: $(ABCD \cdots F)' = F' \cdots D'C'B'A'$. In words: *the transpose of the product of any number of matrices is equal to the product of the transposes of the individual matrices formed in the reverse order.*

Examples:

(1) $A = \begin{pmatrix} 1 & 2 \\ 3 & 4 \end{pmatrix}$, $B = \begin{pmatrix} 1 & -1 \\ -1 & -1 \end{pmatrix}$. $AB = \begin{pmatrix} -1 & -3 \\ -1 & -7 \end{pmatrix}$. Therefore $(AB)' = \begin{pmatrix} -1 & -1 \\ -3 & -7 \end{pmatrix}$. But, $B' = \begin{pmatrix} 1 & -1 \\ -1 & -1 \end{pmatrix}$, $A' = \begin{pmatrix} 1 & 3 \\ 2 & 4 \end{pmatrix}$ so that $B'A' = \begin{pmatrix} -1 & -1 \\ -3 & -7 \end{pmatrix} = (AB)'$.

(2) If A and B are symmetric matrices, prove that the matrix ABA is also symmetric. One might do this in two ways: (a) by examining the individual elements of the matrices, or (b) by making use of the laws of the transpose. The latter method is by far the easier of the two. $(ABA)' = A'B'A'$. But if A and B are both symmetric, $A = A'$ and $B = B'$. Hence, $A'B'A' = ABA$. Therefore, $(ABA)' = ABA$, so that ABA must be symmetric.

PROBLEMS

1. If

$$A = \begin{pmatrix} 1 & 1 & 1 \\ -1 & 1 & -1 \\ 1 & 1 & -1 \end{pmatrix} \text{ and } B = \begin{pmatrix} 1 & -1 & 1 \\ 1 & 1 & 1 \\ -1 & -1 & 1 \end{pmatrix},$$

show by a direct computation that $(AB)' = B'A'$.

2. Prove that AA' is always a symmetric matrix.
3. Prove that $(A^n)' = (A')^n$.
4. If A is skew symmetric (that is, $A' = -A$), prove A^2 must be symmetric.
5. If A and B are both symmetric, prove $ABABA$ is symmetric.
6. If the matrices A and B commute, prove that A' and B' commute.
7. Show that $(A(B + C))' = B'A' + C'A'$.
8. Suppose that a square matrix A satisfies the equation

$$A^3 - 6A^2 + 9A - 3I = 0.$$

Show that the matrix A' satisfies the same equation.

9. Prove a theorem that generalizes the result of Problem 8.
10. Prove that $((A^n)')^m = (A^{mn})' = (A')^{mn}$.

2.9 Matrix Multiplication at Work

Now that matrix multiplication has been introduced and its more important laws have been explained, we shall exhibit a variety of things that can be accomplished with it.

1. Formation of Simultaneous Linear Equations (Multiplication of a Square Matrix by a Column Matrix). The following matrix product is easily worked out.

$$\begin{pmatrix} a_{11} & a_{12} & \cdots & a_{1n} \\ a_{21} & a_{22} & \cdots & a_{2n} \\ \cdot & \cdot & \cdots & \cdot \\ a_{n1} & a_{n2} & \cdots & a_{nn} \end{pmatrix} \begin{pmatrix} x_1 \\ x_2 \\ \cdot \\ x_n \end{pmatrix} = \begin{pmatrix} a_{11}x_1 + a_{12}x_2 + \cdots + a_{1n}x_n \\ a_{21}x_1 + a_{22}x_2 + \cdots + a_{2n}x_n \\ \cdots \\ a_{n1}x_1 + a_{n2}x_2 + \cdots + a_{nn}x_n \end{pmatrix}.$$

Designate the first matrix factor by A and the second factor by X. The product AX is particularly important since it is intimately related to systems of simultaneous linear equations. If we introduce the column matrix

$$B = \begin{pmatrix} b_1 \\ b_2 \\ \cdot \\ \cdot \\ b_n \end{pmatrix},$$

then the system of n simultaneous equations in n unknowns $x_1, x_2, \ldots, x_n$ can be abbreviated by means of the single matrix equation $AX = B$.

Example: The system of two equations in two unknowns x_1, x_2,

$$\begin{cases} 2x_1 - 3x_2 = 1 \\ -3x_1 - 4x_2 = 6 \end{cases}$$

is completely equivalent to the matrix equation

$$\begin{pmatrix} 2 & -3 \\ -3 & -4 \end{pmatrix} \begin{pmatrix} x_1 \\ x_2 \end{pmatrix} = \begin{pmatrix} 1 \\ 6 \end{pmatrix}.$$

PROBLEMS

1. Express the following systems of equations in matrix form:

$$\begin{cases} 2x_1 + x_2 = 7 \\ x_1 - x_2 = 6, \end{cases} \qquad \begin{cases} 3x_1 + x_2 + x_3 = 4 \\ x_1 - x_2 + x_3 = 0 \\ 4x_1 + 6x_2 + 7x_3 = 18, \end{cases} \qquad \begin{cases} x_1 + x_2 + x_3 = 6 \\ x_1 + x_3 = 0 \\ 2x_1 - x_2 + x_3 = 5. \end{cases}$$

2. Express these systems in matrix form:

$$\begin{cases} x_1 + x_2 = -3 \\ x_1 \qquad = \quad 4, \end{cases} \qquad \begin{cases} x_1 + x_3 = 1 \\ x_2 + x_3 = 1 \\ x_1 + x_2 = 1, \end{cases} \qquad \begin{cases} x_1 + 2x_2 - x_3 = 2 \\ x_1 \qquad\quad - x_3 = 6 \\ \qquad\qquad\quad x_3 = 1. \end{cases}$$

3. Write the matrix equation $\begin{pmatrix} 6 & 8 \\ 7 & 9 \end{pmatrix} \begin{pmatrix} x_1 \\ x_2 \end{pmatrix} = \begin{pmatrix} 4 \\ 2 \end{pmatrix}$ as a system of equations, and find its solution.

4. Find x_1 and x_2 if

$$\begin{pmatrix} 2 & 1 \\ 7 & 4 \end{pmatrix} \begin{pmatrix} x_1 \\ x_2 \end{pmatrix} = \begin{pmatrix} 0 \\ 1 \end{pmatrix}.$$

5. Do the same for

$$\begin{pmatrix} 0 & 0 & 1 & 0 \\ 1 & 0 & 0 & 0 \\ 0 & 1 & 0 & 0 \\ 0 & 0 & 0 & 1 \end{pmatrix} \begin{pmatrix} x_1 \\ x_2 \\ x_3 \\ x_4 \end{pmatrix} = \begin{pmatrix} 1 \\ 9 \\ 6 \\ 4 \end{pmatrix} \quad \text{and for} \quad \begin{pmatrix} 1 & 0 & 1 & 0 \\ 0 & 1 & 0 & 0 \\ 0 & 0 & 0 & 1 \\ 0 & 0 & 1 & 0 \end{pmatrix} \begin{pmatrix} x_1 \\ x_2 \\ x_3 \\ x_4 \end{pmatrix} = \begin{pmatrix} 1 \\ 0 \\ 6 \\ 6 \end{pmatrix}.$$

6. If $AX = B$, prove that $X'A' = B'$. Hence show that a system of linear equations can be written in either of these forms. Express the systems of Problems 1 and 2 in this alternate form.

2. *Multiplication of a Rectangular Matrix by a Column Matrix.* There are instances in which the number of unknowns is not equal to the number of equations. Let us see what happens when we try to interpret the matrix equation $AX = B$ as a system of equations when A is not square. For example, consider the product

$$\begin{pmatrix} 2 & 1 & 1 \\ 1 & 3 & 2 \end{pmatrix} \begin{pmatrix} x_1 \\ x_2 \\ x_3 \end{pmatrix} = \begin{pmatrix} 3 \\ 2 \end{pmatrix}.$$

This matrix equation leads to

$$\begin{cases} 2x_1 + \ x_2 + \ x_3 = 3 \\ \ x_1 + 3x_2 + 2x_3 = 2, \end{cases}$$

which is a system of two linear equations in three unknowns. This system is *underdetermined.* This means that there are many solutions to the system; the equations do not contain enough information to determine a unique answer. The values $x_1 = 1$, $x_2 = 1$, $x_3 = 2$ are a solution. The values $x_1 = 0$, $x_2 = -4$, $x_3 = 7$ are also a solution. But there are infinitely many solutions. In fact, if you choose any value of t whatever, the values $x_1 = -t$, $x_2 = -4 - 3t$, $x_3 = 7 + 5t$ will satisfy the simultaneous equations. This can be shown as follows:

$$\begin{cases} 2(-t) + (-4 - 3t) + (7 + 5t) = 3 \\ (-t) + 3(-4 - 3t) + 2(7 + 5t) = 2. \end{cases}$$

Suppose we take a matrix A that has more rows than columns:

$$\begin{pmatrix} 1 & 2 \\ 1 & 1 \\ 2 & 1 \end{pmatrix} \begin{pmatrix} x_1 \\ x_2 \end{pmatrix} = \begin{pmatrix} 1 \\ 1 \\ 1 \end{pmatrix}.$$

This matrix product is equivalent to the system

$$\begin{cases} x_1 + 2x_2 = 1 \\ x_1 + x_2 = 1 \\ 2x_1 + x_2 = 1. \end{cases}$$

This system is *overdetermined*. This means that is impossible to find values that simultaneously satisfy the equations. For, subtracting the second equation from the first equation, we learn that $x_2 = 0$. Subtraction of the second equation from the third leads to $x_1 = 0$. But the pair of values $x_1 = 0$, $x_2 = 0$ satisfies none of the equations.

If there are n simultaneous equations and n unknowns, there is usually one and only one solution to the system. If there are fewer equations than unknowns, the system is usually underdetermined. If there are more equations than unknowns, the system is usually overdetermined. Matrix theory elucidates the circumstances under which these three possibilities occur.

Underdetermined equations represent a situation that is *incomplete*. Overdetermined equations represent a situation that is *contradictory*. Both correspond more closely to our conception of what goes on in life than precisely determined situations; both are more realistic in practical problems. One of the characteristics of applied mathematics in recent years is its great concern with the resolution of incomplete or contradictory problems. It does this by introducing additional criteria for the selection of answers.

PROBLEMS

1. Show that the system of equations

$$\begin{cases} 2x_1 + 3x_2 + 4x_3 = 13 \\ x_1 - x_2 + x_3 = 2 \end{cases}$$

is underdetermined, and that for every value of t, $x_1 = 1 + 7t$, $x_2 = 1 + 2t$, $x_3 = 2 - 5t$ is a solution.

2. Show that the system

$$\begin{cases} x_1 + x_2 + x_3 = 3 \\ 2x_1 + x_2 + 2x_3 = 5 \\ 3x_1 + x_2 + 2x_3 = 6 \\ x_1 - x_2 + x_3 = 4 \end{cases}$$

is overdetermined.

3. Is the system

$$\begin{cases} 2x_1 + x_2 = 5 \\ x_1 + 2x_2 = 4 \\ 3x_1 - 2x_2 = 4 \end{cases}$$

overdetermined or underdetermined?

4. Is the system

$$\begin{cases} x_1 + 3x_2 = 7 \\ 3x_1 + 6x_2 = 14 \\ -x_1 - 3x_2 = -7 \end{cases}$$

overdetermined or underdetermined?

5. Write the systems in Problems 1–4 in matrix form.

6. Show that the system of equations

$$\begin{cases} x = 1 - y \\ 2x + 2y = 2 \end{cases}$$

is underdetermined and determine that solution of the system which is closest to the point (0, 0).

7. Prove that the system

$$\begin{cases} x - y = 0 \\ 3x - 2y = 1 \\ 4x - 2y = 3 \end{cases}$$

is overdetermined and hence has no solution. Suppose that we adopt the following procedure for "solving" the system. Take the equations two by two and solve them. This will give values (x_1, y_1), (x_2, y_2), (x_3, y_3) that may not agree. Then, accept as the answer, the average value:

$$\left(\frac{x_1 + x_2 + x_3}{3}, \quad \frac{y_1 + y_2 + y_3}{3}\right).$$

(a) "Solve" the above system in the sense just explained.

(b) Give a geometrical interpretation of this process.

3. Linear Changes of Variable: Multiplication of a Rectangular Matrix by a Column Matrix. We have already had an inkling of this in Section 5 of this chapter. If A is an $m \times n$ matrix, and X is an $n \times 1$ matrix, then A and X are conformable for multiplication in this order and their product is an $m \times 1$ matrix. We have

$$\begin{pmatrix} a_{11} & a_{12} & \cdots & a_{1n} \\ a_{21} & a_{22} & \cdots & a_{2n} \\ \cdot & \cdot & \cdots & \cdot \\ a_{m1} & a_{m2} & \cdots & a_{mn} \end{pmatrix} \begin{pmatrix} x_1 \\ x_2 \\ \cdot \\ x_n \end{pmatrix} = \begin{pmatrix} a_{11}x_1 + a_{12}x_2 + \cdots + a_{1n}x_n \\ a_{21}x_1 + a_{22}x_2 + \cdots + a_{2n}x_n \\ \cdot \quad \cdot \quad \cdots \quad \vdots \\ a_{m1}x_1 + a_{m2}x_2 + \cdots + a_{mn}x_n \end{pmatrix}.$$

Suppose that we write

$$AX = Y \qquad \text{or} \qquad Y = AX$$

where

$$Y = \begin{pmatrix} y_1 \\ y_2 \\ \cdot \\ \cdot \\ y_m \end{pmatrix}.$$

This matrix equation is therefore equal to the system of equations

$$\begin{cases} y_1 = a_{11}x_1 + a_{12}x_2 + \cdots + a_{1n}x_n \\ y_2 = a_{21}x_1 + a_{22}x_2 + \cdots + a_{2n}x_n \\ \cdot \quad \cdot \quad \cdot \quad \cdot \\ y_m = a_{m1}x_1 + a_{m2}x_2 + \cdots + a_{mn}x_n. \end{cases}$$

This system expresses the m variables $y_1, y_2, \ldots, y_m$ in terms of n variables $x_1, x_2, \ldots, x_n$. Only first degree terms appear, and the y's are called *linear combinations* of the x's. The system of equations can be considered as a *transformation* that changes x's into y's. It is known as a *linear transformation.*

Suppose that the y's, on their part, are related to further quantities, which we will call z's; suppose that there are p z's each of which is a linear combination of the y's:

$$\begin{cases} z_1 = b_{11}y_1 + b_{12}y_2 + \cdots + b_{1m}y_m \\ z_2 = b_{21}y_1 + b_{22}y_2 + \cdots + b_{2m}y_m \\ \cdot \quad \cdot \quad \cdot \quad \cdot \\ z_p = b_{p1}y_1 + b_{p2}y_2 + \cdots + b_{pm}y_m. \end{cases}$$

By the same token, this relationship may be expressed in matrix fashion by means of the equation

$$Z = BY$$

where $$B = \begin{pmatrix} b_{11} & \cdots & b_{1m} \\ \cdot & & \cdot \\ b_{p1} & \cdots & b_{pm} \end{pmatrix} \quad \text{and} \quad Z = \begin{pmatrix} z_1 \\ z_2 \\ \cdot \\ \cdot \\ z_p \end{pmatrix}.$$

If we substitute the values of y in terms of x in the equations that relate the z's to the y's, we will have the z's expressed in terms of the x's. But this process can be carried out by matrix multiplication. If $Z = BY$ and $Y = AX$, then, $Z = B(AX) = (BA)X$. Since B is $p \times m$ and A is $m \times n$, the matrix BA is $p \times n$, and this last matrix equation is equivalent to expressing the p quantities $z_1, z_2, \ldots, z_p$ as linear combinations of the n quantities $x_1, x_2, \ldots, x_n$.

The situation can be summed up in the following way.

If we change from the variables x *to the variables* y *by a linear transformation with matrix* A, *and if we change from the variables* y *to the variables* z *by another linear transformation with matrix* B, *then the matrix* BA *automatically gives us the linear transformation that changes the variables* x *into the variables* z.

Note the sequence of matrices in the product BA. It is important to have the sequence in the correct order inasmuch as BA and AB are usually different.

It naturally follows that if one has more than two transformations to carry out, one only needs to increase the number of matrix factors appropriately.

Example:

If $\begin{cases} y_1 = 3x_1 + 4x_2 \\ y_2 = x_1 - x_2, \end{cases}$ $\begin{cases} z_1 = y_1 + 2y_2 \\ z_2 = 3y_1 - y_2 \end{cases}$ and $\begin{cases} w_1 = z_1 - 2z_2 \\ w_2 = 2z_1 + z_2 \end{cases}$

then,

$$\begin{pmatrix} w_1 \\ w_2 \end{pmatrix} = \begin{pmatrix} 1 & -2 \\ 2 & 1 \end{pmatrix} \begin{pmatrix} 1 & 2 \\ 3 & -1 \end{pmatrix} \begin{pmatrix} 3 & 4 \\ 1 & -1 \end{pmatrix} \begin{pmatrix} x_1 \\ x_2 \end{pmatrix}.$$

Hence,

$$\begin{pmatrix} w_1 \\ w_2 \end{pmatrix} = \begin{pmatrix} -11 & -24 \\ 18 & 17 \end{pmatrix} \begin{pmatrix} x_1 \\ x_2 \end{pmatrix}, \quad \text{or,}$$

$$\begin{cases} w_1 = -11x_1 - 24x_2 \\ w_2 = 18x_1 + 17x_2. \end{cases}$$

If values of w_1 and w_2 are sought that correspond to particular values of x_1 and x_2, say to $x_1 = 1$, $x_2 = -1$, we may write

$$\begin{pmatrix} w_1 \\ w_2 \end{pmatrix} = \begin{pmatrix} -11 & -24 \\ 18 & 17 \end{pmatrix} \begin{pmatrix} 1 \\ -1 \end{pmatrix} = \begin{pmatrix} 13 \\ 1 \end{pmatrix},$$

and hence $w_1 = 13$ and $w_2 = 1$.

PROBLEMS

1. If

$$\begin{cases} y_1 = 6x_1 + 5x_2 \\ y_2 = -x_1 + x_2, \end{cases} \quad \begin{cases} z_1 = y_1 + y_2 \\ z_2 = y_1 - y_2, \end{cases} \quad \text{and} \quad \begin{cases} w_1 = 2z_1 + z_2 \\ w_2 = z_1 - 3z_2, \end{cases}$$

express the w's directly in terms of the x's by means of matrix multiplication. Verify your answer by means of direct substitution.

2. If

$$\begin{cases} y_1 = x_1 + 2x_2 \\ y_2 = 2x_1 - x_2 \\ y_3 = 2x_1 + 3x_2, \end{cases} \quad \begin{cases} z_1 = y_1 - y_2 \\ z_2 = 2y_1 + 3y_2 \\ z_3 = y_1 + 3y_2, \end{cases} \quad \text{and} \quad \begin{cases} w_1 = 2z_1 + z_2 - z_3 \\ w_2 = 3z_1 - z_2 + 2z_3 \end{cases}$$

express the w's directly in terms of the x's by means of matrix multiplication.

3. If

$$\begin{cases} y_1 = x_1 + x_2 + x_3 \\ y_2 = 2x_1 + 2x_2 - x_3 \\ y_3 = -x_1 - x_2 + x_3 \end{cases} \quad \text{and} \quad \begin{cases} z_1 = 2y_1 + y_2 + 2y_3 \\ z_2 = -y_1 + y_2 + 2y_3, \end{cases}$$

express the z's directly in terms of the x's by means of matrix multiplication.

4. If

$$\begin{cases} y_1 = x_1 + 2x_2 + 3x_3 - x_4 \\ y_2 = 5x_1 + x_2 - x_3 + x_4 \end{cases} \quad \text{and} \quad z_1 = 3y_1 + y_2,$$

express z_1 directly in terms of the x's by matrix multiplication.

5. In Problems 1 and 2, use matrix multiplication to find the values of the w's when $x_1 = 1$ and $x_2 = 2$.

6. In Problems 1 and 2, suppose that the w's are related by means of the equation $2w_1 - 3w_2 = 0$. Find in each case, by matrix multiplication, the corresponding relationship between x_1 and x_2.

7. Give an interpretation of the following statement in terms of changes of variable: if X satisfies the equation $AX = B$, and if $X = CY$, then Y satisfies the equation $(AC)Y = B$.

4. The Action of Permutation Matrices. A very special case of changes of variable are those given by permutation matrices. Recall that a permutation matrix is a square matrix that has precisely one 1 in every row and column, and represents a permutation of objects. Let us see how this works out from our present point of view. For example. write

$$(y_1 \quad y_2 \quad y_3) = (x_1 \quad x_2 \quad x_3) \begin{pmatrix} 0 & 1 & 0 \\ 0 & 0 & 1 \\ 1 & 0 & 0 \end{pmatrix}.$$

By expanding this equation, we obtain

$$\begin{cases} y_1 = x_3 \\ y_2 = x_1 \\ y_3 = x_2. \end{cases}$$

In other words, the effect of this transformation is to permute the subscripts 1 2 3 into 3 1 2.

Since a first permutation followed by a second permutation is obviously a third permutation, it must follow that *the product of two permutation matrices is itself a permutation matrix.* For example,

$$\begin{pmatrix} 0 & 1 & 0 & 0 \\ 0 & 0 & 1 & 0 \\ 1 & 0 & 0 & 0 \\ 0 & 0 & 0 & 1 \end{pmatrix}\begin{pmatrix} 1 & 0 & 0 & 0 \\ 0 & 0 & 1 & 0 \\ 0 & 0 & 0 & 1 \\ 0 & 1 & 0 & 0 \end{pmatrix} = \begin{pmatrix} 0 & 0 & 1 & 0 \\ 0 & 0 & 0 & 1 \\ 1 & 0 & 0 & 0 \\ 0 & 1 & 0 & 0 \end{pmatrix}.$$

What is the effect of multiplying a "full" matrix by a permutation matrix? Consider the product

$$\begin{pmatrix} 0 & 1 & 0 \\ 0 & 0 & 1 \\ 1 & 0 & 0 \end{pmatrix}\begin{pmatrix} a_{11} & a_{12} & a_{13} \\ a_{21} & a_{22} & a_{23} \\ a_{31} & a_{32} & a_{33} \end{pmatrix} = \begin{pmatrix} a_{21} & a_{22} & a_{23} \\ a_{31} & a_{32} & a_{33} \\ a_{11} & a_{12} & a_{13} \end{pmatrix}.$$

Multiplication on the left side by this permutation matrix causes a permutation of the rows.

PROBLEMS

1. What is the effect of multiplying a matrix on the right side by a permutation matrix?
2. If P is a permutation matrix, prove that $PJ = JP = J$.
3. If P is a permutation matrix and if $P^2 = I$, explain what kind of permutation P effects.
4. If P is a permutation matrix, prove that the sequence of powers $P, P^2, P^3, \ldots$ cannot all be different matrices.
5. A matrix A is multiplied on the right (or on the left) by J. Contrast the elements of the product with those of A.
6. A pseudo-permutation matrix has been defined in Problem 11 on page 21. Prove that the product of two pseudo-permutation matrices is itself a pseudo-permutation matrix.
7. Describe the effect of multiplying J on the left by a diagonal matrix. On the right.

5. *Quadratic Forms.* First degree expressions come about by multiplying a matrix of constants by a matrix of variables. Second degree expressions

can come about by multiplying two matrices of variables. Constant matrices can be thrown in for good measure.

Example 1:

$$(x_1 \quad x_2 \quad x_3)\begin{pmatrix} x_1 \\ x_2 \\ x_3 \end{pmatrix} = (x_1^2 + x_2^2 + x_3^2).$$

If we let $X = (x_1 \quad x_2 \quad x_3)$, then we can also express this matrix equation as

$$XX' = (x_1^2 + x_2^2 + x_3^2).$$

Example 2:

$$(x_1 \quad x_2)\begin{pmatrix} 2 & 1 \\ 1 & 1 \end{pmatrix}\begin{pmatrix} x_1 \\ x_2 \end{pmatrix} = (2x_1^2 + 2x_1x_2 + x_2^2).$$

If we let $X = (x_1 \quad x_2)$ and $A = \begin{pmatrix} 2 & 1 \\ 1 & 1 \end{pmatrix}$, then this equation can be expressed as

$$XAX' = (2x_1^2 + 2x_1x_2 + x_2^2).$$

Expressions that arise from a matrix product of type XAX' are called *quadratic forms*.

Suppose that we would like to change variables in a quadratic form. What does $2x_1^2 + 2x_1x_2 + x_2^2$ become in terms of y_1 and y_2 if

$$\begin{cases} x_1 = y_1 + 2y_2 \\ x_2 = y_1 - y_2 \end{cases}?$$

The "conventional" way of doing this would be to substitute the values of x_1 and x_2 into the quadratic form and simplify:

$$\begin{aligned} 2x_1^2 + 2x_1x_2 + x_2^2 &= 2(y_1 + 2y_2)^2 + 2(y_1 + 2y_2)(y_1 - y_2) + (y_1 - y_2)^2 \\ &= 5y_1^2 + 8y_1y_2 + 5y_2^2. \end{aligned}$$

But there is also a matrix solution to this type of problem. Suppose that we let $Y = (y_1 \quad y_2)$ and $C = \begin{pmatrix} 1 & 2 \\ 1 & -1 \end{pmatrix}$. Then the relationship between the x's and the y's can be expressed by the matrix equation

$$X' = CY'$$

or

$$X = (CY')' = YC'.$$

Hence, $XAX' = (YC')A(CY') = Y(C'AC)Y'$. Since the variables are in the matrices Y and Y' and the constants are in $C'AC$, this means that the matrix associated with the transformed quadratic form is $C'AC$. Let us see how this works out with the above example:

$$C'AC = \begin{pmatrix} 1 & 1 \\ 2 & -1 \end{pmatrix}\begin{pmatrix} 2 & 1 \\ 1 & 1 \end{pmatrix}\begin{pmatrix} 1 & 2 \\ 1 & -1 \end{pmatrix} = \begin{pmatrix} 5 & 4 \\ 4 & 5 \end{pmatrix}.$$

Hence the new quadratic form is

$$Y(C'AC)Y' = (y_1 \quad y_2)\begin{pmatrix}5 & 4\\4 & 5\end{pmatrix}\begin{pmatrix}y_1\\y_2\end{pmatrix} = (5y_1^2 + 8y_1y_2 + 5y_2^2).$$

PROBLEMS

1. Expand:

$$(x_1 \quad x_2)\begin{pmatrix}2 & 2\\4 & -2\end{pmatrix}\begin{pmatrix}x_1\\x_2\end{pmatrix}, \qquad (x_1 \quad x_2)\begin{pmatrix}\frac{1}{2} & 0\\0 & \frac{1}{2}\end{pmatrix}\begin{pmatrix}x_1\\x_2\end{pmatrix},$$

$$(x_1 \quad x_2)\begin{pmatrix}0 & 2\\2 & 0\end{pmatrix}\begin{pmatrix}x_1\\x_2\end{pmatrix}, \qquad (x_1 \quad x_2)\begin{pmatrix}a & b\\b & c\end{pmatrix}\begin{pmatrix}x_1\\x_2\end{pmatrix},$$

$$(x_1 \quad x_2)\begin{pmatrix}2 & 3\\3 & -2\end{pmatrix}\begin{pmatrix}x_1\\x_2\end{pmatrix}.$$

2. Expand:

$$(x_1 \quad x_2 \quad x_3)\begin{pmatrix}1 & 2 & 1\\1 & 1 & 1\\2 & 2 & 3\end{pmatrix}\begin{pmatrix}x_1\\x_2\\x_3\end{pmatrix}, \qquad (x_1 \quad x_2 \quad x_3)\begin{pmatrix}2 & 0 & 2\\1 & 2 & 1\\1 & 2 & 1\end{pmatrix}\begin{pmatrix}x_1\\x_2\\x_3\end{pmatrix},$$

$$(x_1 \quad x_2 \quad x_3)\begin{pmatrix}1 & 0 & 0\\0 & 2 & 0\\0 & 0 & -7\end{pmatrix}\begin{pmatrix}x_1\\x_2\\x_3\end{pmatrix}, \qquad (x_1 \quad x_2 \quad x_3)\begin{pmatrix}1 & 0 & 0\\1 & 1 & 0\\1 & 1 & 1\end{pmatrix}\begin{pmatrix}x_1\\x_2\\x_3\end{pmatrix}.$$

3. Find a matrix product for the expressions:
$$3x_1^2 + 4x_1x_2 + 5x_2^2,\ x_1^2 + x_2^2 + x_3^2 + x_1x_2 + x_1x_3 + x_2x_3.$$
Show that the matrix in the central portion of the product can be selected so as to be symmetric.

4. Use matrix multiplication to find the values of the expressions in Problem 2 if $x_1 = 1 \quad x_2 = -1 \quad x_3 = 2$.

5. Describe (or plot) the set of points with coordinates (x, y) that satisfy the equation $(x \quad y)\ (x \quad y)' = (6)$.

6. Describe (or plot) the set of points with coordinates (x, y) that satisfy the matrix equation $(x \quad y)\begin{pmatrix}4 & 3\\3 & 5\end{pmatrix}\begin{pmatrix}x\\y\end{pmatrix} = (60)$.

7. By means of matrices introduce the variables y_1 and y_2 into the first expression in Problem 1 if

$$\begin{cases}x_1 = 4y_1 + 2y_2\\x_2 = y_1 - y_2.\end{cases}$$

8. By means of matrices, introduce the variables y_1, y_2, y_3 into the first expression in Problem 2 if

$$\begin{cases} x_1 = y_1 + y_2 + y_3 \\ x_2 = y_1 + y_2 - y_3 \\ x_3 = y_1 - y_2 + y_3. \end{cases}$$

9. Prove that if A is symmetric, then $C'AC$ is also symmetric.

10. Suppose that A is a diagonal matrix, and $X = (x_1, x_2, \ldots, x_n)$. Write out XAX' explicitly.

2.10 Multiplication of a Rectangular Matrix by a Column Matrix: Some Practical Problems

1. Crates and Weights. Turn to the example of the citrus production of the State of Limonia given on page 9, and designate the matrix there by C. Suppose that in Limonia, oranges are packed 50 lbs. to the crate, lemons 45 lbs. to the crate, limes 45 lbs., grapefruit 60 lbs., and citrons 20 lbs. Introduce the matrix $W = \begin{pmatrix} 50 \\ 45 \\ 45 \\ 60 \\ 20 \end{pmatrix}$. The matrix product CW is a 5×1 column matrix. Each element of the product equals (number of crates of oranges times lbs. per crate) plus (number of crates of lemons times lbs. per crate) plus $\cdots$ plus (number of crates of citrons times lbs. per crate). Each row of C refers to one year's production, and hence the elements of CW are the total weights of fruit grown over the years in question. More exactly, since the elements of C are listed in 1000 crate units, the matrix $1000\ CW$ gives the total weight in pounds. CW would give it in 1000's of pounds.

This example is typical of a wide variety of problems that come up in practice. After the reader has examined this example, he might exclaim that matrices do not really give him a new method for finding total weights; he would go through the same arithmetic operations even if he were ignorant of matrices. This observation is certainly justified, and we are therefore led to ask just what the matrix approach accomplishes in the present example. It accomplishes several things. (1) It gathers together into two separate conceptual units two different types of data: crate data and weight data. Each is then available for subsequent manipulation in its own right. Some of these data may be fixed, and some variable. For example, if a different state packs its fruit in the same weights, then W will be the same. But if we were interested in total value of the fruit, we would multiply the same C by a column matrix V that listed the value for 1000 crates of each of the different kinds of fruit. (2) It shows that a certain type of problem fits a certain abstract pattern: in this case, matrix multiplication. If it were desired to handle this problem on a computing machine, one would need merely to use a standard code for matrix multiplication, and not be concerned whether one is talking about crates of oranges, dozens of light bulbs, the results of a physical experiment, et cetera.

2. *Maxwell's Influence Coefficients.* Here is an example that comes from the branch of mechanics known as the *theory of elasticity.* When a weight is attached to a spring, the elongation of the spring is proportional to the weight. If 1 pound causes the spring to stretch $\frac{1}{10}''$, then 2 pounds will cause it to stretch $\frac{2}{10}''$. This is known as *Hooke's Law** (Robert Hooke, 1635–1703). The renowned physicist James Clerk Maxwell (1831–1879) derived a simple method for describing the deformations of a more complicated elastic body when it has been subjected to a variety of concentrated loads.

Suppose we have an elastic body supported in some manner—think of a wooden or metallic beam B supported at its ends (Figure 2.3).

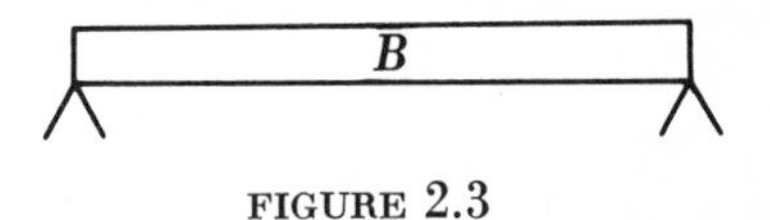

FIGURE 2.3

If a load of 1 lb. is concentrated at some portion of the beam, the beam will be deflected very slightly. Figure 2.4 is exaggerated.

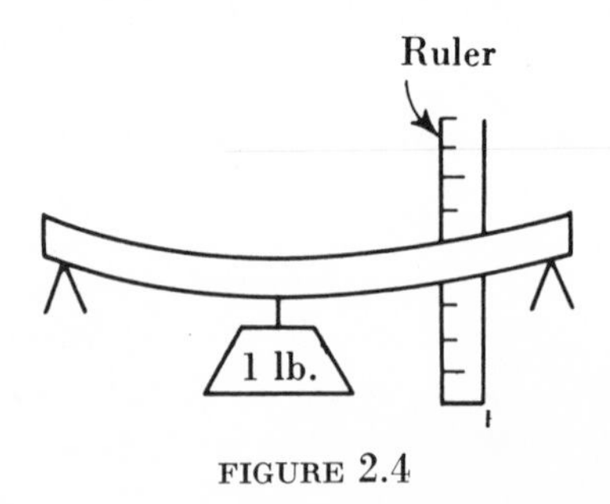

FIGURE 2.4

* This "law" is merely a description of observed behavior. It applies to many types of materials and to many types of distortion. It applies, for example, to (a) the stretching of a spring, (b) the twisting of a metal rod or wire, (c) the bending of a beam. See Section 3 of Chapter 7 for a discussion of its limitations.

Each point on the beam will be displaced downward and the amount of the displacement will depend upon where along the beam the point is and where along the beam the load has been concentrated. To make matters simple, suppose we distinguish three points or "stations" ①, ②, ③ along the beam (Figure 2.5).

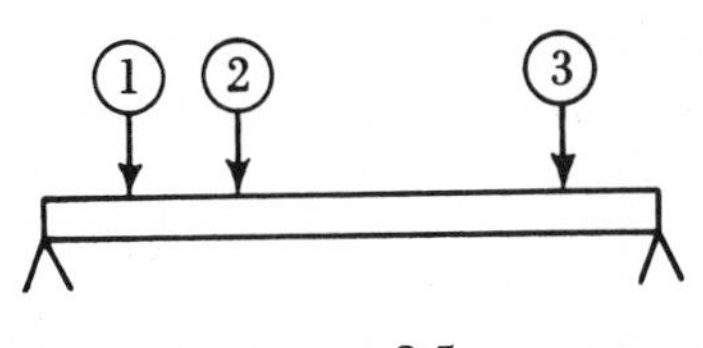

FIGURE 2.5

At each of these stations successively, we will apply a load of 1 lb. and then measure the deflection of the beam—also at these stations. The deflection (in inches) at station ① due to a 1 lb. load at station ① will be designated by d_{11}. The deflection at station ② due to a 1 lb. load at station ① will be designated by d_{21}. In general, the deflection (in inches) at station i due to a 1 lb. load at station j will be designated by d_{ij}. The quantities d_{ij} which serve to characterize the beam are known as Maxwell's *influence coefficients*, and the matrix (d_{ij}) is called the *influence matrix*. It is also called the *flexibility matrix*.

It is a surprising fact that the influence matrix is *symmetric*, that is, $d_{ij} = d_{ji}$. In physical language, this means that the deflection at station i due to a 1 lb. weight at station j is the same as the deflection at station j due to a 1 lb. weight at station i.

Suppose now that weights of w_1, w_2, and w_3 lbs. are placed at stations ①, ②, and ③ (Figure 2.6). What will the deflection of the beam be? It can be shown—and this is a form of *Hooke's Law*—that the deflections D_1, D_2, D_3 at stations ①, ②, ③ will be

$$\begin{aligned} D_1 &= d_{11}w_1 + d_{12}w_2 + d_{13}w_3 \\ D_2 &= d_{21}w_1 + d_{22}w_2 + d_{23}w_3 \\ D_3 &= d_{31}w_1 + d_{32}w_2 + d_{33}w_3 \end{aligned}$$

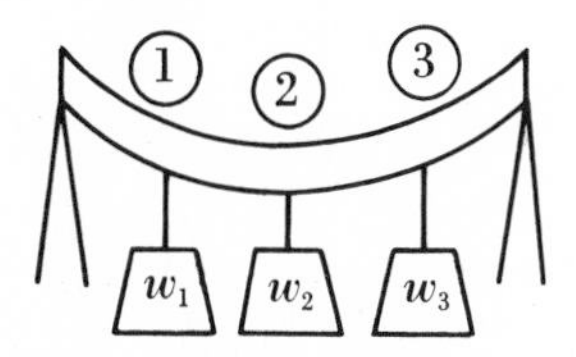

FIGURE 2.6

These equations hold providing the weights w_1, w_2, and w_3 are sufficiently small so that the beam is not loaded beyond its elastic limit. A typical equation, say the first, can be analyzed in the following manner. The deflection at station ① is due to three loads w_1, w_2, and w_3. The influence of load w_1 amounts to $d_{11}w_1$ (number of inches per 1 lb. load times the number of pounds in the load w_1). The influence of load w_2 amounts to $d_{12}w_2$ while that of w_3 is $d_{13}w_3$.

These three quantities may be expressed by the matrix multiplication

$$\begin{pmatrix} D_1 \\ D_2 \\ D_3 \end{pmatrix} = \begin{pmatrix} d_{11} & d_{12} & d_{13} \\ d_{21} & d_{22} & d_{23} \\ d_{31} & d_{32} & d_{33} \end{pmatrix} \begin{pmatrix} w_1 \\ w_2 \\ w_3 \end{pmatrix}.$$

Let us consider a numerical example. Suppose that our beam is symmetric about its center and that three stations have been selected, also

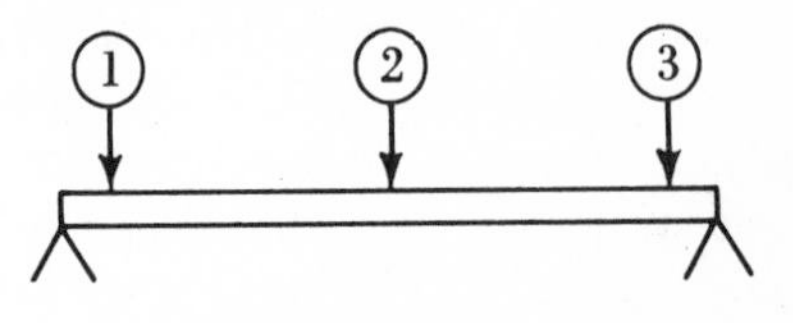

FIGURE 2.7

symmetrically about the center (Figure 2.7). A series of measurements yielded the following influence matrix:

$$\begin{pmatrix} \frac{1}{200} & \frac{1}{400} & \frac{1}{800} \\ \frac{1}{400} & \frac{1}{200} & \frac{1}{400} \\ \frac{1}{800} & \frac{1}{400} & \frac{1}{200} \end{pmatrix}.$$

Each number in the matrix has for its associated unit inches per pound. Compute the displacements when weights of 10, 20, and 30 lbs. are applied simultaneously to stations ①, ②, and ③. Solution:

$$\begin{pmatrix} \frac{1}{200} & \frac{1}{400} & \frac{1}{800} \\ \frac{1}{400} & \frac{1}{200} & \frac{1}{400} \\ \frac{1}{800} & \frac{1}{400} & \frac{1}{200} \end{pmatrix} \begin{pmatrix} 10 \\ 20 \\ 30 \end{pmatrix} = \begin{pmatrix} \frac{11}{80} \\ \frac{1}{5} \\ \frac{17}{80} \end{pmatrix}.$$

PROBLEMS

The object in Problems 1–5 is conceptual. Numbers need not be inserted, nor products worked out.

1. A university has investments in the form of bonds that pay five different rates of interest. The amount invested at each rate of interest varies from year to year. Express as a matrix product the total interest income per annum over a sequence of years.

2. Meat loaf recipes call for beef, pork, oatmeal, eggs, and condiments in varying amounts. Each of these ingredients contains vitamins A, B, C, D, and E. Express as a matrix product the total amounts of the various nutritive elements in a meat loaf whose composition is given.

3. An airline has terminals in five cities with direct service between any two of the cities. A matrix M gives the distance in air miles between any two of the cities. A matrix P gives the total number of passengers between any two cities over the past fiscal year. Show that the sum of the elements of the principal diagonal of MP' gives the total number of passenger-miles flown by the airline. Tabulate the ticket fares between cities as a matrix N and interpret the sum of the principal diagonal of NP'.

4. A professor of mathematics computes final grades on the following basis: daily assignments, 40%; midterm examinations, 25%; final examinations, 35%. Express the final grades of the class as a matrix product.

5. A daily record is kept at the foreign exchange window of a bank. The till collects pounds, liras, francs, pesos, and marks. It is desired to set up a matrix product that gives the value in dollars of the daily accumulation of foreign currency.

6. In the numerical example on page 70, the beam carries concentrated loads of 50 and 60 lbs. at stations 1 and 3 and no load at station 2. Compute the deflections.

7. If deflections of $\frac{1}{2}''$, $\frac{7}{10}''$, $\frac{13}{20}''$ are registered at stations 1, 2, and 3, what loads must have been applied?

8. It is shown in the theory of elasticity that if a unit load is placed at x_1 on a cantilever beam (Figure 2.8), the deflection at the point x_2 is given by the formula $\frac{1}{6EI} x_1^2(3x_2 - x_1)$. Here we assume that $x_1 \leq x_2$. E and I are certain constants that depend on the cross section of the beam and the type of material. Write a 2×2 influence matrix for a cantilever beam.

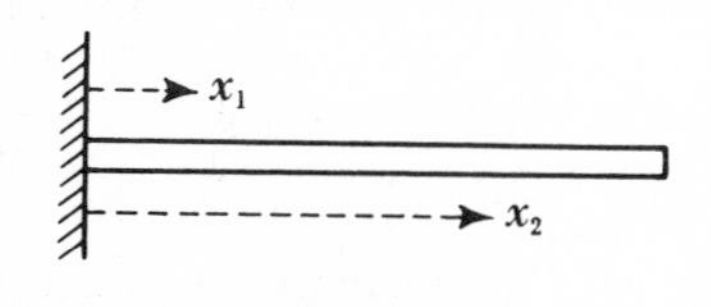

FIGURE 2.8

CHAPTER 3

The Arithmetic of Matrices, Part II

3.1 Remembrance of Things Past: The Solution of Linear Equations

The reader surely recalls how to solve a system of linear equations such as

$$\begin{cases} 3x + 4y + 5z = 18 & (1) \\ 2x - y + 8z = 13 & (2) \\ 5x - 2y + 7z = 20. & (3) \end{cases}$$

In fact, we have already drawn on this knowledge. But let us begin at the beginning. Here is one way of tackling this problem. Multiply Equation (2) by four and add it to Equation (1). This eliminates the y:

$$11x + 37z = 70.$$

Multiply Equation (2) by two and subtract it from Equation (3):

$$x - 9z = -6.$$

This eliminates the y once again.

We now have to deal with a system of two equations in x and z:

$$\begin{cases} 11x + 37z = 70 & (4) \\ x - 9z = -6. & (5) \end{cases}$$

Multiply Equation (5) by eleven and subtract it from Equation (4). This eliminates the x:

$$136z = 136. \tag{6}$$

Hence,

$$z = 1. \tag{7}$$

To obtain the values of other unknowns, we use "backward substitution." By placing $z = 1$ in Equation (5) we obtain

$$x - 9(1) = -6.$$

Hence

$$x = 3.$$

Finally, placing $x = 3$, $z = 1$ in Equation (2) we obtain

$$2(3) - y + 8(1) = 13.$$

Hence,

$$y = 1.$$

The solution is now determined: $x = 3$, $y = 1$, $z = 1$.

This method of solving systems of linear equations is known as the elimination method. Actually, we have not given a complete description of the method; we merely indicated how it works in a helter-skelter fashion. It can be applied to systems of linear equations in any number of unknowns; but if the number of unknowns were large, it would be crucial to formulate it in a systematic way.

There are many methods of solving linear equations (probably several hundred) and each method has advantages and disadvantages. A second method will now be expounded. It is related to the method just discussed, and is *called the Gauss-Jordan elimination* method (Figure 3.1). By studying it, we will learn a systematic method, and one which is frequently employed in electronic computer codes, and we will also learn some related matrix mathematics. The method is somewhat harder to carry out with pencil and paper than the one above.

Begin by writing the matrix of coefficients of the system of equations to which the right-hand sides of the equations have been adjoined:

$$\begin{pmatrix} 3 & 4 & 5 & 18 \\ 2 & -1 & 8 & 13 \\ 5 & -2 & 7 & 20 \end{pmatrix}.$$

The reader should compare this matrix with the Equations (1), (2), and (3). We will not bother with the letters x, y, and z. When we are through with our arithmetic we will put them back in.

1. Examine the first column and select an element that is largest in absolute value. (The absolute value of a number a is $+a$ if a is positive or zero and $-a$ if a is negative.) In our case, it is the element 5. This number will be called the *pivot*.

2. Interchange the third and first rows so that the pivot comes into the (1, 1) position: Leave the other row alone:

$$\begin{pmatrix} 5 & -2 & 7 & 20 \\ 2 & -1 & 8 & 13 \\ 3 & 4 & 5 & 18 \end{pmatrix}.$$

3. Divide each element of the first row by the pivot:

$$\begin{pmatrix} 1 & -\frac{2}{5} & \frac{7}{5} & 4 \\ 2 & -1 & 8 & 13 \\ 3 & 4 & 5 & 18 \end{pmatrix}.$$

4. Multiply the first row by the first element of the second row, 2, and subtract this multiple of the first row from the second row. That is, form

$$(2 \quad -1 \quad 8 \quad 13) - 2(1 \quad -\tfrac{2}{5} \quad \tfrac{7}{5} \quad 4) = (0 \quad -\tfrac{1}{5} \quad \tfrac{26}{5} \quad 5).$$

5. Multiply the first row by the first element of the third row, 3, and subtract this multiple of the first row from the third row. That is, form

$$(3 \quad 4 \quad 5 \quad 18) - 3(1 \quad -\tfrac{2}{5} \quad \tfrac{7}{5} \quad 4) = (0 \quad \tfrac{26}{5} \quad \tfrac{4}{5} \quad 6).$$

After steps 4 and 5 we are left with the matrix

$$\begin{pmatrix} 1 & -\frac{2}{5} & \frac{7}{5} & 4 \\ 0 & -\frac{1}{5} & \frac{26}{5} & 5 \\ 0 & \frac{26}{5} & \frac{4}{5} & 6 \end{pmatrix}.$$

The steps now repeat—with proper modifications.

6. Examine the elements of the second column below the first row and select as a *pivot* the one with the largest absolute value: $\frac{26}{5}$. Interchange the third and second rows so that this pivot comes into the (2, 2) position in the matrix:

$$\begin{pmatrix} 1 & -\frac{2}{5} & \frac{7}{5} & 4 \\ 0 & \frac{26}{5} & \frac{4}{5} & 6 \\ 0 & -\frac{1}{5} & \frac{26}{5} & 5 \end{pmatrix}.$$

FIGURE 3.1 (*on page 75*) *Portion of the Flow Diagram for the Gauss-Jordan Elimination Method. In computing machine codes, the computation is broken down to atomic computational units and all contingencies must be provided for. From* Mathematical Methods for Digital Computers, *A. Ralston and H. S. Wilf, editors (John Wiley, New York, 1960).*

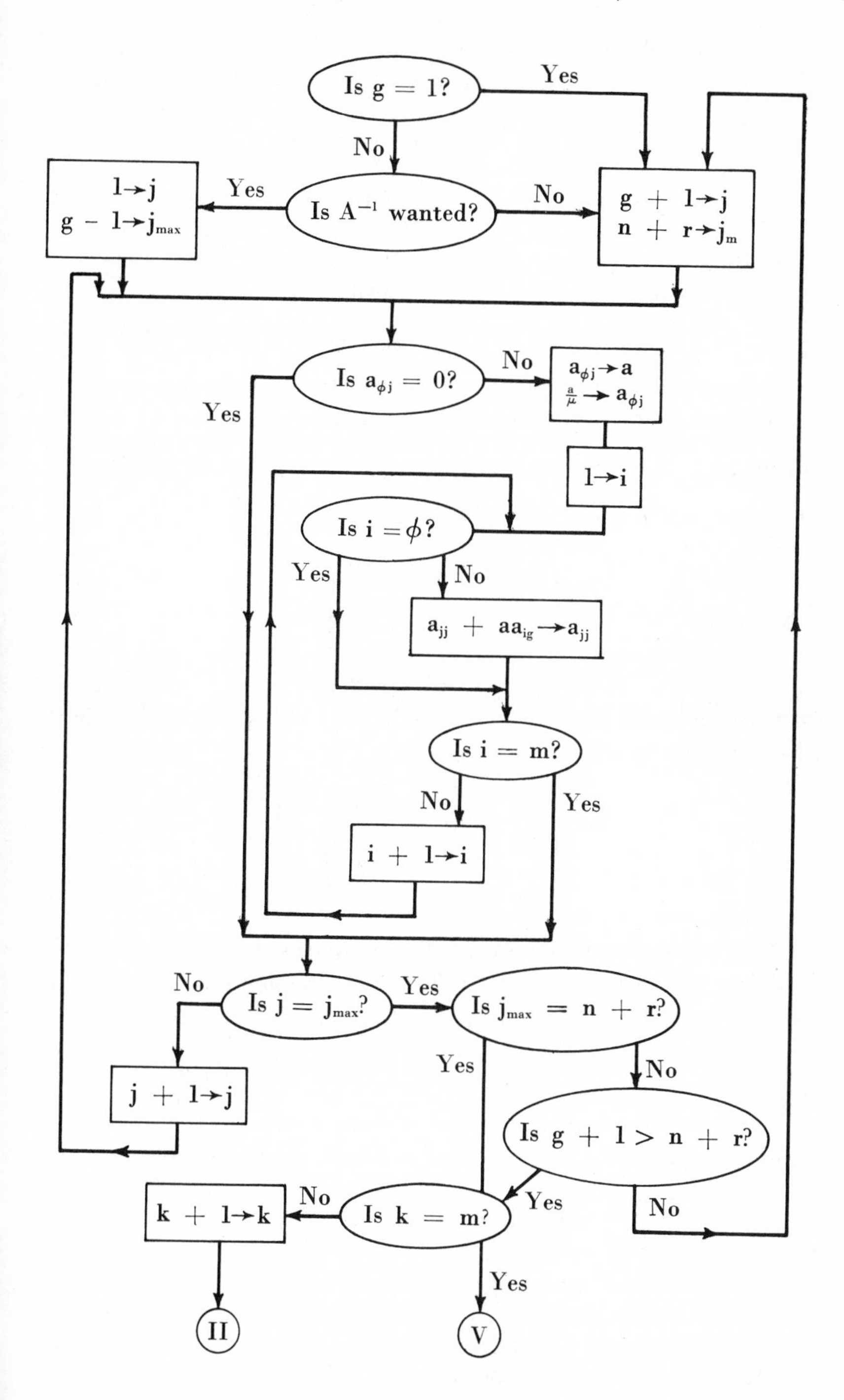

Is g = 1?
Yes
No
1→j
g – 1→j_max
Yes
Is A⁻¹ wanted?
No
g + 1→j
n + r→j_m
Is a_φj = 0?
No
a_φj→a
a/μ → a_φj
Yes
1→i
Is i = φ?
Yes
No
a_jj + aa_ig→a_jj
Is i = m?
No
Yes
i + 1→i
No
Is j = j_max?
Yes
Is j_max = n + r?
Yes
No
j + 1→j
Is g + 1 > n + r?
No
Is k = m?
k + 1→k
Yes
No
Yes
II
V

7. Divide the elements of the second row by the second pivot:

$$\begin{pmatrix} 1 & -\frac{2}{5} & \frac{7}{5} & 4 \\ 0 & 1 & \frac{4}{26} & \frac{30}{26} \\ 0 & -\frac{1}{5} & \frac{26}{5} & 5 \end{pmatrix}.$$

8. Multiply the second row by the element in the (1, 2) position, $-2/5$, and subtract from the first row. That is, form

$$(1 \quad -\tfrac{2}{5} \quad \tfrac{7}{5} \quad 4) + \tfrac{2}{5}(0 \quad 1 \quad \tfrac{4}{26} \quad \tfrac{30}{26}) = (1 \quad 0 \quad \tfrac{190}{130} \quad \tfrac{580}{130}).$$

9. Multiply the second row by the element in the (3, 2) position, $-1/5$, and subtract it from the third row. That is, form

$$(0 \quad -\tfrac{1}{5} \quad \tfrac{26}{5} \quad 5) + \tfrac{1}{5}(0 \quad 1 \quad \tfrac{4}{26} \quad \tfrac{30}{26}) = (0 \quad 0 \quad \tfrac{680}{130} \quad \tfrac{680}{130}).$$

After steps 8 and 9 we are left with the matrix

$$\begin{pmatrix} 1 & 0 & \frac{190}{130} & \frac{580}{130} \\ 0 & 1 & \frac{4}{26} & \frac{30}{26} \\ 0 & 0 & \frac{680}{130} & \frac{680}{130} \end{pmatrix}.$$

10. Select as third pivot the element in the (3, 3) position. Divide the third row by this pivot yielding

$$\begin{pmatrix} 1 & 0 & \frac{190}{130} & \frac{580}{130} \\ 0 & 1 & \frac{4}{26} & \frac{30}{26} \\ 0 & 0 & 1 & 1 \end{pmatrix}.$$

11. Multiply the third row by the element in the (1, 3) position, $190/130$, and subtract this multiple of the third row from the first row. That is, form

$$\begin{aligned}(1 \quad 0 \quad \tfrac{190}{130} \quad \tfrac{580}{130}) - \tfrac{190}{130}(0 \quad 0 \quad 1 \quad 1) &= (1 \quad 0 \quad 0 \quad \tfrac{390}{130}) \\ &= (1 \quad 0 \quad 0 \quad 3).\end{aligned}$$

12. Multiply the third row by the element in the (2, 3) position, $4/26$, and subtract this multiple of the third row from the second row:

$$(0 \quad 1 \quad \tfrac{4}{26} \quad \tfrac{30}{26}) - \tfrac{4}{26}(0 \quad 0 \quad 1 \quad 1) = (0 \quad 1 \quad 0 \quad 1)$$

After steps 11 and 12 we are left with

$$\begin{pmatrix} 1 & 0 & 0 & 3 \\ 0 & 1 & 0 & 1 \\ 0 & 0 & 1 & 1 \end{pmatrix}.$$

The first three columns of the above matrix form a unit matrix, and the last column gives the answers:

$$x = 3, \quad y = 1, \quad z = 1.$$

If this process seems mysterious and unmotivated, the reader should carry out the steps with the letters x, y, and z attached and an equal sign between the third and fourth columns of the matrix. He will find that (a) interchanging two rows corresponds to interchanging two equations; (b) multiplying or dividing a matrix row by a constant corresponds to multiplying all the terms of the equation by that constant; (c) adding or subtracting a multiple of one row to another row corresponds to adding or subtracting a multiple of one equation to another equation.

In this way, the method proceeds from one system of equations to another system of equations that is equivalent. At the last stage, all the variables, which originally were interlocked with one another, are separated, and the answer is immediate.

Producing the unit matrix to the left is a convenient way of insuring the proper identification of the unknowns in the answer: the value of the first unknown comes out first, the second unknown comes out second, etcetera. Taking as pivot the column element that is *largest* in absolute value is unnecessary when simple pencil and paper calculations are done. Any nonzero element may be selected. When calculations are done on an electronic computer, working with a fixed number of decimal places, it is a somewhat more accurate procedure. Note that in the Gauss-Jordan elimination method (Figure 3.1), as contrasted with the plain elimination method, there is no part of the process that corresponds to backward substitution.

This method brings out clearly another feature of the solution of linear systems of equations. In the above example, a system of three equations in three unknowns, three divisions occurred: three matrix rows were divided by three pivots. If any of these pivots happen to equal zero, the division cannot be carried out. The system of equations is either an overdetermined system (no answer) or an underdetermined system (more than one answer).

The solution of linear equations can be a long and tedious process. There are no methods which reduce the work substantially. The solution of a system of ten equations in ten unknowns with pencil and paper, including a desk calculator as an aid, can take several hours. It requires the full strength of an electronic calculator to handle large systems of equations.

PROBLEMS

Solve by means of the Gauss-Jordan elimination method.

1. $\begin{cases} 2x + 3y = 8 \\ 2x - y = 0. \end{cases}$

2. $\begin{cases} x + 2y = -2 \\ 2x + y = 2. \end{cases}$

3. $\begin{cases} 2x + 3y + 4z = 4 \\ x - y + z = 1 \\ 2x - y + z = 1. \end{cases}$

4. $\begin{cases} x + y + z = 1 \\ 2x + y + z = 2 \\ x + 2y + 2z = 1. \end{cases}$

5. $\begin{cases} 11x + 12y = a \\ 10x + 11y = b. \end{cases}$

The reader should try to work these problems in a completely mechanical and automatic way following steps 1–12. In other words, he should try to act like a machine. In this way, he will get an idea—through some of the inadequacies of description of steps 1–12—of just what it takes to reduce a complicated process to atomic steps and just what distinguishes normal, imprecise human action from precise but stupid, machine action. The writer does not recommend that one build a life on the imitation of machines, but occasionally it is important to see how our more mechanical brother organisms live.

3.2 Elementary Row Transformations

If you go back over the Gauss-Jordan elimination method just described, you will see that the rows of the matrix of coefficients were subjected to the following three types of transformation.

Type I: Two rows were interchanged.

Type II: All the elements of a particular row were multiplied (or divided) by the same constant. This constant was not equal to zero.

Type III: Two rows were selected. All the elements of the first row were multiplied by the same constant and then added element by element to the second row.

These transformations were applied over and over again in a fixed sequence until the solution of the system of equations emerged. Transformations or operations of this type are known as *elementary row transformations* and are of considerable theoretical importance. We shall now study their algebraic significance, and in Chapter 4, shall learn about their geometric significance.

We have already suggested that the elementary row transformations correspond to simple manipulations of equations. Let us see about this in some detail. Suppose that the system of equations

$$\begin{cases} x + y + z = 3 \\ x + 2y + 3z = 6 \\ x + 4y + 9z = 14 \end{cases}$$

is represented by the matrix

$$\begin{pmatrix} 1 & 1 & 1 & 3 \\ 1 & 2 & 3 & 6 \\ 1 & 4 & 9 & 14 \end{pmatrix}.$$

The interchanging of two rows (say the first and the second) corresponds to the interchanging of two equations (the first and the second). That is,

$$\begin{pmatrix} 1 & 2 & 3 & 6 \\ 1 & 1 & 1 & 3 \\ 1 & 4 & 9 & 14 \end{pmatrix}.$$

represents the system of equations

$$\begin{cases} x + 2y + 3z = 6 \\ x + y + z = 3 \\ x + 4y + 9z = 14. \end{cases}$$

Though the two systems of equations are not the same, they represent the same interlocking relationship between the quantities x, y, and z and so are equivalent: *if a set of numbers satisfies the first set of equations, it must also satisfy the second set, and conversely*. In the language of sets, two systems of equations are *equivalent* if they have identical solution sets.

In a transformation of Type II, the elements of a row are multiplied by the same nonzero constant. For example, the third row is multiplied by three. This corresponds to a multiplication of the third equation by three. That is,

$$\begin{pmatrix} 1 & 1 & 1 & 3 \\ 1 & 2 & 3 & 6 \\ 3 & 12 & 27 & 42 \end{pmatrix}$$

represents the system of equations

$$\begin{cases} x + y + z = 3 \\ x + 2y + 3z = 6 \\ 3x + 12y + 27z = 42. \end{cases}$$

The original system, and this new system are also equivalent. For if $x + 4y + 9z = 14$ then $3x + 12y + 27z = 42$ and vice versa.

(It should be noted that if a row of a system were multiplied by zero, the two systems would not necessarily be equivalent. Whereas $x + 4y + 9z = 14$ implies $0 \cdot x + 0 \cdot y + 0 \cdot z = 0$, the latter equation is true for all x, y, and z and hence does not necessarily imply the former equation.)

In a transformation of Type III, a certain equation is multiplied by a constant and then is added to another equation. Thus, if the first row of

$$\begin{pmatrix} 1 & 1 & 1 & 3 \\ 1 & 2 & 3 & 6 \\ 1 & 4 & 9 & 14 \end{pmatrix}$$

is multiplied by -1 and then added to the second row, element by element, we obtain $\begin{pmatrix} 1 & 1 & 1 & 3 \\ 0 & 1 & 2 & 3 \\ 1 & 4 & 9 & 14 \end{pmatrix}$. This matrix corresponds to the system

$$\begin{cases} x + y + z = 3 \\ (x + 2y + 3z) - (x + y + z) = 6 - 3 \\ x + 4y + 9z = 14 \end{cases}$$

or

$$\begin{cases} x + y + z = 3 \\ \quad y + 2z = 3 \\ x + 4y + 9z = 14. \end{cases}$$

Again, the new system and the original system are equivalent. For $x + y + z = 3$ and $x + 2y + 3z = 6$ implies $x + y + z = 3$ and $y + 2z = 3$. The reverse is also true. (Add the two equations.)

The upshot of this discussion is that an elementary row-transformation converts a matrix that represents one system of equations into a matrix that represents an equivalent system of equations.

PROBLEMS

Are the following systems of equations equivalent?

1. $\begin{cases} x + y = 3 \\ x - y = 4 \end{cases}$ and $\begin{cases} x - y = 4 \\ x + y = 3. \end{cases}$

2. $x + y = 3$ and $\begin{cases} x - y = 4 \\ x + y = 3. \end{cases}$

3. $\begin{cases} x + y = 1 \\ 2x + 2y = 3 \end{cases}$ and $\begin{cases} x + y = 1 \\ x - y = 0. \end{cases}$

4. $\begin{cases} x = 1 \\ y = 1 \\ z = 1 \end{cases}$ and $\begin{cases} x + y + z = 3 \\ 2x + y + z = 4 \\ x + y + 2z = 4. \end{cases}$

5. $\begin{cases} x + 2y = 3 \\ 2x + 4y = 6 \end{cases}$ and $3x + 6y = 9.$

6. $\begin{cases} x + y = 2 \\ x + z = 2 \\ y + z = 2 \end{cases}$ and $\begin{cases} x + y \quad = 2 \\ x - y \quad = 0 \\ x + y + z = 4. \end{cases}$

Elementary row transformations can be effected by multiplication on the left by an appropriate matrix. We have already had an intimation of this in Section 9 of Chapter 2 when we discussed the action of permutation matrices. We shall illustrate this principle using the matrix of the previous paragraph.

We would like to interchange the first and second row. Note that

$$\begin{pmatrix} 0 & 1 & 0 \\ 1 & 0 & 0 \\ 0 & 0 & 1 \end{pmatrix}\begin{pmatrix} 1 & 1 & 1 & 3 \\ 1 & 2 & 3 & 6 \\ 1 & 4 & 9 & 14 \end{pmatrix} = \begin{pmatrix} 1 & 2 & 3 & 6 \\ 1 & 1 & 1 & 3 \\ 1 & 4 & 9 & 14 \end{pmatrix}.$$

Multiplication on the left by $\begin{pmatrix} 0 & 1 & 0 \\ 1 & 0 & 0 \\ 0 & 0 & 1 \end{pmatrix}$ accomplishes this task.

We would like to multiply the third row by three. Note that

$$\begin{pmatrix} 1 & 0 & 0 \\ 0 & 1 & 0 \\ 0 & 0 & 3 \end{pmatrix}\begin{pmatrix} 1 & 1 & 1 & 3 \\ 1 & 2 & 3 & 6 \\ 1 & 4 & 9 & 14 \end{pmatrix} = \begin{pmatrix} 1 & 1 & 1 & 3 \\ 1 & 2 & 3 & 6 \\ 3 & 12 & 27 & 42 \end{pmatrix},$$

so that multiplication on the left by $\begin{pmatrix} 1 & 0 & 0 \\ 0 & 1 & 0 \\ 0 & 0 & 3 \end{pmatrix}$ does just this. We would like, finally, to multiply the first row by -1 and add it to the second row leaving the first and third rows unchanged. Note that

$$\begin{pmatrix} 1 & 0 & 0 \\ -1 & 1 & 0 \\ 0 & 0 & 1 \end{pmatrix}\begin{pmatrix} 1 & 1 & 1 & 3 \\ 1 & 2 & 3 & 6 \\ 1 & 4 & 9 & 14 \end{pmatrix} = \begin{pmatrix} 1 & 1 & 1 & 3 \\ 0 & 1 & 2 & 3 \\ 1 & 4 & 9 & 14 \end{pmatrix}.$$

so that multiplication on the left by $\begin{pmatrix} 1 & 0 & 0 \\ -1 & 1 & 0 \\ 0 & 0 & 1 \end{pmatrix}$ carries out this transformation of the third type.

The various matrices that effect these elementary transformations are called *elementary matrices*.

Note what happens when several elementary matrices are multiplied together:

$$\begin{pmatrix} 1 & 0 & 0 \\ 0 & 1 & 0 \\ 0 & 0 & 3 \end{pmatrix}\begin{pmatrix} 0 & 1 & 0 \\ 1 & 0 & 0 \\ 0 & 0 & 1 \end{pmatrix}\begin{pmatrix} 1 & 1 & 1 & 3 \\ 1 & 2 & 3 & 6 \\ 1 & 4 & 9 & 14 \end{pmatrix} = \begin{pmatrix} 1 & 2 & 3 & 6 \\ 1 & 1 & 1 & 3 \\ 3 & 12 & 27 & 42 \end{pmatrix}.$$

Since matrix multiplication is associative, we may work from right to left in the matrix product. The first elementary matrix interchanges the first two rows, while the second multiplies the third row by three. The product,

$$\begin{pmatrix} 1 & 0 & 0 \\ 0 & 1 & 0 \\ 0 & 0 & 3 \end{pmatrix}\begin{pmatrix} 0 & 1 & 0 \\ 1 & 0 & 0 \\ 0 & 0 & 1 \end{pmatrix} = \begin{pmatrix} 0 & 1 & 0 \\ 1 & 0 & 0 \\ 0 & 0 & 3 \end{pmatrix}$$

considered as a multiplier on the left must have the combined effect.

Since each elementary row transformation can be regarded as having changed one system of equations into an equivalent system of equations, the combined effect of several elementary row transformations is to do the same, that is to say, the product of several elementary matrices must also have the effect of changing systems of equations into equivalent systems.

PROBLEMS

1. Explain the effect of multiplication on the left by

$$\begin{pmatrix} 1 & 0 & 0 \\ 0 & 0 & 1 \\ 0 & 1 & 0 \end{pmatrix}, \quad \begin{pmatrix} 1 & 0 & 0 \\ 0 & -7 & 0 \\ 0 & 0 & 1 \end{pmatrix}, \quad \begin{pmatrix} 3 & 0 & 0 \\ 0 & 1 & 0 \\ 0 & 0 & 1 \end{pmatrix}.$$

2. The same for

$$\begin{pmatrix} 1 & 0 & 0 \\ 0 & 1 & 0 \\ 0 & -1 & 1 \end{pmatrix}, \quad \begin{pmatrix} 1 & 0 & 0 \\ 0 & 1 & 0 \\ -1 & 0 & 1 \end{pmatrix}, \quad \begin{pmatrix} 1 & 0 & -1 \\ 0 & 1 & 0 \\ 0 & 0 & 1 \end{pmatrix}.$$

3. Explain the effect of multiplication on the left by the products

$$\begin{pmatrix} 1 & 0 & -1 \\ 0 & 1 & 0 \\ 0 & 0 & 1 \end{pmatrix}\begin{pmatrix} 1 & 0 & 0 \\ 0 & 2 & 0 \\ 0 & 0 & 1 \end{pmatrix}, \quad \begin{pmatrix} 1 & 0 & 0 \\ 0 & 1 & 0 \\ 0 & 0 & -6 \end{pmatrix}\begin{pmatrix} 1 & 0 & 0 \\ 0 & 1 & -1 \\ 0 & 0 & 1 \end{pmatrix},$$

$$\begin{pmatrix} 0 & 1 & 0 \\ 1 & 0 & 0 \\ 0 & 0 & 1 \end{pmatrix}\begin{pmatrix} 1 & 0 & 0 \\ 0 & 1 & 0 \\ 0 & -1 & 1 \end{pmatrix}\begin{pmatrix} 2 & 0 & 0 \\ 0 & 1 & 0 \\ 0 & 0 & 1 \end{pmatrix}.$$

4. Construct several elementary 4×4 matrices and test their effect.

5. In a 4×4 matrix, it is desired to multiply the second row by -3 and add this, element by element, to the fourth row. The first, second, and third rows are to remain unchanged. Find an elementary matrix that effects this.

3.3 Matrix Inversion

We have described matrix addition, subtraction, and multiplication; it remains for us to talk about division. Suppose that we agree to proceed by analogy with ordinary arithmetic. Since $7 \times 6 = 42$, we write $6 = {}^{42}/_{7}$ or $7 = {}^{42}/_{6}$. More generally, if $ab = c$, then $b = c/a$ (if $a \neq 0$) and $a = c/b$ (if $b \neq 0$). In this way, division is related to multiplication.

When we try to do something similar for matrix division, we strike a grave difficulty immediately. Suppose that we observe the matrix product $(1 \quad 1)\begin{pmatrix} 2 \\ 1 \end{pmatrix} = (3)$. If we were to proceed by analogy with the ordinary case we might be inclined to write

$$(1 \quad 1) = \frac{(3)}{\begin{pmatrix} 2 \\ 1 \end{pmatrix}}$$

and interpret this equation as saying that "the matrix (3) divided by the matrix $\begin{pmatrix} 2 \\ 1 \end{pmatrix}$ equals the matrix $(1 \quad 1)$." But notice that $(2 \quad -1)\begin{pmatrix} 2 \\ 1 \end{pmatrix} = (3)$. By the same token, we might say that "the matrix (3) divided by the matrix $\begin{pmatrix} 2 \\ 1 \end{pmatrix}$ equals the matrix $(2 \quad -1)$." This would put us in a dilemma, for then the quotient of (3) by $\begin{pmatrix} 2 \\ 1 \end{pmatrix}$ would have two answers. Which answer would we select as *the* answer? The situation is worse than this. There really would be an unlimited number of answers since any matrix of the form $(a \quad b)$ with $2a + b = 3$ would be an answer. You can check this very easily.

In order to construct a theory of matrix division that is not subject to this difficulty, some kind of limitation is necessary. One limits the discussion to *square matrices*. When this is done matrix division is found to have similarities to ordinary division. It will also have a very striking interpretation in terms of linear transformations (Chapter 4).

It is convenient, in building up a theory of matrix division, to begin with *reciprocals* or *inverses*. We proceed by analogy. The reciprocal of 7 is 1/7, and the meaning of 1/7 is elucidated by the product $(7)(1/7) = 1$ or by the product $(1/7)\, 7 = 1$. Every number—zero excepted—has a reciprocal. These considerations lead us to the following definition.

Definition: *Given a square matrix* A, *a second square matrix* B (*of the same order*) *is called an inverse of* A *if the following equations both hold:*

$$\mathrm{AB} = \mathrm{I} \qquad \text{and} \qquad \mathrm{BA} = \mathrm{I}.$$

Example 1:

$$\begin{pmatrix} 1 & 4 \\ 2 & 9 \end{pmatrix} \begin{pmatrix} 9 & -4 \\ -2 & 1 \end{pmatrix} = \begin{pmatrix} 1 & 0 \\ 0 & 1 \end{pmatrix}$$

and

$$\begin{pmatrix} 9 & -4 \\ -2 & 1 \end{pmatrix} \begin{pmatrix} 1 & 4 \\ 2 & 9 \end{pmatrix} = \begin{pmatrix} 1 & 0 \\ 0 & 1 \end{pmatrix}.$$

If we set

$$A = \begin{pmatrix} 1 & 4 \\ 2 & 9 \end{pmatrix} \quad \text{and} \quad B = \begin{pmatrix} 9 & -4 \\ -2 & 1 \end{pmatrix},$$

the equations for inverses are satisfied, and B is therefore an inverse of A.

But note also that we could equally well have set

$$A = \begin{pmatrix} 9 & -4 \\ -2 & 1 \end{pmatrix} \quad \text{and} \quad B = \begin{pmatrix} 1 & 4 \\ 2 & 9 \end{pmatrix}$$

in the previous example.

The two equations for inverses are also satisfied and we can equally well say that A is an inverse of B.

This is a general principle: *If a matrix* A *has an inverse* B, *then the matrix* B *has an inverse* A.

Example 2: Since $II = I$, (II means the matrix I multiplied by the matrix I), the unit matrix I is its own inverse. This matrix fact corresponds to the ordinary equation $1 = 1/1$, and shows that all is right in this corner of the algebraic universe.

Just as the ordinary number zero has no inverse, it is too much to expect that every matrix will have an inverse.

Example 3: Suppose we are given the problem of finding the inverse of the matrix $\begin{pmatrix} 1 & 1 \\ 1 & 1 \end{pmatrix}$. Assume it has an inverse, and write this inverse in the form $\begin{pmatrix} x & y \\ z & w \end{pmatrix}$ where x, y, z, and w are to be determined. We must have

$$\begin{pmatrix} 1 & 1 \\ 1 & 1 \end{pmatrix}\begin{pmatrix} x & y \\ z & w \end{pmatrix} = \begin{pmatrix} 1 & 0 \\ 0 & 1 \end{pmatrix}.$$

By expanding this matrix equation, we find

$$\begin{pmatrix} x+z, & y+w \\ x+z, & y+w \end{pmatrix} = \begin{pmatrix} 1 & 0 \\ 0 & 1 \end{pmatrix}.$$

Upon equating the two matrices element by element, we find that

$$\begin{cases} x+z=1 \\ x+z=0, \end{cases} \qquad \begin{cases} y+w=0 \\ y+w=1. \end{cases}$$

Each of these systems of equations is obviously overdetermined and incompatible (for example, $x + z$ cannot both be 0 and 1), and hence there is no solution to them. The matrix $\begin{pmatrix} 1 & 1 \\ 1 & 1 \end{pmatrix}$ therefore has no inverse.

If a matrix has no inverse, it is called a *singular** matrix. Singular matrices are analogous to 0 when it comes to division. A matrix that has an inverse is called a *nonsingular* matrix. $\begin{pmatrix} 1 & 1 \\ 1 & 1 \end{pmatrix}$ is a singular matrix. $\begin{pmatrix} 1 & 4 \\ 2 & 9 \end{pmatrix}$ is a nonsingular† matrix.

Example 4: If the matrix has an inverse, the device employed in Example 3 will lead us to it. Suppose we would like to find an inverse of $\begin{pmatrix} 2 & 1 \\ 1 & 1 \end{pmatrix}$. Write the presumed inverse in the form $\begin{pmatrix} x & y \\ z & w \end{pmatrix}$ with the unknowns x, y, z, and w to be determined. We must have

$$\begin{pmatrix} x & y \\ z & w \end{pmatrix}\begin{pmatrix} 2 & 1 \\ 1 & 1 \end{pmatrix} = \begin{pmatrix} 1 & 0 \\ 0 & 1 \end{pmatrix}.$$

---

* The word "singular" is not used here in the ordinary sense of "single" or "individual." The word also means "strange" or "unusual" and this is how it should be understood in the case of matrix inversion. A. Conan Doyle was fond of using the word with this meaning in his Sherlock Holmes stories.

† The expression "is nonsingular" is synonymous with "has an inverse." I prefer the latter expression because it accentuates the positive and avoids a bad double negative. But the former expression is so firmly established that I have not been able to stay clear of it, and the reader should become familiar with it.

By working through the matrix multiplication, we find that

$$\begin{pmatrix} 2x + y & x + y \\ 2z + w & z + w \end{pmatrix} = \begin{pmatrix} 1 & 0 \\ 0 & 1 \end{pmatrix}.$$

If we now equate these two matrices element by element, we are led to two systems of linear equations each in two unknowns:

$$\begin{cases} 2x + y = 1 \\ x + y = 0 \end{cases}$$

and

$$\begin{cases} 2z + w = 0 \\ z + w = 1. \end{cases}$$

Each set of equations is compatible and when they are solved, we find $x = 1$, $y = -1$; $z = -1$, $w = 2$.

Thus, $\begin{pmatrix} 1 & -1 \\ -1 & 2 \end{pmatrix}\begin{pmatrix} 2 & 1 \\ 1 & 1 \end{pmatrix} = \begin{pmatrix} 1 & 0 \\ 0 & 1 \end{pmatrix}$. Now note also that

$$\begin{pmatrix} 2 & 1 \\ 1 & 1 \end{pmatrix}\begin{pmatrix} 1 & -1 \\ -1 & 2 \end{pmatrix} = \begin{pmatrix} 1 & 0 \\ 0 & 1 \end{pmatrix}.$$

The factors here are switched around; and this second product must be verified by a computation. It does not follow "automatically," for the commutativity of multiplication conceivably might break down. These two matrix equations now tell us that the inverse of $\begin{pmatrix} 2 & 1 \\ 1 & 1 \end{pmatrix}$ is $\begin{pmatrix} 1 & -1 \\ -1 & 2 \end{pmatrix}$.

In our definition of inverses, we stated that B is *an* inverse of A if $AB = I$ and $BA = I$. The word "an" seems to imply that matrix A might conceivably have several different inverses. If this were true, the dilemma posed at the beginning of this section would hardly have been resolved. Actually, this is not the case, and the fact is important enough to be formulated as a theorem.

Theorem: *If a matrix has an inverse it has only one inverse.*

PROOF: Let the matrix A have the matrix B as its inverse. This means that $AB = I$ and that $BA = I$. Suppose that somebody claims that he also has an inverse, C, of the matrix A. This means that $AC = I$ and $CA = I$. The problem, then is to show that B and C are really the same: $B = C$.

If $BA = I$, then $(BA)C = I(C) = C$. But $(BA)C = B(AC)$. Since $AC = I$, $B(AC) = BI = B$. By putting these equalities together we learn that $B = C$.

A further word is in order about this theorem. It belongs to the category of theorems known as *uniqueness theorems*. It tells us that the requirements of the inverse lead to a unique object satisfying the requirements.

To appreciate the force of the theorem, it is useful to look at a situation in which this conclusion is not possible. Suppose that we say that the square root of four is a number x that satisfies the requirement $x^2 = 4$. Now the number $x = 2$ satisfies the requirement, but it is not true that it is the only number that does. The number $x = -2$ satisfies it equally well. Square roots are not unique.

Since we now know that a matrix with an inverse has only one inverse, we can speak of it as *the* inverse. More than this: a special notation, reminiscent of ordinary algebra, is given to inverses.

Definition: *If* A *has an inverse, its inverse will be denoted by* A^{-1}.

In formulating our requirements for an inverse, we demanded that B is inverse to A if *both* $AB = I$ and $BA = I$. Actually, these two requirements are more than we need. It is a fact—but in this book we shall prove it only for 2×2 and 3×3 matrices—that if $AB = I$ then $BA = I$, or vice versa, if $BA = I$ then $AB = I$. Hence if either equation is fulfilled, the other equation is also fulfilled and the matrices have inverses.

PROBLEMS

1. Verify that $\begin{pmatrix} -6 & 7 \\ 7 & -8 \end{pmatrix}$ is the inverse of $\begin{pmatrix} 8 & 7 \\ 7 & 6 \end{pmatrix}$.
2. Verify that $\begin{pmatrix} \frac{1}{3} & 0 \\ 0 & 5 \end{pmatrix}$ is the inverse of $\begin{pmatrix} 3 & 0 \\ 0 & \frac{1}{5} \end{pmatrix}$.
3. Prove that the 1×1 matrix (a) has the inverse (a^{-1}) provided that $a \neq 0$.
4. Find the inverse of $\begin{pmatrix} 5 & 3 \\ 3 & 2 \end{pmatrix}$.
5. If $A = \begin{pmatrix} 1 & 2 \\ 3 & 4 \end{pmatrix}$, find A^{-1}.
6. Does $\begin{pmatrix} 1 & 2 \\ 4 & 8 \end{pmatrix}$ have an inverse? If so, what is it?
7. Find the inverse of $\begin{pmatrix} 0 & 1 & 0 \\ 1 & 0 & 0 \\ 0 & 0 & 1 \end{pmatrix}$.
8. If $A = \begin{pmatrix} 5 & 3 \\ 7 & 4 \end{pmatrix}$ find $A + A^{-1}$.
9. Does $J + I$ have an inverse? Use 2×2 matrices.
10. Prove that every nonsingular matrix commutes with its inverse.
11. Prove that the 2×2 zero matrix has no inverse.

12. Prove that the 2×2 J matrix has no inverse.

13. Prove that if a matrix has a row of zeros or a column of zeros, it cannot have an inverse.

As a general thing, the determination of the inverse of a given matrix is not easy. We have already seen that it requires the solution of a system of linear equations, and so becomes more and more involved as the size of the matrix increases. However, there are some special matrices that are not too difficult to invert (that is, to determine the inverses for).

(1) The matrix I is its own inverse: $I^{-1} = I$.

(2) If D is a diagonal matrix,

$$D = \begin{pmatrix} d_1 & 0 & 0 & 0 & 0 & \cdots \\ 0 & d_2 & 0 & 0 & 0 & \\ 0 & 0 & d_3 & 0 & 0 & \\ \vdots & & & & & \end{pmatrix}$$

and if none of the d's is zero, then

$$D^{-1} = \begin{pmatrix} d_1^{-1} & 0 & 0 & 0 & \cdots \\ 0 & d_2^{-1} & 0 & 0 & \\ 0 & 0 & d_3^{-1} & 0 & \\ 0 & 0 & 0 & d_4^{-1} & \cdots \\ \vdots & & & \vdots & \end{pmatrix}.$$

This is readily proved by showing that the product of D by D^{-1} (formed in either way) is I.

(3) The inverse of a permutation is the transpose of that matrix. This means that there is practically no work involved in finding the inverse of a permutation matrix. For example, the inverse of

$$\begin{pmatrix} 0 & 1 & 0 & 0 \\ 0 & 0 & 1 & 0 \\ 0 & 0 & 0 & 1 \\ 1 & 0 & 0 & 0 \end{pmatrix} \quad \text{is} \quad \begin{pmatrix} 0 & 0 & 0 & 1 \\ 1 & 0 & 0 & 0 \\ 0 & 1 & 0 & 0 \\ 0 & 0 & 1 & 0 \end{pmatrix}.$$

Check the multiplication and then see if you can discover the general reason for this.

(4) All the elementary matrices have inverses, and their inverses are simple to compute. Let us examine samples of three types. We work with 4×4's.

Type I. First and third rows interchanged. This row operation is effected by

$$A = \begin{pmatrix} 0 & 0 & 1 & 0 \\ 0 & 1 & 0 & 0 \\ 1 & 0 & 0 & 0 \\ 0 & 0 & 0 & 1 \end{pmatrix}.$$

The inverse of this operation is to interchange the first and third rows once again. This will set things in their original order. Hence A is its own inverse: $A = A^{-1}$.

Type II. Second row multiplied by -6. This row operation is effected by the matrix

$$A = \begin{pmatrix} 1 & 0 & 0 & 0 \\ 0 & -6 & 0 & 0 \\ 0 & 0 & 1 & 0 \\ 0 & 0 & 0 & 1 \end{pmatrix}.$$

The inverse of this operation is to multiply the second row by $-1/6$. Hence

$$A^{-1} = \begin{pmatrix} 1 & 0 & 0 & 0 \\ 0 & -\frac{1}{6} & 0 & 0 \\ 0 & 0 & 1 & 0 \\ 0 & 0 & 0 & 1 \end{pmatrix}.$$

Type III. Third row multiplied by -2 and added to the fourth row. First three rows are not changed. This is effected by

$$A = \begin{pmatrix} 1 & 0 & 0 & 0 \\ 0 & 1 & 0 & 0 \\ 0 & 0 & 1 & 0 \\ 0 & 0 & -2 & 1 \end{pmatrix}.$$

This operation can be undone by multiplying the third row by 2 and adding it to the fourth row. Hence,

$$A^{-1} = \begin{pmatrix} 1 & 0 & 0 & 0 \\ 0 & 1 & 0 & 0 \\ 0 & 0 & 1 & 0 \\ 0 & 0 & 2 & 1 \end{pmatrix}.$$

The reader should now verify that for each of the three types the presumed inverse obtained from an argument about operations does, indeed, satisfy the proper equations for the inverse.

(5) If a matrix is upper triangular or lower triangular, then it is not too difficult to compute its inverse. The inverse will also be upper triangular or lower triangular and its elements can be computed by several backward substitutions. For simple coefficients, this work can be done in one's head.

For example, find the inverse of $\begin{pmatrix} 1 & 2 & -1 \\ 0 & 1 & 3 \\ 0 & 0 & 1 \end{pmatrix}$. Suppose that the inverse is $\begin{pmatrix} a & b & c \\ d & e & f \\ g & h & k \end{pmatrix}$. Then we must have

$$\begin{pmatrix} a & b & c \\ d & e & f \\ g & h & k \end{pmatrix}\begin{pmatrix} 1 & 2 & -1 \\ 0 & 1 & 3 \\ 0 & 0 & 1 \end{pmatrix} = \begin{pmatrix} 1 & 0 & 0 \\ 0 & 1 & 0 \\ 0 & 0 & 1 \end{pmatrix}.$$

Therefore,

$$\begin{cases} a\cdot 1 + b\cdot 0 + c\cdot 0 = 1 \\ a\cdot 2 + b\cdot 1 + c\cdot 0 = 0 \\ a\cdot(-1) + b\cdot 3 + c\cdot 1 = 0 \end{cases} \quad \text{so that} \quad \begin{cases} a = 1 \\ b = -2 \\ c = 7 \end{cases}$$

Also

$$\begin{cases} d\cdot 1 + e\cdot 0 + f\cdot 0 = 0 \\ d\cdot 2 + e\cdot 1 + f\cdot 0 = 1 \\ d\cdot(-1) + e\cdot 3 + f\cdot 1 = 0 \end{cases} \quad \text{so that} \quad \begin{cases} d = 0 \\ e = 1 \\ f = -3. \end{cases}$$

Finally,

$$\begin{cases} g\cdot 1 + h\cdot 0 + k\cdot 0 = 0 \\ g\cdot 2 + h\cdot 1 + k\cdot 0 = 0 \\ g\cdot(-1) + h\cdot 3 + k\cdot 1 = 1 \end{cases} \quad \text{so that} \quad \begin{cases} g = 0 \\ h = 0 \\ k = 1. \end{cases}$$

The inverse matrix is therefore

$$\begin{pmatrix} 1 & -2 & 7 \\ 0 & 1 & -3 \\ 0 & 0 & 1 \end{pmatrix}.$$

PROBLEMS

1. Find the inverse of

$$\begin{pmatrix} \frac{1}{2} & 0 & 0 \\ 0 & \frac{1}{3} & 0 \\ 0 & 0 & -\frac{7}{4} \end{pmatrix}.$$

2. Find the inverse of

$$\begin{pmatrix} 1 & 0 & 0 & 0 & 0 \\ 0 & 0 & 1 & 0 & 0 \\ 0 & 1 & 0 & 0 & 0 \\ 0 & 0 & 0 & 0 & 1 \\ 0 & 0 & 0 & 1 & 0 \end{pmatrix}.$$

3. Find the inverse of $\begin{pmatrix} 1 & 0 \\ 2 & 1 \end{pmatrix}$ and of $\begin{pmatrix} 1 & 0 \\ a & 1 \end{pmatrix}$.

4. Find the inverse of

$$\begin{pmatrix} 1 & 2 & 3 \\ 0 & 1 & 2 \\ 0 & 0 & 1 \end{pmatrix}.$$

5. Find the inverse of

$$\begin{pmatrix} 1 & 2 & 3 & 4 \\ 0 & 1 & 2 & 3 \\ 0 & 0 & 1 & 2 \\ 0 & 0 & 0 & 1 \end{pmatrix}.$$

6. Invert

$$\begin{pmatrix} 1 & 0 & 0 \\ 0 & b & 0 \\ a & 0 & b \end{pmatrix}.$$

7. Invert

$$\begin{pmatrix} 0 & 2 \\ \frac{1}{3} & 0 \end{pmatrix}, \qquad \begin{pmatrix} 0 & 0 & 3 \\ 0 & \frac{1}{5} & 0 \\ -2 & 0 & 0 \end{pmatrix}.$$

8. Find the inverse of

$$\begin{pmatrix} 1 & 0 & 0 & 0 \\ 0 & 1 & 0 & 0 \\ 0 & 0 & 1 & 0 \\ 2 & -1 & 2 & 1 \end{pmatrix}.$$

9. Find the inverse of

$$\begin{pmatrix} 1 & 0 & 0 & 0 & 0 \\ 0 & 1 & 0 & 0 & 0 \\ 0 & 0 & 1 & 0 & 0 \\ 0 & 0 & -3 & 1 & 0 \\ 0 & 0 & 0 & 0 & 1 \end{pmatrix}.$$

10. Show by matrix multiplication that the inverse of

$$\begin{pmatrix} 0 & a & 0 & 0 & 0 & 0 \\ f & 0 & b & 0 & 0 & 0 \\ 0 & g & 0 & c & 0 & 0 \\ 0 & 0 & h & 0 & d & 0 \\ 0 & 0 & 0 & k & 0 & e \\ 0 & 0 & 0 & 0 & m & 0 \end{pmatrix} \text{ is } \begin{pmatrix} 0 & \frac{1}{f} & 0 & -\frac{b}{fh} & 0 & \frac{bd}{fhm} \\ \frac{1}{a} & 0 & 0 & 0 & 0 & 0 \\ 0 & 0 & 0 & \frac{1}{h} & 0 & -\frac{d}{hm} \\ -\frac{g}{ac} & 0 & \frac{1}{c} & 0 & 0 & 0 \\ 0 & 0 & 0 & 0 & 0 & \frac{1}{m} \\ \frac{gk}{ace} & 0 & -\frac{k}{ce} & 0 & \frac{1}{e} & 0 \end{pmatrix}.$$

11. Prove that an upper triangular matrix that has 1's on its main diagonal has an inverse that is upper triangular and also has 1's on its main diagonal.

We now undertake the determination of the inverse of the general 2×2 matrix. Suppose we have the matrix $A = \begin{pmatrix} a & b \\ c & d \end{pmatrix}$. Under what circumstances does it have an inverse? If it has an inverse, what is the inverse? To solve the problem, suppose that A has an inverse. Call the inverse $\begin{pmatrix} x & y \\ z & w \end{pmatrix}$ where the quantities x, y, z, and w are to be determined. We must have $\begin{pmatrix} a & b \\ c & d \end{pmatrix} \cdot \begin{pmatrix} x & y \\ z & w \end{pmatrix} = \begin{pmatrix} 1 & 0 \\ 0 & 1 \end{pmatrix}$.

This matrix equation leads to the two systems of equations

$$\begin{matrix} (1) \\ (2) \end{matrix} \begin{cases} ax + bz = 1 \\ cx + dz = 0 \end{cases} \quad \text{and} \quad \begin{matrix} (3) \\ (4) \end{matrix} \begin{cases} ay + bw = 0 \\ cy + dw = 1. \end{cases}$$

Multiply Equations (1) and (3) by c and Equations (2) and (4) by a:

$$\begin{matrix} (5) \\ (6) \end{matrix} \begin{cases} acx + bcz = c \\ acx + adz = 0 \end{cases} \quad \begin{matrix} (7) \\ (8) \end{matrix} \begin{cases} acy + bcw = 0 \\ acy + adw = a. \end{cases}$$

Subtract Equation (5) from (6) and Equation (7) from (8):

$$\underline{(ad - bc)z = -c} \qquad \underline{(ad - bc)w = a}$$

Multiply Equations (1) and (3) by d and Equations (2) and (4) by b:

$$\begin{matrix} (9) \\ (10) \end{matrix} \begin{cases} adx + bdz = d \\ bcx + bdz = 0 \end{cases} \quad \begin{matrix} (11) \\ (12) \end{matrix} \begin{cases} ady + bdw = 0 \\ bcy + bdw = b. \end{cases}$$

Subtract Equation (10) from (9) and Equation (12) from (11):

$$\underline{(ad - bc)x = d} \qquad \underline{(ad - bc)y = -b.}$$

Notice that the quantity $ad - bc$ appears as a coefficient in each of the four equations underlined. It will be convenient to give this quantity a special symbol. Set

$$\Delta = ad - bc.$$

Now, it can be proved that under the assumption that A has an inverse, Δ cannot be $= 0$. For, suppose $\Delta = 0$, then the four underlined equations tell us that $a = 0$, $b = 0$, $c = 0$, and $d = 0$. Hence $A = \begin{pmatrix} 0 & 0 \\ 0 & 0 \end{pmatrix} = 0$.

But this matrix has no inverse, (why?), and this would contradict our assumption that A has an inverse.

We have therefore proved: if A has an inverse then $\Delta = ad - bc \neq 0$.

The converse is also true: if $\Delta \neq 0$ then A has an inverse. To prove this, follow the lead of the equations. If $\Delta \neq 0$, then we can solve the underlined equations for x, y, z, and w:

$$x = \frac{d}{\Delta}, \qquad y = \frac{-b}{\Delta}, \qquad z = \frac{-c}{\Delta}, \qquad w = \frac{a}{\Delta}.$$

This suggests that the matrix

$$\begin{pmatrix} \frac{d}{\Delta} & -\frac{b}{\Delta} \\ -\frac{c}{\Delta} & \frac{a}{\Delta} \end{pmatrix} = \frac{1}{\Delta}\begin{pmatrix} d & -b \\ -c & a \end{pmatrix}$$

is the required inverse. To check it, form the matrix products in both orders.

$$\frac{1}{\Delta}\begin{pmatrix} d & -b \\ -c & a \end{pmatrix}\begin{pmatrix} a & b \\ c & d \end{pmatrix} = \frac{1}{\Delta}\begin{pmatrix} ad - bc & 0 \\ 0 & ad - bc \end{pmatrix} = \begin{pmatrix} 1 & 0 \\ 0 & 1 \end{pmatrix}$$

and

$$\begin{pmatrix} a & b \\ c & d \end{pmatrix}\frac{1}{\Delta}\begin{pmatrix} d & -b \\ -c & a \end{pmatrix} = \frac{1}{\Delta}\begin{pmatrix} ad - bc & 0 \\ 0 & ad - bc \end{pmatrix} = \begin{pmatrix} 1 & 0 \\ 0 & 1 \end{pmatrix}.$$

Multiplication in either order results in the unit matrix.

These conclusions will be summed up as a theorem.

Theorem: *The matrix* $\mathrm{A} = \begin{pmatrix} \mathrm{a} & \mathrm{b} \\ \mathrm{c} & \mathrm{d} \end{pmatrix}$ *has an inverse if and only if* $\Delta = \mathrm{ad} - \mathrm{bc} \neq 0$. *If* $\Delta \neq 0$, *the inverse is given by the formula*

$$\mathrm{A}^{-1} = \frac{1}{\Delta}\begin{pmatrix} \mathrm{d} & -\mathrm{b} \\ -\mathrm{c} & \mathrm{a} \end{pmatrix}.$$

We can phrase part of this result in another way. The matrix A is singular if $ad - bc = 0$. It is nonsingular if $ad - bc \neq 0$.

The quantity $\Delta = ad - bc$ is called the *determinant* of the matrix A. Determinants will be studied in detail in Chapter 5.

PROBLEMS

1. Which of the following matrices are singular and which are nonsingular

$$\begin{pmatrix} 1 & 1 \\ 2 & 3 \end{pmatrix}, \quad \begin{pmatrix} 1 & 2 \\ 5 & 8 \end{pmatrix}, \quad \begin{pmatrix} -1 & -6 \\ 3 & 9 \end{pmatrix}, \quad \begin{pmatrix} 0 & 0 \\ 0 & 1 \end{pmatrix}, \quad \begin{pmatrix} 2 & 3 \\ 4 & 5 \end{pmatrix}.$$

2. Find the inverses of the nonsingular matrices in Problem 1.

3. If $\Delta = ad - bc = 1$, prove the inverse of A is $\begin{pmatrix} d & -b \\ -c & a \end{pmatrix}$.

4. Find the inverse of $\begin{pmatrix} a & \sqrt{1 - a^2} \\ -\sqrt{1 - a^2} & a \end{pmatrix}$.

5. If $\begin{pmatrix} 1 & 1 \\ a & a^2 \end{pmatrix}$ has an inverse, what statement can be made about a?

6. Show that the matrix $\begin{pmatrix} x & y \\ -y & x \end{pmatrix}$ has an inverse provided that x and y are not both zero. Compute the inverse.

7. Show that if A has an inverse and B has an inverse, it does not necessarily follow that $A + B$ has an inverse.

8. Work with 2×2 matrices and describe all the values of m for which $I + mJ$ has an inverse.

9. Under what conditions on a and b does the matrix $\begin{pmatrix} a & 0 \\ 1 & a \end{pmatrix} - \begin{pmatrix} 1 & b \\ b & 0 \end{pmatrix}$ have an inverse?

10. Under what condition on the number λ will the matrix $\begin{pmatrix} 1 - \lambda & 2 \\ 2 & 6 - \lambda \end{pmatrix}$ have an inverse?

11. Apply the explicit formula for A^{-1} (in the 2×2 case) twice to show directly that $(A^{-1})^{-1} = A$.

12. Show that if A is nonsingular and symmetric, A^{-1} is also symmetric.

13. Are there any values of λ for which the matrix $\begin{pmatrix} 1 & 2 \\ 1 & 3 \end{pmatrix} + \lambda \begin{pmatrix} 2 & 0 \\ 1 & 1 \end{pmatrix}$ has no inverse?

3.4 The Algebra of Inverses

In this section, some of the more important algebraic properties of inverses will be developed.

Theorem: *If* A *has an inverse, then* A^{-1} *has an inverse and* $(A^{-1})^{-1} = A$.

This says that the inverse of the inverse of a matrix is the matrix itself. A parallel statement in arithmetic is that 1/6 is the inverse of 6, and the inverse of 1/6 is again 6.

PROOF: $AA^{-1} = I$ and $A^{-1}A = I$ because these are the conditions that an inverse must satisfy. But the same conditions may be construed slightly differently. They say that A satisfies the two conditions for the inverse of A^{-1}. Hence $(A^{-1})^{-1} = A$.

Theorem: *If* A *has an inverse and* c *is a constant that is not* 0, *then* cA *has an inverse and*

$$(cA)^{-1} = c^{-1}A^{-1}.$$

PROOF: $(cA)(c^{-1}A^{-1}) = cc^{-1}(AA^{-1}) = 1 \cdot I = I$. Similarly, $(c^{-1}A^{-1})(cA) = c^{-1}c(A^{-1}A) = 1 \cdot I = I$. Hence $c^{-1}A^{-1}$ is inverse to cA, or: $(cA)^{-1} = c^{-1}A^{-1}$.

Theorem: *If* A *and* B *have inverses, so does* AB *and*

$$(AB)^{-1} = B^{-1}A^{-1}.$$

This says that the inverse of the product is the product of the inverses, *taken in reverse order*. The reversal of order is important to keep in mind.

PROOF: $(AB)(B^{-1}A^{-1}) = A(BB^{-1})A^{-1} = A\,I\,A^{-1} = AA^{-1} = I$.
Similarly,

$$(B^{-1}A^{-1})(AB) = B^{-1}(A^{-1}A)B = B^{-1}\,I\,B = B^{-1}B = I.$$

Corollary: *If* A, B, C, $\cdots$, F *all have inverses, so does the product* ABC $\cdots$ F *and*

$$(ABC \cdots F)^{-1} = F^{-1} \cdots C^{-1}B^{-1}A^{-1}.$$

This extended version is proved in the same way.

Theorem: *If* A *has an inverse, so does* A′ *and*

$$(A')^{-1} = (A^{-1})'.$$

PROOF: $A'(A^{-1})' = (A^{-1}A)' = I' = I$.
Similarly,

$$(A^{-1})'A' = (AA^{-1})' = I' = I.$$

Hence the matrix $(A^{-1})'$ satisfies the requirements of the inverse of A'.

We are now in a position to extend the notion of matrix powers so as to include negative powers.

Definition: *If* A *is a nonsingular matrix, and* m *is a positive integer, then* A^{-m} *will mean* $(A^{-1})^m$. *That is to say,* A^{-m} *is defined as the* m*th power of the inverse of* A.

Negative powers of singular matrices are not defined.

Example:

$$\text{If } A = \begin{pmatrix} 11 & 7 \\ 3 & 2 \end{pmatrix} \quad \text{then} \quad A^{-1} = \begin{pmatrix} 2 & -7 \\ -3 & 11 \end{pmatrix}.$$

Hence,

$$A^{-2} = (A^{-1})^2 = \begin{pmatrix} 2 & -7 \\ -3 & 11 \end{pmatrix}\begin{pmatrix} 2 & -7 \\ -3 & 11 \end{pmatrix} = \begin{pmatrix} 25 & -91 \\ -39 & 142 \end{pmatrix}.$$

Negative powers of a matrix satisfy the usual laws of exponents. This extends the theorem in Section 7, Chapter 2.

Theorem: *If* A *has an inverse, and if* m *and* n *are integers (either positive, negative, or zero) then*

$$A^m A^n = A^{m+n}. \tag{1}$$
$$(A^m)^n = A^{mn}. \tag{2}$$
$$(A')^m = (A^m)'. \tag{3}$$

PROOF: We shall give only an indication of a proof. Suppose we wish to prove that $A^{-3}A^5 = A^{-3+5} = A^2$. A^{-3} means $(A^{-1})^3$ or $A^{-1}A^{-1}A^{-1}$. Hence,

$$\begin{aligned} A^{-3}A^5 &= (A^{-1})(A^{-1})\,(A^{-1})(A)\,A^4 = (A^{-1})(A^{-1})A^4 \\ &= (A^{-1})(A^{-1})AA^3 = (A^{-1})A^3 \\ &= (A^{-1})AA^2 = I\,A^2 = A^2. \text{ This illustrates (1).} \end{aligned}$$

Suppose we would like to prove that

$$Y = (A^{-2})^{-3} = A^{(-2)(-3)} = A^6.$$

Set $X = A^{-2}$. This means that $X = (A^{-1})(A^{-1})$.
Set $Y = X^{-3}$. This means $Y = (X^{-1})(X^{-1})(X^{-1})$.

Now $X^{-1} = ((A^{-1})(A^{-1}))^{-1} = (A^{-1})^{-1}(A^{-1})^{-1} = A \cdot A = A^2$.

Therefore $Y = A^2A^2A^2 = A^6$. This illustrates (2).

Suppose we would like to show that $(A')^{-3} = (A^{-3})'$.

$$\begin{aligned} (A')^{-3} \text{ means } (A')^{-1}(A')^{-1}(A')^{-1} &= (A^{-1})'(A^{-1})'(A^{-1})' \\ &= [(A^{-1})(A^{-1})(A^{-1})]' = (A^{-3})'. \end{aligned}$$

This illustrates (3).

Example: If A is symmetric and is nonsingular then all its powers (positive and negative) are symmetric. $A = A'$. Hence $A^m = (A')^m$. But $(A')^m = (A^m)'$. Hence $A^m = (A^m)'$ or A^m is symmetric.

PROBLEMS

1. What is $((A^{-1})^{-1})^{-1}$? $(((A^{-1})^{-1})^{-1})^{-1}$?
2. Prove by a direct computation that $(AB)^{-1} = B^{-1}A^{-1}$ where $A = \begin{pmatrix} 1 & 6 \\ 2 & 1 \end{pmatrix}$, $B = \begin{pmatrix} 1 & 1 \\ 3 & 2 \end{pmatrix}$.
3. If $A = \begin{pmatrix} 7 & 4 \\ -1 & 0 \end{pmatrix}$ $B = \begin{pmatrix} 2 & 1 \\ 1 & 1 \end{pmatrix}$ $C = \begin{pmatrix} 3 & 4 \\ 7 & 9 \end{pmatrix}$, prove by a numerical computation that $(ABC)^{-1} = C^{-1}B^{-1}A^{-1}$.
4. Use the matrix in Problem 2 and prove by a direct computation that
$$(A')^{-1} = (A^{-1})'.$$
5. If
$$A^{-1} = \begin{pmatrix} 1 & 1 & 1 \\ 1 & 2 & 3 \\ 1 & 4 & 9 \end{pmatrix}$$
find A.
If
$$(A')^{-1} = \begin{pmatrix} 1 & 1 & 1 \\ 3 & 4 & 5 \\ 1 & 2 & 1 \end{pmatrix}$$
find A.
6. Show that $(A^{-1}BA)^{-1} = A^{-1}B^{-1}A$ and that $(A^{-1}B^{-1}A)^{-1} = A^{-1}BA$.
7. If $A = \begin{pmatrix} 2 & 1 \\ 3 & 2 \end{pmatrix}$ find A^{-3}. Show by a direct computation that
$$(A^{-1})^3 = (A^3)^{-1}.$$
8. If $A = \begin{pmatrix} 6 & 7 \\ 5 & 6 \end{pmatrix}$ compute $(A')^{-2}$. Compare with $(A^{-2})'$.
9. Show that $(A^3)'$ is the inverse of $(A')^{-3}$.
10. Prove that $(ABA^{-1})^2 = AB^2A^{-1}$.
11. If n is a positive integer, show that $(ABA^{-1})^n = AB^nA^{-1}$.
12. Show that $[(A'B^{-1}C^{-1})']^{-1} = A^{-1}B'C'$.
13. Verify numerically that the inverse of the symmetric matrix
$$\begin{pmatrix} 1 & 3 & 5 \\ 3 & 6 & 2 \\ 5 & 2 & 1 \end{pmatrix}$$
is also symmetric.

Certain matrix equations can be solved by means of the inverse. Suppose that we have the equation

$$AX = B.$$

The matrix X will be regarded as an unknown, and it will be supposed that A is a square and nonsingular matrix. If we multiply both sides of this equation on the left by A^{-1}, we obtain

$$A^{-1}AX = A^{-1}B$$

or

$$IX = A^{-1}B$$
$$X = A^{-1}B.$$

If we had started with the equation

$$XA = B,$$

then we would obtain the solution

$$XAA^{-1} = BA^{-1}$$
$$XI = BA^{-1}$$
$$X = BA^{-1}.$$

In each instance, we have expressed the value of X in terms of B and the inverse of A. This process is the analog of solving a simple algebraic equation such as $7x = 6$. We can write $(7^{-1})\ 7x = (7^{-1})6$ or $x = (7^{-1})6 = 6/7 = 6$ divided by 7.

We should be tempted to say that the value of X is the matrix B divided by the matrix A, if we think of division by a matrix as multiplication by its reciprocal. But there are two types of division corresponding to two types of multiplication: division on the right and division on the left. $A^{-1}B$ is B divided by A on the left, and BA^{-1} is B divided by A on the right. These two processes must be distinguished very carefully for multiplication is not commutative: In general, it is not true that $A^{-1}B = BA^{-1}$.

On the whole, when dealing with matrices, it is better to speak about multiplication by inverses and to allow the expressions "divide" and "division" to fall into disuse.

PROBLEMS

1. If $AX + B = C$ prove that $X = A^{-1}C - A^{-1}B$. What assumption has been made about A?
2. If $XA - B = C$ prove that $X = CA^{-1} + BA^{-1}$.
3. If $XA = B - XB$ prove that $X = B(A + B)^{-1}$. What assumption has been made here?
4. Prove that $AB^{-1} = B^{-1}A$ if and only if $AB = BA$.
5. Give a numerical example to show that division on the right and division on the left need not be the same.

3.5 Matrix Inversion by the Gauss-Jordan Scheme: Reduction of Matrices

When we come to matrices of higher orders, there are no simple explicit formulas for the inverses.

(1) There are formulas for the inverse that make use of determinants.* These are of interest theoretically.

(2) There are schemes for obtaining inverses numerically.

In this section, we shall show how the Gauss-Jordan elimination scheme can be adapted to produce matrix inverses numerically.

Suppose it is desired to invert the matrix

$$A = \begin{pmatrix} 2 & 1 & 1 \\ 1 & 2 & 1 \\ 1 & 1 & 2 \end{pmatrix}.$$

Augment the given matrix by appending the identity matrix at its right-hand side:

$$\begin{pmatrix} 2 & 1 & 1 & 1 & 0 & 0 \\ 1 & 2 & 1 & 0 & 1 & 0 \\ 1 & 1 & 2 & 0 & 0 & 1 \end{pmatrix}.$$

Now proceed exactly as in the Gauss-Jordan scheme explained in Section 1. We abbreviate somewhat the description of the steps.

1. Select the largest element in absolute value in the first column as a pivot. It is 2 so we do not have to interchange the rows.

2. Divide each element of the first row by the pivot:

$$\begin{pmatrix} 1 & \frac{1}{2} & \frac{1}{2} & 0 & 0 & \frac{1}{2} \\ 1 & 2 & 1 & 0 & 1 & 0 \\ 1 & 1 & 2 & 0 & 0 & 1 \end{pmatrix}.$$

3. By subtracting appropriate multiples of the first row we get

$$\begin{pmatrix} 1 & \frac{1}{2} & \frac{1}{2} & \frac{1}{2} & 0 & 0 \\ 0 & 1\frac{1}{2} & \frac{1}{2} & -\frac{1}{2} & 1 & 0 \\ 0 & \frac{1}{2} & 1\frac{1}{2} & -\frac{1}{2} & 0 & 1 \end{pmatrix}.$$

4. The pivot in the second row is $1\frac{1}{2} = \frac{3}{2}$ and it is also in proper position.

---

* For example, see page 182 for the inverse of the general 3×3 matrix.

5. Divide the elements of the second row by the pivot:

$$\begin{pmatrix} 1 & \frac{1}{2} & \frac{1}{2} & \frac{1}{2} & 0 & 0 \\ 0 & 1 & \frac{1}{3} & -\frac{1}{3} & \frac{2}{3} & 0 \\ 0 & \frac{1}{2} & 1\frac{1}{2} & -\frac{1}{2} & 0 & 1 \end{pmatrix}.$$

6. Subtract the appropriate multiples of the second row:

$$\begin{pmatrix} 1 & 0 & \frac{1}{3} & \frac{2}{3} & -\frac{1}{3} & 0 \\ 0 & 1 & \frac{1}{3} & -\frac{1}{3} & \frac{2}{3} & 0 \\ 0 & 0 & 1\frac{1}{3} & -\frac{1}{3} & -\frac{1}{3} & 1 \end{pmatrix}.$$

7. The third pivot is $1\frac{1}{3}$, and it, too, is in the proper position.
8. Division of the third row by the pivot produces

$$\begin{pmatrix} 1 & 0 & \frac{1}{3} & \frac{2}{3} & -\frac{1}{3} & 0 \\ 0 & 1 & \frac{1}{3} & -\frac{1}{3} & \frac{2}{3} & 0 \\ 0 & 0 & 1 & -\frac{1}{4} & -\frac{1}{4} & \frac{3}{4} \end{pmatrix}.$$

9. Subtract the appropriate multiples of the third row:

$$\begin{pmatrix} 1 & 0 & 0 & \frac{3}{4} & -\frac{1}{4} & -\frac{1}{4} \\ 0 & 1 & 0 & -\frac{1}{4} & \frac{3}{4} & -\frac{1}{4} \\ 0 & 0 & 1 & -\frac{1}{4} & -\frac{1}{4} & \frac{3}{4} \end{pmatrix}.$$

This completes the elimination process. The 3×3 matrix on the left has been reduced to the unit matrix. On the other hand, the 3×3 matrix to the left, which was originally the unit matrix, is now some other matrix. This matrix is precisely the inverse of A. We can check it by multiplying out:

$$\begin{pmatrix} 2 & 1 & 1 \\ 1 & 2 & 1 \\ 1 & 1 & 2 \end{pmatrix} \begin{pmatrix} \frac{3}{4} & -\frac{1}{4} & -\frac{1}{4} \\ -\frac{1}{4} & \frac{3}{4} & -\frac{1}{4} \\ -\frac{1}{4} & -\frac{1}{4} & \frac{3}{4} \end{pmatrix} = \begin{pmatrix} \frac{3}{4} & -\frac{1}{4} & -\frac{1}{4} \\ -\frac{1}{4} & \frac{3}{4} & -\frac{1}{4} \\ -\frac{1}{4} & -\frac{1}{4} & \frac{3}{4} \end{pmatrix} \begin{pmatrix} 2 & 1 & 1 \\ 1 & 2 & 1 \\ 1 & 1 & 2 \end{pmatrix}$$

$$= \begin{pmatrix} 1 & 0 & 0 \\ 0 & 1 & 0 \\ 0 & 0 & 1 \end{pmatrix}.$$

Why is this so? Of course, we could argue crudely that if we do "something" to A and it ends up as I, then the same thing done to I must convert it to A^{-1}. What is this "something"?

It can be explained as a simple extension of the solution of a system of equations by the Gauss-Jordan elimination method. Notice, first of all, that in the process of manipulation, whereas rows are combined or mixed with one another, columns are kept separate. Hence, appending the three columns

$$\begin{pmatrix}1\\0\\0\end{pmatrix}, \quad \begin{pmatrix}0\\1\\0\end{pmatrix}, \quad \begin{pmatrix}0\\0\\1\end{pmatrix}$$

to the right of A is equivalent to appending each of these columns separately and carrying out the elimination process three times.

Now what comes about when we carry out the elimination process with

$$\begin{pmatrix}2 & 1 & 1 & 1\\1 & 2 & 1 & 0\\1 & 1 & 2 & 0\end{pmatrix}?$$

We end up with

$$\begin{pmatrix}1 & 0 & 0 & \frac{3}{4}\\0 & 1 & 0 & -\frac{1}{4}\\0 & 0 & 1 & -\frac{1}{4}\end{pmatrix}.$$

As we know, the column to the extreme right,

$$\begin{pmatrix}\frac{3}{4}\\-\frac{1}{4}\\-\frac{1}{4}\end{pmatrix},$$

must represent the solution of the system of equations

$$\begin{cases}2x + y + z = 1\\x + 2y + z = 0\\x + y + 2z = 0.\end{cases}$$

That is to say, $x = 3/4$, $y = -1/4$, $z = -1/4$ is the solution of this system. You can check it. The process working on

$$\begin{pmatrix}2 & 1 & 1 & 0\\1 & 2 & 1 & 1\\1 & 1 & 2 & 0\end{pmatrix}$$

leads to

$$\begin{pmatrix}1 & 0 & 0 & -\frac{1}{4}\\0 & 1 & 0 & \frac{3}{4}\\0 & 0 & 1 & -\frac{1}{4}\end{pmatrix}.$$

The column to the right,

$$\begin{pmatrix}-\frac{1}{4}\\\frac{3}{4}\\-\frac{1}{4}\end{pmatrix},$$

represents the solution of

$$\begin{cases} 2p + q + r = 0 \\ p + 2q + r = 1 \\ p + q + 2r = 0. \end{cases}$$

Finally, the elimination process working on

$$\begin{pmatrix} 2 & 1 & 1 & 0 \\ 1 & 2 & 1 & 0 \\ 1 & 1 & 2 & 1 \end{pmatrix}$$

leads to

$$\begin{pmatrix} 1 & 0 & 0 & -\frac{1}{4} \\ 0 & 1 & 0 & -\frac{1}{4} \\ 0 & 0 & 1 & \frac{3}{4} \end{pmatrix},$$

and

$$\begin{pmatrix} -\frac{1}{4} \\ -\frac{1}{4} \\ \frac{3}{4} \end{pmatrix}$$

represents the solution of the system

$$\begin{cases} 2t + u + v = 0 \\ t + 2u + v = 0 \\ t + u + 2v = 1. \end{cases}$$

Now suppose we would like to invert A. We can write its inverse (as yet unknown) in the form

$$\begin{pmatrix} x & p & t \\ y & q & u \\ z & r & v \end{pmatrix},$$

and hence

$$\begin{pmatrix} 2 & 1 & 1 \\ 1 & 2 & 1 \\ 1 & 1 & 2 \end{pmatrix}\begin{pmatrix} x & p & t \\ y & q & u \\ z & r & v \end{pmatrix} = \begin{pmatrix} 1 & 0 & 0 \\ 0 & 1 & 0 \\ 0 & 0 & 1 \end{pmatrix}.$$

It will be seen that these unknowns satisfy the three systems of equations in three unknowns that we have just dealt with. This works for matrices of any order.

Here is another proof which makes use of matrix algebra in a more compact way. Suppose that A has an inverse A^{-1}. A certain sequence of elementary row transformations is applied to A and reduces it to I. Now these transformations can be effected by multiplication of A on the left by a certain sequence of elementary matrices $E_1, E_2, \ldots, E_p$ (where p is some integer whose exact value it is not important to know). Form the product $E_pE_{p-1} \cdots E_2E_1$ and call it E. Then,

$$EA = I.$$

Multiply on the right by A^{-1}. This yields

$$(EA)A^{-1} = IA^{-1},$$

or

$$E = A^{-1}.$$

Now, EI represents the result of carrying out the same sequence of elementary row transformation on I. But.

$$EI = E = A^{-1}$$

and hence, the same sequence of transformations will reduce I to A^{-1}.

PROBLEMS

1. Work out carefully a sequence of elementary row transformations which will reduce the matrix $A = \begin{pmatrix} 1 & 2 \\ 2 & 3 \end{pmatrix}$ to the unit matrix. For each row transformation write its corresponding elementary matrix. Call these matrices $E_1, E_2, \ldots, E_p$. Show numerically that $E_pE_{p-1} \cdots E_2E_1 = A^{-1}$.

2. Find the inverse of the following matrices by means of the Gauss-Jordan elimination scheme. Try to go through the steps in a mechanical fashion.

$$\begin{pmatrix} 7 & 5 \\ 4 & 3 \end{pmatrix}, \quad \begin{pmatrix} 3 & 4 & 5 \\ 2 & -1 & 8 \\ 5 & -2 & 7 \end{pmatrix}, \quad \begin{pmatrix} 1 & 1 & 1 \\ 2 & 1 & 2 \\ 2 & 2 & 3 \end{pmatrix}.$$

(Compare the example in Section 1).

3. Suppose that in the Gauss-Jordan elimination method for computing inverses the matrix B is adjoined to A instead of the matrix I. Prove that the sequence of elementary row transformations that reduces A to I will reduce B to $A^{-1}B$. Try this out by appending $\begin{pmatrix} 1 & -3 \\ 2 & 7 \end{pmatrix}$ to the right of $\begin{pmatrix} 5 & 3 \\ 3 & 2 \end{pmatrix}$.

We have employed elementary row operations to reduce a matrix A to I and hence to reduce an adjoined I to A^{-1}. Yet, if A is such that it has no inverse A^{-1}, the process must fail. Let us take a look at how this failure can occur. The only arithmetic operation in the Gauss-Jordan elimination process that might give trouble is a division by pivot. What if this pivot is 0? In such an instance, since division by zero is not allowed, the process will fail.

But we can prove that if A has an inverse, the process will not fail, that the occurrence of a zero pivot is the symptom of a singular matrix. We shall present a proof in the case of a 3×3 matrix, but it can be extended. Suppose that we apply the Gauss-Jordan elimination method to find the inverse of the matrix

$$A = \begin{pmatrix} a & b & c \\ d & e & f \\ g & h & k \end{pmatrix}.$$

(We omit the unit matrix that must be adjoined.) A is assumed to have an inverse. The first step is to look at the first column and select as a pivot the element that is largest in absolute value. Now this pivot cannot be zero. For if it were, a, d, and g would all be 0. Now a matrix of the form

$$\begin{pmatrix} 0 & b & c \\ 0 & e & f \\ 0 & h & k \end{pmatrix}$$

cannot have an inverse, for if it did,

$$\begin{pmatrix} x & y & z \\ \cdot & \cdot & \cdot \\ \cdot & \cdot & \cdot \end{pmatrix}\begin{pmatrix} 0 & b & c \\ 0 & e & f \\ 0 & h & k \end{pmatrix} = \begin{pmatrix} 1 & 0 & 0 \\ 0 & 1 & 0 \\ 0 & 0 & 1 \end{pmatrix}$$

and hence, $0x + 0y + 0z = 1$. This is a contradiction.

Since the pivot is not equal to zero, we can divide through by it, and following the steps of the method, cause the column $\begin{pmatrix} 1 \\ 0 \\ 0 \end{pmatrix}$ to appear at the left. We will now be left with a matrix of the form

$$B = \begin{pmatrix} 1 & l & m \\ 0 & n & p \\ 0 & q & r \end{pmatrix}.$$

The matrix B must also have an inverse. This is so because $B = EA$ where E is the product of certain elementary matrices. As we know, these elementary matrices all have inverses and their product E must also. Since A has an inverse, B must.

We now examine the numbers n and q, selecting the one with the largest absolute value as a second pivot. This pivot, again, cannot be equal to 0.

For if it were, both n and q would be 0 and B would be of the form

$$\begin{pmatrix} 1 & l & m \\ 0 & 0 & p \\ 0 & 0 & r \end{pmatrix}.$$

But such a matrix cannot have an inverse. For if it did,

$$\begin{pmatrix} x & y & z \\ w & u & v \\ . & . & . \end{pmatrix}\begin{pmatrix} 1 & l & m \\ 0 & 0 & p \\ 0 & 0 & r \end{pmatrix}=\begin{pmatrix} 1 & 0 & 0 \\ 0 & 1 & 0 \\ 0 & 0 & 1 \end{pmatrix}.$$

From this follows that $x = 1$, $xl = 0$, and hence $l = 0$. Then, $wl = 1$. This is impossible.

Since the second pivot is not equal to zero, we can divide through by it, and cause the column $\begin{pmatrix} 0 \\ 1 \\ 0 \end{pmatrix}$ to appear in the middle. We are now left with a matrix of the form

$$C = \begin{pmatrix} 1 & 0 & s \\ 0 & 1 & t \\ 0 & 0 & j \end{pmatrix}.$$

A similar argument to the one above shows that C has an inverse.

Finally, j cannot equal 0. For if it did, C would be of the form

$$C = \begin{pmatrix} 1 & 0 & s \\ 0 & 1 & t \\ 0 & 0 & 0 \end{pmatrix}.$$

But

$$\begin{pmatrix} \alpha & \beta & \gamma \\ \delta & \epsilon & \zeta \\ \eta & \theta & \kappa \end{pmatrix}\begin{pmatrix} 1 & 0 & s \\ 0 & 1 & t \\ 0 & 0 & 0 \end{pmatrix}=\begin{pmatrix} 1 & 0 & 0 \\ 0 & 1 & 0 \\ 0 & 0 & 1 \end{pmatrix}$$

implies $\eta = 0$, $\theta = 0$, and then $\kappa \cdot 0 = 1$ which is impossible. Since j is not 0, it is a proper pivot, and the final steps of the elimination can be carried out to complete the reduction.

This argument, written out in some detail, proves the following theorem.

Theorem: *If a matrix* A *has an inverse it can be reduced to the unit matrix by a sequence of elementary row operations. Equivalently, we can find a sequence of elementary matrices* $E_1, E_2, \ldots, E_p$ *such that*

$$E_pE_{p-1} \cdots E_2E_1 A = I.$$

Conversely, if A *can be reduced in this way, it has an inverse.*

This last assertion of the theorem is proved by observing that $E_1, E_2, \ldots, E_p$ all have inverses: ${E_1}^{-1}, {E_2}^{-1}, \ldots, {E_p}^{-1}$. Hence the product $E = E_p E_{p-1} \cdots E_2 E_1$ has an inverse: $E^{-1} = {E_1}^{-1}{E_2}^{-1} \cdots {E_{p-1}}^{-1}{E_p}^{-1}$. Now $EA = I$, so that $EAE = IE = E$. Hence, $E^{-1}EAE = E^{-1}E = I$. Therefore, $AE = I$. Thus both $EA = I$ and $AE = I$ so that E is the inverse of A.

But this long argument also tells more. It tells what can be done by way of reduction if A is *singular*. In such a case we will strike one or more zero pivots during the process of elimination. We will not be able to reduce to zero the numbers in the column above the pivot. However, all the numbers below the pivot will be zero (since the pivot is largest in absolute value). Therefore we have the following result.

Theorem: *If* A *is a singular matrix, it can be reduced by a sequence of elementary row transformations to a matrix* B *which (a) is upper triangular; (b) has either zeros or ones on its main diagonal; (c) has at least one zero on the main diagonal; and (d) has zeros in every column above the main diagonal wherever a 1 appears on the main diagonal.*

Example: Try to reduce the matrix

$$\begin{pmatrix} 1 & 1 & 3 \\ 2 & 0 & 1 \\ 1 & -1 & -2 \end{pmatrix}$$

to the unit matrix by row transformations. Examine the first column. The largest element is 2, so interchange and obtain

$$\begin{pmatrix} 2 & 0 & 1 \\ 1 & 1 & 3 \\ 1 & -1 & -2 \end{pmatrix}.$$

Divide by 2:

$$\begin{pmatrix} 1 & 0 & \frac{1}{2} \\ 1 & 1 & 3 \\ 1 & -1 & -2 \end{pmatrix}.$$

Subtract the first row from the second and third rows:

$$\begin{pmatrix} 1 & 0 & \frac{1}{2} \\ 0 & 1 & \frac{5}{2} \\ 0 & -1 & -\frac{5}{2} \end{pmatrix}.$$

Examine the second column; either 1 or -1 will do for a pivot. The 1 is in the proper position. Add the second row to the third:

$$\begin{pmatrix} 1 & 0 & \frac{1}{2} \\ 0 & 1 & \frac{5}{2} \\ 0 & 0 & 0 \end{pmatrix}.$$

Examine the third column for a pivot. The only choice is 0. The matrix is singular and no further reduction is possible. We have reduced

$$\begin{pmatrix} 2 & 0 & 1 \\ 1 & 1 & 3 \\ 1 & -1 & -2 \end{pmatrix} \quad \text{to} \quad \begin{pmatrix} 1 & 0 & \frac{1}{2} \\ 0 & 1 & \frac{5}{2} \\ 0 & 0 & 0 \end{pmatrix}$$

which is upper triangular, has 0's and 1's on its main diagonal, and has at least one 0.

PROBLEMS

1. Reduce the following matrices as far as possible, and interpret the results.

$$\begin{pmatrix} 1 & 1 & 2 \\ 2 & 0 & 2 \\ 3 & 0 & 1 \end{pmatrix}, \quad \begin{pmatrix} 1 & 1 & 2 \\ 1 & 1 & 2 \\ 2 & 5 & 8 \end{pmatrix}, \quad \begin{pmatrix} 2 & 2 & 2 \\ 2 & 2 & 2 \\ 2 & 2 & 2 \end{pmatrix}, \quad \begin{pmatrix} 1 & 2 & 3 \\ 3 & 2 & 1 \\ 7 & 6 & 7 \end{pmatrix}.$$

2. Try to invert

$$\begin{pmatrix} 1 & 0 & 3 & 1 \\ 0 & 1 & 2 & -1 \\ 0 & 0 & 0 & 3 \\ 0 & 0 & 0 & 1 \end{pmatrix}$$

by assuming an inverse with unknown numbers and setting up the system of linear equations for the unknowns. What happens?

3.6 Tricks of the Matrix Trade

This section contains a matrix trick, or rather, a paradox. Suppose we set

$$A = \begin{pmatrix} 1 & 1 & 0 \\ 2 & 0 & 2 \\ 0 & 5 & 5 \end{pmatrix}, \qquad B = \begin{pmatrix} 0 & 0 & -1 \\ 0 & -2 & 0 \\ -5 & 0 & 0 \end{pmatrix}, \qquad C = \begin{pmatrix} 3 & 4 & 2 \\ -2 & -1 & -1 \\ -1 & -3 & -1 \end{pmatrix}.$$

It is easily verified that

$$\begin{pmatrix} 1 & 1 & 0 \\ 2 & 0 & 2 \\ 0 & 5 & 5 \end{pmatrix}\begin{pmatrix} 3 & 4 & 2 \\ -2 & -1 & -1 \\ -1 & -3 & -1 \end{pmatrix} = \begin{pmatrix} 1 & 3 & 1 \\ 4 & 2 & 2 \\ -15 & -20 & -10 \end{pmatrix}.$$

Furthermore,

$$\begin{pmatrix} 0 & 0 & -1 \\ 0 & -2 & 0 \\ -5 & 0 & 0 \end{pmatrix}\begin{pmatrix} 3 & 4 & 2 \\ -2 & -1 & -1 \\ -1 & -3 & -1 \end{pmatrix} = \begin{pmatrix} 1 & 3 & 1 \\ 4 & 2 & 2 \\ -15 & -20 & -10 \end{pmatrix}.$$

In symbols then, these numerical products prove that $AC = BC$. By "cancelling" the C from both sides of the equation (that is, multiplying both sides of the equation on the right by C^{-1}), we are led to $ACC^{-1} = BCC^{-1}$. Hence $AI = BI$, or $A = B$. But this equation means that

$$\begin{pmatrix} 1 & 1 & 0 \\ 2 & 0 & 2 \\ 0 & 5 & 5 \end{pmatrix} = \begin{pmatrix} 0 & 0 & -1 \\ 0 & -2 & 0 \\ -5 & 0 & 0 \end{pmatrix}.$$

From this matrix equation, we can conclude all sorts of interesting absurdities such as $1 = 0$, $2 = 0$, $0 = -5$, et cetera. What is wrong? Verification of the arithmetic shows that all is in order there. And the formal matrix algebra follows well-established rules.

The reader may recall similar paradoxes or fallacies in ordinary algebra; "proofs" which purported to prove that $1 = 2$, et cetera.* It may be further recalled that the trouble with these "proofs" is that at a crucial stage a division by zero is performed. This is an undefined operation in algebra and can lead to a contradiction.

Something similar was done here. There was one division, or rather multiplication by an inverse in the "proof," namely, multiplication by C^{-1}. But whenever the symbol C^{-1} is written and utilized, it is tacitly assumed that C has an inverse. In this case, nothing of the sort is true. C has no inverse: it is a singular matrix. (Prove this directly). C^{-1} is entirely without meaning, and to conclude $A = B$ from $AC = BC$ is illegitimate.

There is a second aspect to this paradox. The equation $AC = BC$ is surely true, as we have seen. Hence

$$AC - BC = 0$$

or

$$(A - B)C = 0.$$

This matrix product can be verified by a direction computation:

$$A - B = \begin{pmatrix} 1 & 1 & 1 \\ 2 & 2 & 2 \\ 5 & 5 & 5 \end{pmatrix},$$

and hence

$$(A - B)C = \begin{pmatrix} 1 & 1 & 1 \\ 2 & 2 & 2 \\ 5 & 5 & 5 \end{pmatrix} \begin{pmatrix} 3 & 4 & 2 \\ -2 & -1 & -1 \\ -1 & -3 & -1 \end{pmatrix} = \begin{pmatrix} 0 & 0 & 0 \\ 0 & 0 & 0 \\ 0 & 0 & 0 \end{pmatrix} = 0.$$

---

* One such "proof" goes as follows. Set $x = 1$. Then $x^2 = x$. Hence $x^2 - x = x^2 - 1$. Therefore $x(x - 1) = (x + 1)(x - 1)$. Division of both sides of the equation by $(x - 1)$ yields $x = x + 1$. But $x = 1$, and hence $1 = 2$.

Now this is a strange thing, for we have here two matrices, neither of which is zero, but whose matrix product is zero! Ordinary arithmetic is vastly different, for if $xy = 0$, we can conclude that *either* $x = 0$, *or* $y = 0$. Not so with matrices: if the product of two matrices is zero, we cannot conclude that one of the factors must be zero. The most we can say is this: if the product of two matrices is zero and neither factor is zero, then both factors are singular (that is, have no inverses). For suppose that

$$AB = 0$$

while $A \neq 0$ and $B \neq 0$. If A had an inverse, A^{-1}, then

$$A^{-1}AB = A^{-1}0,$$

or

$$IB = 0.$$

Hence,

$$B = 0.$$

But this conclusion contradicts the known fact that $B \neq 0$. Hence the assumption that A^{-1} exists must be false. A similar argument shows that B must also be singular.

These investigations tell us further, that although the zero matrix is the analog of the ordinary zero when it comes to addition and subtraction, when it comes to division, *the whole class of singular matrices must be considered as the analog of zero.*

A special name is given to a pair of matrices, A, B neither of which is zero but whose product is zero. They are called *zero divisors*. In ordinary arithmetic, there are no zero divisors.

PROBLEMS

1. Show that $\begin{pmatrix} 1 & 0 \\ 2 & 0 \end{pmatrix}$, $\begin{pmatrix} 0 & 0 \\ 1 & 1 \end{pmatrix}$ are a pair of zero divisors.
2. Prove if $A = \begin{pmatrix} bc, & -b^2 \\ c^2, & -bc \end{pmatrix}$, then for all values of b and c, $A^2 = 0$.
3. Refer to the previous problem and show directly that the matrix A is always singular.
4. Find a pair of 3×3 zero divisors. Find a pair of 4×4 zero divisors.
5. Is it true that if $AB = 0$, then $BA = 0$?
6. Prove if A, B is a pair of zero divisors, so are B', A'.
7. Make up a paradox similar to the one given in the text.
8. If $C^2 = C$, show that C and $C - I$ are a pair of zero divisors. What about $C - I$ and C?

3.7 The Sense of Identity

The basic matrix operations have now been introduced: addition, subtraction, scalar multiplication, matrix multiplication, and matrix division —or as we have preferred to call it—multiplication by an inverse matrix. Besides these, we have introduced the transpose operation, which has no analog in ordinary algebra. We have found that with several exceptions, the manipulation of matrix expressions is very much like the manipulation of ordinary algebraic expressions. But these exceptions are important to keep in mind. They are:

(a) Matrix multiplication is not necessarily commutative.

(b) The inverse (or the transpose) of a product equals the product of the inverses (or the transposes) of the factors taken in the reverse order.

(c) The equation $AB = 0$ does not imply that either $A = 0$ or $B = 0$.

Symbolic manipulation with matrix inverses preassumes that these inverses exist. In specific instances, this may or may not be so.

Our aim in this section is to acquire more skill at formal matrix algebra by working through a variety of identities. We pursue them without seeking applications or interpretations. They may be considered as mere drill.

It is neither possible nor desirable to get away from drill in a mathematics course. Does the ballerina dance *Giselle* without her endless hours at the bar? The practice of mathematics also demands that certain thought muscles be kept in tone.

But there are compensations for the hard and frequently dull work that accompanies drill. Gertrude Stein—panjandrum of literature and art in the twenties—once wrote that "nothing is meaningless if one likes to do it." I know a lady who teaches classic languages in the Berkshires and who likes nothing better than to relax by simplifying a long and complicated algebraic expression. Or think of the cadenza in a famous violin concerto; the cadenza may be pure ostentatious fiddle drill, but it can be a wonderful experience to hear it.

Example 1: Expand $(A + B)^2$. We have $(A + B)^2 = (A + B)(A + B) = A^2 + AB + BA + B^2$. No further simplification is possible, for we do not normally have $AB = BA$. If A and B commute, then, of course $(A + B)^2 = A^2 + 2AB + B^2$, as in ordinary algebra. Until one gets used to noncommutativity, it may be best to expand products by the distributive law, writing down the intermediate steps. Thus,

$$(A + B)(A + B) = A(A + B) + B(A + B) = A^2 + AB + BA + B^2.$$

Example 2: Expand $(A + B)^3$. We have $(A + B)^3 = (A + B)(A + B)^2 = (A + B)(A^2 + AB + BA + B^2) = A(A^2 + AB + BA + B^2) + B(A^2 + AB + BA + B^2) = A^3 + A^2B + ABA + AB^2 + BA^2 + BAB + B^2A + B^3$.

No further simplification is possible.

Example 3: If A and B commute, then the result in Example (2) can be simplified. From $AB = BA$, we obtain $A(AB) = A(BA) = (AB)A = (BA)A$. Hence, $A^2B = ABA = BA^2$. In a similar way, we can show that $AB^2 = BAB = B^2A$. Therefore we have the usual binomial expansion

$$(A + B)^3 = A^3 + 3A^2B + 3AB^2 + B^3.$$

Example 4: If $A^2 - 3A + 2I = 0$. Then, assuming that A has an inverse, we can prove that $A^{-1} = \frac{3}{2}I - \frac{1}{2}A$. For,

$$2I = 3A - A^2, \qquad I = \tfrac{3}{2}A - \tfrac{1}{2}A^2.$$

Multiplication of both sides of the equation by A^{-1} gives us the required identity.

Example 5: If $A^3 = 0$, then we have

$$(I - A)(I + A + A^2) = I + A + A^2 - A - A^2 - A^3 = I.$$

Similarly, $(I + A + A^2)(I - A) = I$. It follows from these two equations that the matrix $I - A$ is nonsingular and

$$(I - A)^{-1} = I + A + A^2.$$

Example 6: If $P^{-1} + Q^{-1} = I$, find P. We have

$$I - Q^{-1} = P^{-1}.$$

Hence,

$$(P^{-1})^{-1} = P = (I - Q^{-1})^{-1}.$$

PROBLEMS

1. Show that $(A + B)^2 - (A - B)^2 = 2(AB + BA)$.
2. Expand $(A + B + C)^2$.
3. Expand $(A + B)^4$.
4. Expand $(A + I)^4$.
5. Simplify $CB^{-1}A(C^{-1}BA)^{-1}(B^{-1}C)^{-1}$.
6. If $S = (X + A)^{-1} + (X - A)^{-1}$, prove $XSX - XSA + ASX - ASA = 2X$.
7. $A(B + C) - (B + C)A = (AB - BA) + (AC - CA)$.
8. If $P^{-1} + Q^{-1} = I$ prove $P + Q = PQ$.
9. If $A^4 = 0$, prove $(I - A)^{-1} = I + A + A^2 + A^3$.
10. Prove that $(I + A + A^2 + \cdots + A^n) = (I - A)^{-1}(I - A^{n+1})$. What if $A^{n+1} = 0$?
11. If $A^3 = 0$, prove that $(I - A)^{-2} = I + 2A + 3A^2$.
12. If $A^n = 0$, prove that $I - A$ is nonsingular.
13. Prove the transpose of $(I + A)(I - A)^{-1}$ is $(I - A')^{-1}(I + A')$.
14. Prove that if A and B commute then the Binomial Theorem of ordinary algebra is valid:

$$(A + B)^n = A^n + nA^{n-1}B + \frac{n(n-1)}{2}A^{n-2}B^2 + \cdots + nAB^{n-1} + B^n.$$

15. If $A + B = 0$, does $A^2 + 2AB + B^2 = 0$?
16. If $B = QAQ^{-1}$, prove $A = Q^{-1}BQ$.
17. If $aM = bM$, and $M \neq 0$, does $a = b$?

18. Solve for X: $X = B + (I - BA)X$.

19. In the theory of alternating current circuits, the following system of simultaneous matrix equations arises:

$$\begin{cases} XG + RB = 0 \\ RG - XB = I. \end{cases}$$

Solve the equations for G and B in terms of R and X and show that

$$\begin{cases} G = (R + XR^{-1}X)^{-1} \\ B = -R^{-1}X\,(R + XR^{-1}X)^{-1}. \end{cases}$$

20. Solve the simultaneous matrix equations for the unknown matrices X and Y

$$\begin{cases} AX + BY = C \\ DX + EY = F. \end{cases}$$

What assumptions need to be made to guarantee the validity of the answer?

21. What is wrong with the following argument?

$$\text{Let } A = \begin{pmatrix} 1 & 8 \\ 2 & 1 \end{pmatrix}. \qquad \text{Then, } A^2 = \begin{pmatrix} 17 & 16 \\ 4 & 17 \end{pmatrix}.$$

Summary of the Laws of Matrix Arithmetic

ADDITION

$$A + B = B + A$$
$$(A + B) + C = A + (B + C)$$

SCALAR MULTIPLICATION

$$a(A + B) = aA + aB$$
$$(a + b)A = aA + bA$$
$$(ab)A = a(bA)$$
$$(1)A = A$$
$$(-1)A = -A$$
$$a0 = 0$$
$$0A = 0$$

MATRIX MULTIPLICATION

$$(AB)C = A(BC)$$
$$(A + B)C = AC + BC$$
$$A(B + C) = AB + AC$$
$$0A = A0 = 0$$
$$AI = IA = A$$

It follows that $A^2 - 2A - 15I = 0$. But, $A^2 - 2A - 15I = (A - 5I)(A + 3I)$. Therefore $(A - 5I)(A + 3I) = 0$. Thus, either $A = 5I$ or $A = -3I$. This means that either $\begin{pmatrix} 1 & 8 \\ 2 & 1 \end{pmatrix} = \begin{pmatrix} 5 & 0 \\ 0 & 5 \end{pmatrix}$ or $\begin{pmatrix} 1 & 8 \\ 2 & 1 \end{pmatrix} = \begin{pmatrix} -3 & 0 \\ 0 & -3 \end{pmatrix}$!

22. Let $A = \begin{pmatrix} 2 & 4 \\ 3 & 6 \end{pmatrix}$. Then $A^2 = \begin{pmatrix} 2 & 4 \\ 3 & 6 \end{pmatrix}\begin{pmatrix} 2 & 4 \\ 3 & 6 \end{pmatrix} = \begin{pmatrix} 16 & 32 \\ 24 & 48 \end{pmatrix} = 8\begin{pmatrix} 2 & 4 \\ 3 & 6 \end{pmatrix}$.

Hence, $A^2 = 8A$. Therefore $A^2A^{-1} = 8AA^{-1}$ or $A = 8I$. Hence, $\begin{pmatrix} 2 & 4 \\ 3 & 6 \end{pmatrix} = \begin{pmatrix} 8 & 0 \\ 0 & 8 \end{pmatrix}$. What is wrong with this argument?

23. Write $\begin{pmatrix} a & b \\ b & a \end{pmatrix} = aI + bE$ where $E = \begin{pmatrix} 0 & 1 \\ 1 & 0 \end{pmatrix}$.

Use the fact that $E^n = I$, n = even

$E^n = E$, n = odd

to compute $\begin{pmatrix} a & b \\ b & a \end{pmatrix}^4$. Can you develop a formula for $\begin{pmatrix} a & b \\ b & a \end{pmatrix}^n$?

Summary of the Laws of Matrix Arithmetic—*Continued*

SCALAR AND MATRIX MULTIPLICATION

$$a(AB) = (aA)B = A(aB)$$

INVERSES

$$AA^{-1} = A^{-1}A = I$$
$$(A^{-1})^{-1} = A$$
$$I^{-1} = I$$
$$(aA)^{-1} = a^{-1}A^{-1}$$
$$(AB)^{-1} = B^{-1}A^{-1}$$
$$(ABC \cdots F)^{-1} = F^{-1} \cdots C^{-1}B^{-1}A^{-1}$$

EXPONENTS

$$A^mA^n = A^{m+n}$$
$$(A^m)^n = (A^n)^m = A^{mn}$$
$$A^0 = I$$

TRANSPOSES

$$(A')' = A$$
$$(A + B)' = A' + B'$$
$$(aA)' = aA'$$
$$(AB)' = B'A'$$
$$(ABC \cdots F)' = F' \cdots C'B'A'$$
$$(A^{-1})' = (A')^{-1}$$

3.8 Matrix Inversion and the Solution of Systems of Linear Equations

We have already noticed several times that the system of equations

$$\begin{cases} a_{11}x_1 + \cdots + a_{1n}x_n = b_1 \\ \quad\vdots \qquad\qquad\quad \vdots \qquad \vdots \\ a_{n1}x_1 + \cdots + a_{nn}x_n = b_n \end{cases}$$

can be written in the form

$$AX = B \tag{1}$$

where A is the $n \times n$ matrix

$$\begin{pmatrix} a_{11} & \cdots & a_{1n} \\ \vdots & & \vdots \\ a_{n1} & \cdots & a_{nn} \end{pmatrix},$$

X is the $n \times 1$ matrix

$$\begin{pmatrix} x_1 \\ \vdots \\ x_n \end{pmatrix}$$

and B is the $n \times 1$ matrix

$$\begin{pmatrix} b_1 \\ \vdots \\ b_n \end{pmatrix}.$$

Let us make the assumption that A has an inverse, A^{-1}, and multiply Equation (1) on the left by A^{-1}:

$$A^{-1}AX = A^{-1}B.$$

Hence,

$$IX = A^{-1}B,$$

or

$$X = A^{-1}B.$$

This formula gives us the "solution" of the system of equations. The word solution has been put in quotes to emphasize that it is only a solution in a theoretical sense, and that to obtain numerical solutions, we need to know or to have computed A^{-1}.

The relationship between the matrices and the solution of a system of equations is governed by the following theorem.

Theorem: *If* A *has an inverse then for every* B *the system* AX = B *has one and only one solution. Conversely, if* AX = B *has a solution for every* B, *then the matrix* A *has an inverse.*

PROOF: If A has an inverse A^{-1}, then $X = A^{-1}B$ is a solution inasmuch as $A(A^{-1}B) = (AA^{-1})(B) = IB = B$. Now if X and Y are both solutions, then $AX = B$ and $AY = B$. Hence $AX = AY$. Hence $A^{-1}AX = AA^{-1}Y$ so that $X = Y$.

Suppose, conversely, that $AX = B$ has a solution for every right-hand side. Then, in particular, it has solutions when

$$B = \begin{pmatrix} 1 \\ 0 \\ \cdot \\ \cdot \\ \cdot \\ 0 \end{pmatrix} \quad \text{or} \quad \begin{pmatrix} 0 \\ 1 \\ 0 \\ \cdot \\ \cdot \\ 0 \end{pmatrix}, \quad \cdots, \quad \text{or} \quad \begin{pmatrix} 0 \\ 0 \\ \cdot \\ \cdot \\ \cdot \\ 1 \end{pmatrix}.$$

This means that we can find matrices

$$\begin{pmatrix} x_{11} \\ x_{21} \\ \cdot \\ \cdot \\ \cdot \\ x_{n1} \end{pmatrix}, \quad \begin{pmatrix} x_{12} \\ x_{22} \\ \cdot \\ \cdot \\ \cdot \\ x_{n2} \end{pmatrix}, \quad \cdots, \quad \begin{pmatrix} x_{1n} \\ x_{2n} \\ \cdot \\ \cdot \\ \cdot \\ x_{nn} \end{pmatrix}$$

such that

$$\begin{pmatrix} a_{11} & \cdots & a_{1n} \\ \vdots & & \vdots \\ a_{n1} & \cdots & a_{nn} \end{pmatrix} \begin{pmatrix} x_{11} \\ \vdots \\ x_{n1} \end{pmatrix} = \begin{pmatrix} 1 \\ 0 \\ \cdot \\ \cdot \\ \cdot \\ 0 \end{pmatrix}$$

$$\vdots \qquad \vdots \qquad \vdots$$

$$\begin{pmatrix} a_{11} & \cdots & a_{1n} \\ \vdots & & \vdots \\ a_{n1} & \cdots & a_{nn} \end{pmatrix} \begin{pmatrix} x_{1n} \\ \vdots \\ x_{nn} \end{pmatrix} = \begin{pmatrix} 0 \\ 0 \\ \vdots \\ 1 \end{pmatrix}.$$

Hence,

$$\begin{pmatrix} a_{11} & \cdots & a_{1n} \\ \vdots & & \vdots \\ a_{n1} & \cdots & a_{nn} \end{pmatrix} \begin{pmatrix} x_{11} & \cdots & x_{1n} \\ \vdots & & \vdots \\ x_{n1} & \cdots & x_{nn} \end{pmatrix} = I$$

and therefore A has an inverse. (The reader should expand this last matrix equation and verify that it is equivalent to the n matrix equations standing above it.)

PROBLEMS

1. Show that $\begin{pmatrix} 1 & 2 \\ 2 & 4 \end{pmatrix}$ is singular by finding numbers b_1, b_2 such that

$$\begin{cases} x_1 + 2x_2 = b_1 \\ 2x_2 + 4x_2 = b_2 \end{cases}$$

has no solution.

2. Do the same for

$$\begin{pmatrix} 1 & 1 & 2 \\ 2 & 0 & 2 \\ 1 & -1 & 0 \end{pmatrix}$$

and for

$$\begin{pmatrix} 1 & 0 & 1 \\ 1 & 1 & 2 \\ 1 & 2 & 3 \end{pmatrix}.$$

The theorem we have just proved has an amusing interpretation in terms of number games. By a number game, I mean the kind of game played by two people in which the first person selects a number. The second person then has the first person subject his number to a variety of operations at the end of which the first reveals his "answer." The second person then tells the first person the number he selected originally.

Consider this number game: have a person think of two numbers. Tell him to add the first to the second and write the answer down as a third number. Have him add the second to the third and to write this answer down as a fourth number. Have him then add the third to the fourth; write it down as a fifth number, add the fourth to the fifth and write it down as a sixth number. If your foil now reveals the last two numbers in the sequence, you can tell him his original numbers in the proper order.

Solution: Let the numbers selected be x and y. The sequence of six numbers is therefore x, y, $x + y$, $x + 2y$, $2x + 3y$, $3x + 5y$. If you call the numbers that have been revealed w and v, then,

$$\begin{cases} w = 2x + 3y \\ v = 3x + 5y. \end{cases}$$

Now $\begin{pmatrix} 2 & 3 \\ 3 & 5 \end{pmatrix}^{-1} = \begin{pmatrix} 5 & -3 \\ -3 & 2 \end{pmatrix}$, so that all you have to do to recover x and y from w and v is to carry out the matrix multiplication $\begin{pmatrix} 5 & -3 \\ -3 & 2 \end{pmatrix}\begin{pmatrix} w \\ v \end{pmatrix}$. For example, your foil thinks of 5 and 2, and following instructions, writes down 5, 2, 7 9, 16, 25. He reveals 16 and 25. You then compute $\begin{pmatrix} 5 & -3 \\ -3 & 2 \end{pmatrix}\begin{pmatrix} 16 \\ 25 \end{pmatrix} = \begin{pmatrix} 5 \\ 2 \end{pmatrix}$, yielding the original numbers in their proper order.

One can now consider number games which lead to other coefficients:

$$\begin{cases} w = a_{11}x + a_{12}y \\ v = a_{21}x + a_{22}y \end{cases}$$

or to similar expressions in three or more variables. Designate the coefficient matrix by A. If now, A has an inverse, the second person can tell the first person's number unambiguously, for every choice of revealed answers. Conversely, if the second person can give a solution no matter what answer the first person revealed, then A has an inverse, and the solutions given were the only possible ones.

A topic somewhat related to this is *Matrix Cryptography* in Chapter 10.

PROBLEMS

1. Show that it is possible to solve the number game example in the text as follows. Start with 25, 16. Subtract the second from the first yielding 25, 16, 9. Subtract the third from the second yielding 25, 16, 9, 7. Two more subtractions yield 25, 16, 9, 7, 2, 5. Give a general proof.

2. Develop a number game where your quarry writes down three numbers. Add the first three to produce a fourth. Add the second, third, and fourth to produce a fifth, and so forth.

We return to the discussion of the use of matrix inverses in the solution of linear systems of equations. It is important to note that if A^{-1} has to be computed, it may be a long job, and involve the solution of simultaneous equations. It would seem, then, that we are going around in circles: we have solved a system of equations using the inverse matrix, but we must compute such an inverse by solving a system of equations. The truth of the matter is that the gain is largely a theoretical one and only occasionally a numerical one.

(1) This mode of solution exhibits the unknowns as linear combinations of the terms on the right-hand side. For example, if

$$\begin{cases} x_1 + 3x_2 + 7x_3 = y_1 \\ 4x_1 + 2x_2 + 3x_3 = y_2 \\ x_1 + 2x_2 + x_3 = y_3 \end{cases}$$

and if we compute (by any of the numerical schemes presented)

$$\begin{pmatrix} 1 & 3 & 7 \\ 4 & 2 & 3 \\ 1 & 2 & 1 \end{pmatrix}^{-1} = \tfrac{1}{35}\begin{pmatrix} -4 & 11 & -5 \\ -1 & -6 & 25 \\ 6 & 1 & -10 \end{pmatrix},$$

then

$$\begin{pmatrix} x_1 \\ x_2 \\ x_3 \end{pmatrix} = \tfrac{1}{35}\begin{pmatrix} -4 & 11 & -5 \\ -1 & -6 & 25 \\ 6 & 1 & -10 \end{pmatrix}\begin{pmatrix} y_1 \\ y_2 \\ y_3 \end{pmatrix}$$

or

$$\begin{cases} x_1 = -\tfrac{4}{35}y_1 + \tfrac{11}{35}y_2 - \tfrac{5}{35}y_3 \\ x_2 = -\tfrac{1}{35}y_1 - \tfrac{6}{35}y_2 + \tfrac{25}{35}y_3 \\ x_3 = \tfrac{6}{35}y_1 + \tfrac{1}{35}y_2 - \tfrac{10}{35}y_3. \end{cases}$$

(2) In numerous practical examples, we have to solve a system where there are different sets of numbers on the right-hand side, but only *one* set of coefficients on the left. The matrix mode of solution is very economical under such circumstances. Once the inverse matrix has been computed, all that is required for each set of numbers on the right side of the equation is a simple matrix multiplication.

(3) Finally, it may happen that what is really wanted is not the values of the unknowns, but some further expressions involving them. Suppose, in the example given under (1), that we want, for each set of numbers y_1, y_2, y_3, not the values x_1, x_2, x_3, but the combination $x_1 + x_2 + x_3$. We may compute, using the explicit solution,

$$x_1 + x_2 + x_3 = \tfrac{1}{35}y_1 + \tfrac{6}{35}y_2 + \tfrac{10}{35}y_3$$

and we have our answer directly in terms of y_1, y_2, y_3.

This process may be given a matrix formulation. Suppose that $AX = Y$ is a system of n linear equations and we would like to compute CX where $C = (c_1, c_2, \ldots, c_n)$. Now $X = A^{-1}Y$ and hence $CX = CA^{-1}Y = (CA^{-1})Y$.

The matrix CA^{-1} is a $1 \times n$ matrix, and if we compute it, $(CA^{-1})Y$ gives CX automatically as a linear combination of the y's.

PROBLEMS

1. Solve the system

$$\begin{cases} 13x_1 + 14x_2 = y_1 \\ 14x_1 + 15x_3 = y_2 \end{cases}$$

for the following values of $\begin{pmatrix} y_1 \\ y_2 \end{pmatrix}$: $\begin{pmatrix} 1 \\ 0 \end{pmatrix}, \begin{pmatrix} 0 \\ 1 \end{pmatrix}, \begin{pmatrix} 0 \\ 0 \end{pmatrix}, \begin{pmatrix} 6 \\ -2 \end{pmatrix}, \begin{pmatrix} 1 \\ 3 \end{pmatrix}, \begin{pmatrix} -1 \\ -1 \end{pmatrix}$.

Use the inverse matrix.

2. If the x's and y's are related as in Problem 1, find, using matrices, the value of $2x_1 + 3x_2$ in terms of y_1 and y_2.

3. If $\begin{cases} x - 6y + z = a \\ 2x + y + z = b \\ x + 2y + z = c, \end{cases}$

express x, y, and z directly in terms of a, b, and c.

4. Suppose that $AX = Y$, and what is desired is not $X = \begin{pmatrix} x_1 \\ \cdot \\ \cdot \\ \cdot \\ x_n \end{pmatrix}$, but

$$x_1^2 + x_2^2 + \cdots + x_n^2.$$

Show that $(x_1^2 + x_2^2 + \cdots + x_n^2) = X'X$, and hence,

$$(x_1^2 + x_2^2 + \cdots + x_n^2) = Y' (A^{-1})' (A^{-1}) Y.$$

5. Try out the scheme in Problem 4 with

$$\begin{cases} 6x_1 + 7x_2 = y_1 \\ 7x_1 + 8x_2 = y_2. \end{cases}$$

6. In Problem 3 suppose that we know the three sets of values of x, y, z corresponding to the three sets of values of a, b, c: $\begin{pmatrix} a \\ b \\ c \end{pmatrix} = \begin{pmatrix} 1 \\ 0 \\ 0 \end{pmatrix}, \begin{pmatrix} 0 \\ 1 \\ 0 \end{pmatrix}, \begin{pmatrix} 0 \\ 0 \\ 1 \end{pmatrix}$. Show that it is then a very simple matter to obtain the general solution.

3.9 Some Further Applications

1. The Analysis of Nuts. Imagine the following project—admittedly artificial and idealized. We would like to determine the retail cost of various types of nuts. The only data available to us has been obtained from cans of mixed nuts. For simplicity, suppose that we distinguish only the following three types of nuts: Spanish peanuts (S), "cocktail" peanuts (P), and cashew nuts (C). We go to the store and buy three one pound cans of mixed nuts of different brands that have these three components in different proportions. Our analysis reveals the following information.

BRAND \ COMPONENT	S	P	C	COST
"JUANITA"	50%	50%	0%	\$ .75
"KASHEW KING"	40%	40%	20%	.80
"AULD SALT"	10%	50%	40%	.91

If we use the symbols S, P, and C to designate the dollar cost per pound of the respective nuts, and the symbols J, K, and A for the number of dollars in the cost per pound of the respective brands, then we may set up the following system of equations

$$\begin{cases} \frac{50}{100}S + \frac{50}{100}P + \frac{0}{100}C = \frac{75}{100} = J \\ \frac{40}{100}S + \frac{40}{100}P + \frac{20}{100}C = \frac{80}{100} = K \\ \frac{10}{100}S + \frac{50}{100}P + \frac{40}{100}C = \frac{91}{100} = A \end{cases}$$

At this stage of the analysis it would be useful to stop and to examine the assumptions, both mathematical and marketing, that underlie these three equations. If the assumptions seem rather naive in the sense that they seem hardly to capture what goes on in the real world of distributors and supermarkets, it may be comforting to realize that when the physicist or engineer sets up equations that are to be a model of the real world, he too, simplifies in the very same way.

Write

$$\frac{1}{10}\begin{pmatrix} 5 & 5 & 0 \\ 4 & 4 & 2 \\ 1 & 5 & 4 \end{pmatrix}\begin{pmatrix} S \\ P \\ C \end{pmatrix} = \begin{pmatrix} J \\ K \\ A \end{pmatrix}.$$

Hence

$$\begin{pmatrix} S \\ P \\ C \end{pmatrix} = 10\begin{pmatrix} 5 & 5 & 0 \\ 4 & 4 & 2 \\ 1 & 5 & 4 \end{pmatrix}^{-1}\begin{pmatrix} J \\ K \\ A \end{pmatrix} = \frac{1}{2}\begin{pmatrix} -3 & 10 & -5 \\ 7 & -10 & 5 \\ -8 & 10 & 0 \end{pmatrix}\begin{pmatrix} J \\ K \\ A \end{pmatrix}.$$

By substituting the particular prices $J = .75$, $K = .80$, $A = .91$, we find that $S = .60$, $P = .90$, and $C = 1.00$. These are the prices of the unmixed nuts.

This solution has a wider utility than to our isolated determination of prices. Perhaps we would like to monitor the prices from week to week. We observe J, K, and A from week to week. We assume that the mixture percentages remain constant. Assume the matrix inversion is done once for all, and S, P, then C can be obtained by a simple matrix multiplication.

2. *Maxwell's Influence Matrices, Once Again.* Refer back to Chapter 2, pages 68–70. Maxwell's influence matrix gives us a method for computing deflections on an elastic structure if loads are known. We have,

$$\begin{pmatrix} D_1 \\ D_2 \\ D_3 \end{pmatrix} = \begin{pmatrix} d_{11} & d_{12} & d_{13} \\ d_{21} & d_{22} & d_{23} \\ d_{31} & d_{32} & d_{33} \end{pmatrix} \begin{pmatrix} w_1 \\ w_2 \\ w_3 \end{pmatrix}.$$

In numerous instances, we would like to reverse the process: we know the individual deflections D_1, D_2, D_3, and we would like to compute the loads, w_1, w_2, w_3. We have

$$\begin{pmatrix} w_1 \\ w_2 \\ w_3 \end{pmatrix} = \begin{pmatrix} d_{11} & d_{12} & d_{13} \\ d_{21} & d_{22} & d_{23} \\ d_{31} & d_{32} & d_{33} \end{pmatrix}^{-1} \begin{pmatrix} D_1 \\ D_2 \\ D_3 \end{pmatrix}.$$

The matrix (d_{ij}) has been called the flexibility matrix for the elastic body; its inverse, $(d_{ij})^{-1}$—the matrix that solves the reverse problem—is called the *stiffness matrix.* Flexibility is a measure of inches of deflection per pound of load; stiffness, on the other hand, is a measure of pounds of load per inch of deflection.

3. *Straight Line and Parabolic Interpolation.* Through every pair of distinct points one and only one straight line can be passed. Let us see how this simple geometrical fact can be given a matrix interpretation.

Suppose that the two points are (x_1, y_1) and (x_2, y_2). Suppose, further, that $x_1 \neq x_2$ so that the points are neither identical nor do they lie on a vertical line. We would like to obtain the equation of the line that passes through them. This equation must be of the form $y = ax + b$ where the quantities a and b are to be determined in terms of x_1, y_1, x_2, y_2. Since the line passes through the points, we have

$$\begin{cases} ax_1 + b = y_1 \\ ax_2 + b = y_2 \end{cases}$$

or

$$\begin{pmatrix} x_1 & 1 \\ x_2 & 1 \end{pmatrix} \begin{pmatrix} a \\ b \end{pmatrix} = \begin{pmatrix} y_1 \\ y_2 \end{pmatrix}.$$

Hence,

$$\begin{pmatrix} a \\ b \end{pmatrix} = \begin{pmatrix} x_1 & 1 \\ x_2 & 1 \end{pmatrix}^{-1} \begin{pmatrix} y_1 \\ y_2 \end{pmatrix}.$$

Now,

$$\begin{pmatrix} x_1 & 1 \\ x_2 & 1 \end{pmatrix}^{-1} = \frac{1}{x_1 - x_2} \begin{pmatrix} 1 & -1 \\ -x_2 & x_1 \end{pmatrix}.$$

(We have assumed that $x_1 \neq x_2$ so that division by zero does not occur.) Hence,

$$\begin{pmatrix} a \\ b \end{pmatrix} = \frac{1}{x_1 - x_2} \begin{pmatrix} 1 & -1 \\ -x_2 & x_1 \end{pmatrix} \begin{pmatrix} y_1 \\ y_2 \end{pmatrix}.$$

By expanding this equation:

$$\begin{cases} a = \text{slope of line} = \dfrac{y_1 - y_2}{x_1 - x_2} \\ b = \text{intercept on } y \text{ axis} = \dfrac{x_1 y_2 - y_1 x_2}{x_1 - x_2}. \end{cases}$$

If x_1 and x_2 are considered to be fixed numbers, the values of a and b are certain linear combinations of y_1 and y_2. Example: If $x_1 = -1$, $x_2 = 1$, then

$$\begin{pmatrix} a \\ b \end{pmatrix} = \frac{1}{2} \begin{pmatrix} -1 & 1 \\ 1 & 1 \end{pmatrix} \begin{pmatrix} y_1 \\ y_2 \end{pmatrix}$$

or

$$\begin{cases} a = -\frac{1}{2} y_1 + \frac{1}{2} y_2 \\ b = -\frac{1}{2} y_1 + \frac{1}{2} y_2. \end{cases}$$

Just as two points determine a straight line, three points determine a parabola. Here the algebra is sufficiently complicated so that we will illustrate this with an example that is partly numerical. Let the three points be $(-1, y_1)$, $(0, y_2)$, $(1, y_3)$. (See Figure 3.2.) The equation of the parabola can be written as $y = ax^2 + bx + c$.

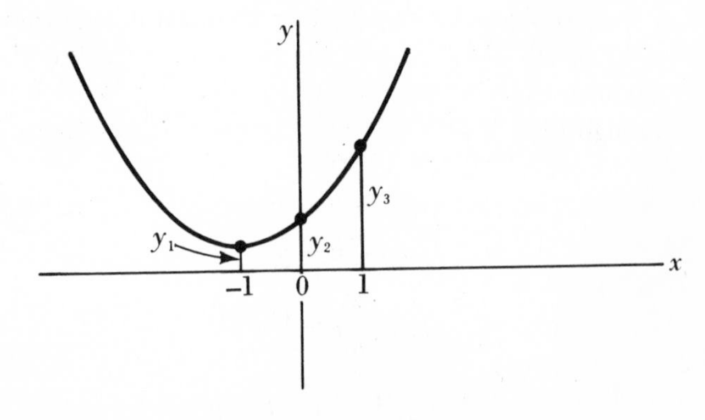

FIGURE 3.2

The quantities a, b, and c are to be determined. From the condition that the three points lie on the curve. We have

$$\begin{cases} y_1 = a - b + c \\ y_2 = \qquad\quad\; c \\ y_3 = a + b + c \end{cases}$$

or,

$$\begin{pmatrix} 1 & -1 & 1 \\ 0 & 0 & 1 \\ 1 & 1 & 1 \end{pmatrix} \begin{pmatrix} a \\ b \\ c \end{pmatrix} = \begin{pmatrix} y_1 \\ y_2 \\ y_3 \end{pmatrix}.$$

Now
$$\begin{pmatrix} 1 & -1 & 1 \\ 0 & 0 & 1 \\ 1 & 1 & 1 \end{pmatrix}^{-1} = \begin{pmatrix} \frac{1}{2} & -1 & \frac{1}{2} \\ -\frac{1}{2} & 0 & \frac{1}{2} \\ 0 & 1 & 0 \end{pmatrix}$$

so that
$$\begin{pmatrix} a \\ b \\ c \end{pmatrix} = \begin{pmatrix} \frac{1}{2} & -1 & \frac{1}{2} \\ -\frac{1}{2} & 0 & \frac{1}{2} \\ 0 & 1 & 0 \end{pmatrix} \begin{pmatrix} y_1 \\ y_2 \\ y_3 \end{pmatrix}.$$

This gives us the coefficients directly as linear combinations of the y's.

Suppose now that it is desired to find the height at x of the parabola that passes through these three points. We have $(y(x)) = (ax^2 + bx + c) =$ $(x^2 \quad x \quad 1) \begin{pmatrix} a \\ b \\ c \end{pmatrix}$. Hence

$$(y(x)) = (x^2 \quad x \quad 1) \begin{pmatrix} \frac{1}{2} & -1 & \frac{1}{2} \\ -\frac{1}{2} & 0 & \frac{1}{2} \\ 0 & 1 & 0 \end{pmatrix} \begin{pmatrix} y_1 \\ y_2 \\ y_3 \end{pmatrix}.$$

PROBLEMS

1. If pound cans of Juanita, Kashew King, and Auld Salt sold for \$ .75, \$ .84, and \$ .95 respectively, determine the price of the unmixed nuts.
2. If J, K, and A each sold for \$ .80 a can, determine the price of the unmixed nuts.
3. In the numerical example on page 120, the sum of each row in the multiplier of $\begin{pmatrix} S \\ P \\ C \end{pmatrix}$ is 1. What fact does this reflect? In the inverse of this multiplier (the multiplier of $\begin{pmatrix} J \\ K \\ A \end{pmatrix}$), the sum of the rows is also 1. What fact does this reflect?

4. A matrix A has all its row sums equal to 1. Suppose that A has an inverse. Does A^{-1} have all its row sums equal to 1? Can you prove your conclusion? Hint: $AJ = J$.

5. Discuss the following problem from the matrix point of view. No numerical values are required. Three mixtures of Spanish peanuts, cocktail peanuts, and cashews have been analyzed. Predict the price of a fourth mixture whose percentage of nuts is different from the first three.

6. Use the flexibility matrix given on page 70 and find the corresponding stiffness matrix.

7. In reference to Problem 6, deflections of $7/8''$, $1''$, and $7/8''$ were recorded at stations 1, 2, and 3. What loads were applied?

8. Find the 2×2 stiffness matrix of a cantilever beam. (See Problem 8 page 71).

9. A series of straight lines cut the two lines $x = -1$, $x = 2$ at heights of 1,2; 2,2; 3,0; 4,0; $-1,-1$; $-1,5$ respectively. Determine the slopes and intercepts on the y axis of these lines.

10. A series of parabolas cut the three lines $x = -1$, $x = 1$, $x = 2$ at heights of 1,2,2; 2,2,1; 1,0,0; 0,1,0; $-1,-2,6$ respectively. Determine where these parabolas cut the line $x = 3$.

CHAPTER 4

Linear Transformations of the Plane

In this chapter we shall develop and study one of the major interpretations of matrices: that of linear transformations of space.

4.1 Functions, Correspondences, Transformations, and Mappings

The expressions in the section heading are used more or less synonymously in mathematics, although each has its own special flavor. The concept they represent is a fundamental one, and it will be worthwhile to spend some time discussing it. Our object is not to lay a rigorous, logical foundation for the concept of a function, but to introduce a few terms and to obtain a feeling for the scope of the definitions.

To have a function (or a correspondence, a transformation, or a mapping) we need, first of all, two sets of objects. These objects may be of any sort, but usually will be the kind of objects that come up in mathematical discussions: numbers, points, lines, matrices, et cetera.* The two sets of objects may actually be the same. We need, secondly, a relation between the two sets wherein to each element of the first set, there is related (or there corresponds) an element of the second set.

Example 1: The first set of objects is composed of the numbers 1, 2, 3, and 4. The second set is composed of the numbers 5, 6, 7, and 8. The number 1 will be related to the number 5, 2 to 6, 3 to 7, and 4 to 8.

Just as there are many synonyms for a function, there are many notations for

---

* A colleague of mine, spoofing the generality of the functional concept, once defined a function, f, for which $f(1) = 1$, $f(2) = 2$, and $f(3) =$ horse. Shortly thereafter, he became a patron of the race tracks, but whether this function helped him place his bets he steadfastly refused to say.

functions in current use. Each notation has its own particular utility. One way of exhibiting the relationship set up in Example 1 is to write

$$\begin{aligned} 1 &\to 5 \\ 2 &\to 6 \\ 3 &\to 7 \\ 4 &\to 8. \end{aligned}$$

These symbols can be read in a variety of ways: 1 "goes into" 5, 1 "becomes" 5, 1 is "mapped onto" 5, 1 is "transformed into" 5, the "image" of 1 is 5, and so forth. Another way of exhibiting the relationship is by writing

$$\begin{aligned} f(1) &= 5 \\ f(2) &= 6 \\ f(3) &= 7 \\ f(4) &= 8. \end{aligned}$$

These lines tell us that we are dealing with a function f whose value at 1 is 5, at 2 is 6, et cetera.

Example 2: Both the first and second set of objects are the set of all two by two matrices. A' designates the transpose of A and

$$A \to A'$$

is an example of a function or of a mapping. What is the image of $\begin{pmatrix} 1 & 3 \\ -2 & 4 \end{pmatrix}$ under this mapping?

Example 3: Let the first set of objects be the positive integers, and let the second set be the integers that are squares. The correspondence

$$\begin{aligned} 1 &\to 1 \\ 2 &\to 4 \\ 3 &\to 9 \\ &\cdot \\ &\cdot \\ &\cdot \end{aligned}$$

relates to every integer n its square n^2: $n \to n^2$.

Example 4: A permutation can be regarded as a function. Let both the first and second sets consist of three objects A, B, C. If

$$\begin{cases} A \to B \\ B \to C \\ C \to A \end{cases} \quad \text{or if} \quad \begin{cases} A \to A \\ B \to C \\ C \to B, \end{cases}$$

then each of these functions or mappings is a permutation of the objects.

The first set of elements (the set that has images) is called the *domain* of the function; while the set of images is called the *range* of the function.

Example 5: If $f(x) = x + 1$, and if the domain of the function is the set of all numbers (both positive and negative) then the range is also the set of all positive and negative numbers.

Example 6: If $f(x) = x^2 + 1$, and if the domain is the set of all positive and negative numbers and zero, the range is the set of all numbers that are equal to or greater than 1.

Two functions are considered *identical* when

1. The domain of each function is the same
2. Each function associates with a given object in the domain the same object in the range.

Example 7: Let $f(x) = x^3 - x^2$, $g(x) = x^2(x - 1)$ and suppose that both functions are considered on a domain consisting of all the numbers. Since for every x, $x^3 - x^2 = x^2(x - 1)$, the two functions are identical. But the formulas which prescribe the values of the points at x (that is, the images of the number x) are not identical. After all, the computational prescription $x^3 - x^2$ involves different arithmetic operations than does the prescription $x^2(x - 1)$. This is something like saying that the first President of the United States is identical to George Washington. Though the words are not the same, whatever is true of the first President of the United States is also true of George Washington and vice versa.

A particularly simple correspondence is obtained by associating each element of a set with itself. This is known as the *identity function* or the *identity mapping*.

Examples 5 and 6 exhibit two diverse types of behavior whose difference it is important to understand. In Example 5, a number in the range is the image of only one number in the domain. Specifically, x is the image only of $x - 1$. But in Example 6 a number in the range may be the image of several numbers in the domain. Specifically, x is the image of $+\sqrt{x^2 - 1}$ but it is also the image of $-\sqrt{x^2 - 1}$.

A function such as that in Example 5 is called *one-to-one*, for it relates one element in the domain with one element in the range and conversely, with one element in the range, it associates one element in the domain.

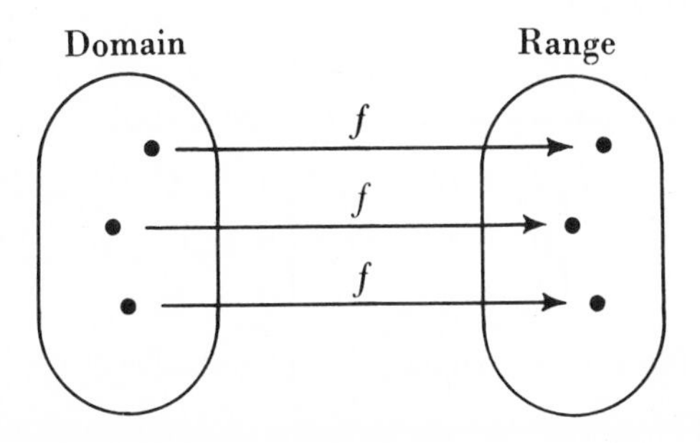

FIGURE 4.1

A function that is one-to-one can be visualized as illustrated in Figure 4.1.

A function that is not one-to-one can be symbolized by Figure 4.2.

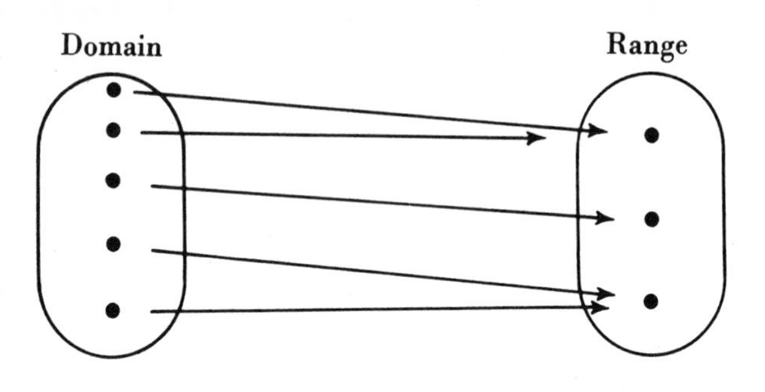

FIGURE 4.2

This exhibits elements in the range that are the images of several elements in the domain.

When we have a function that establishes one-to-one correspondence between two sets, it is possible to define the *inverse function* (also known as the *inverse mapping*, *inverse transformation*, et cetera). This is the function

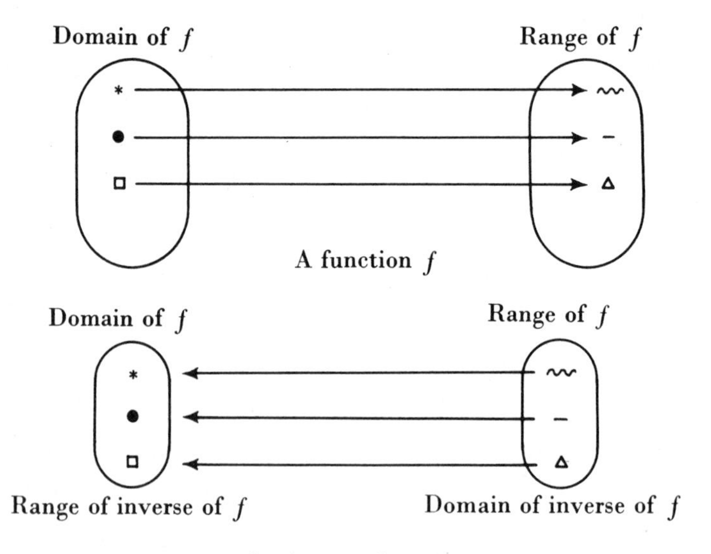

FIGURE 4.3 *Symbolic Representation of the Inverse Function*

that associates with each element of the range, the element of the domain of which it is the image (Figure 4.3).

For example, consider the function $x \to 3x$ where the domain as well as the range is the set of all numbers. This function is one-to-one. Its inverse is $x \to x/3$, for x is the image of $x/3$.

If f is a function, its inverse is frequently designated by f^{-1}. This notation should be distinguished from a similar notation used in algebra to designate reciprocals (for example, $3^{-1} = 1/3$). Although there are a number of differences between the idea of inverse and that of reciprocal, there are also a number of similarities and this accounts for our willingness to put up with the ambiguity. This notation is, of course, used with matrices.

The inverse function "undoes" what the function has done. This means that if we apply a function and then apply its inverse, it is as though we had accomplished nothing; we end up where we started from. The composite of the two is merely the identity function.

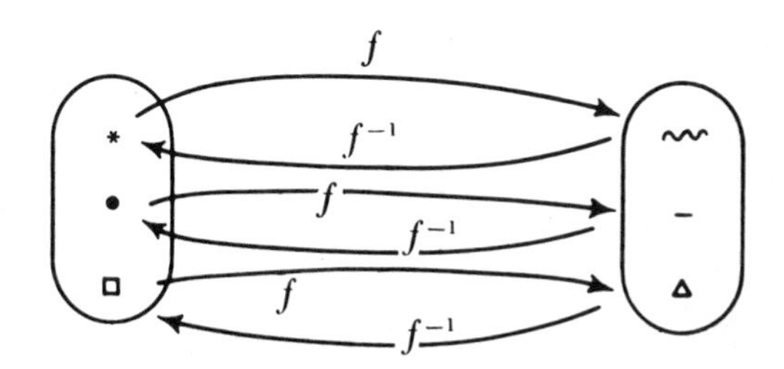

FIGURE 4.4 *Composite of* f *and* f^{-1} *to yield Identity*

Example: Let B be a fixed nonsingular 3×3 matrix. Consider the transformation of 3×3 matrices A given by $A \to AB$. That is, the image of each matrix A is the 3×3 matrix AB. Now, any 3×3 matrix is the image of a matrix under this transformation. For let C be a 3×3 matrix. Then C is the image of CB^{-1}. For $CB^{-1} \to CB^{-1}B = C$. Moreover, the correspondence is one-to-one. This means that distinct matrices have distinct images. To prove this, suppose that $D \neq F$. Then $DB \neq FB$. For if $DB = FB$ then $DBB^{-1} = FBB^{-1}$ or $D = F$. This transformation may therefore be described as a one-to-one transformation of the set of 3×3 matrices onto itself.

The inverse transformation is $A \to AB^{-1}$. The transformation followed by its inverse is $A \to AB \to (AB)B^{-1} = A$ or $A \to A$. This is the identity transformation.

When functions are described by formulas, the inverse function can be found by "solving backwards," and the possibility of a unique backward solution demonstrates the one-to-one character of the function.

Example 1: If $y = x + 1$ is a function (supply domain and range), its inverse is given by $x = y - 1$ (Figure 4.5).

Example 2: If $y = x^2 + 1$ is a function mapping the set $x \geq 0$ onto the set $y \geq 1$, the inverse function is given by $x = +\sqrt{y - 1}$ (Figure 4.6).

PROBLEMS

1. Let set number one be the set of all words in the English language. Set number two is the set of positive integers. A correspondence is obtained by allowing the number of letters in some standard spelling of the word to correspond to the word. Thus,

$$\text{ptarmigan} \rightarrow 9, \text{ brave} \rightarrow 5.$$

Exhibit a few more such correspondences. Is each positive integer the image of a word? Is the correspondence one-to-one? What difficulties would arise in defining an inverse function?

2. Both the first and second sets consist of all positive integers. To each integer we make correspond the sum of its digits (for example, $9 \rightarrow 9$, $103 \rightarrow 4$, $13248 \rightarrow 18$). Answer the same questions as in Problem 1.

3. A telegraphic code book condenses commonly employed phrases. Thus, "Return Immediately" might be condensed to RI; "Having a fine time, wish you were here" might correspond to HFH, "Love and Kisses" to LXX. In making up such a code book why should the correspondence be one-to-one? What purpose does the inverse correspondence serve?

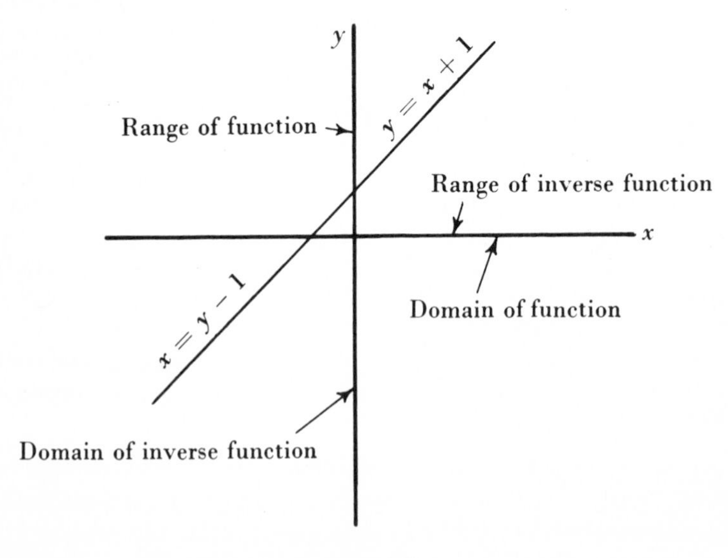

FIGURE 4.5

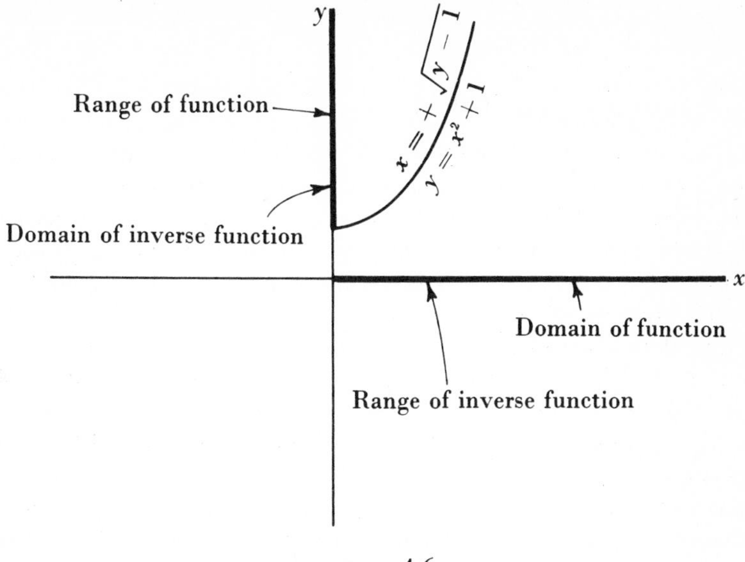

FIGURE 4.6

4. Both the domain and range of a function are the set of all positive numbers. The correspondence is given by $x \to \sqrt{x}$. The symbol $\sqrt{x}$ means the positive square root of x. Is the function one-to-one? If so, find its inverse.

5. A designates a 2×2 matrix. Discuss the mapping $A \to 2A$. Domain? Range? One-to-one? Inverse?

6. Under the transformation $x \to x^3 - x^2$ what is the image of 1? Of 0? Of -1? Find a number whose image is -12.

7. The transformation from Fahrenheit to Centigrade temperatures is given by $C = \frac{5}{9}(F - 32)$. Is this transformation one-to-one? What is the inverse function? What temperature is the same in both systems of measurement?

8. A designates a 2×2 matrix. Discuss the transformation $A \to 2A + I$.

9. A designates a 2×2 matrix. Is the transformation $A \to A^2$ one-to-one?

10. The word "mapping," which is a very popular one in mathematics these days, comes from cartography where the earth is transformed to a plane. Consider the Mercator projection of the earth. Discuss its domain and range. Is it one-to-one?

11. Change dollars to lira. Lira to francs. Francs to pounds. How many dollars in a pound? Discuss this problem from the point of view of transformations.

12. Under the transformation $A \to \begin{pmatrix} 2 & 1 \\ 1 & 3 \end{pmatrix} A$, what matrix has $\begin{pmatrix} 0 & 1 \\ 1 & 0 \end{pmatrix}$ as its image?

13. Deal with 2×2 matrices and discuss the mapping $A \to AB + I$, where B is a fixed nonsingular matrix.

14. The correspondence $n \to n^2$, where n designates a positive integer, formed the basis of a paradox discussed by Galileo Galilei (1564–1642). Galileo observed that this correspondence showed that there are "as many" square numbers as

integers. Yet, how can this be, since not all integers are squares? Discuss this correspondence.

4.2 Transformations of the Plane

Anybody who has seen photographic enlargements, distortions on a television screen or in a "crazy" mirror, knows about transformations of the plane (Figure 4.7). We shall make this notion mathematically precise and shall study in detail a special type of transformation that is known as a *linear transformation*. These transformations will be studied geometrically, and then algebraically by means of matrices.

A transformation of the plane is a function whose domain is a set of points of one plane and whose range is a set of points of another plane. To say this in another way: a transformation of the plane is a correspondence wherein points in a second plane are made to correspond to points in a first plane.

This correspondence is frequently given by means of formulas, and then it is convenient to utilize two coordinate systems, one in the first plane and one in the second plane. For example, rectangular coordinates may be

FIGURE 4.7 *A Transformation of the Plane (Nonlinear)*

employed in both planes. Call the coordinates of the first plane x, y and those in the second x', y'. Then the formulas

$$\begin{cases} x' = x + 1 \\ y' = 2y + 1, \end{cases}$$

considered as a single entity, set up a correspondence between the points of the two planes. To a point (x, y) in the first plane corresponds the point $(x + 1, 2y + 1)$ in the second plane.

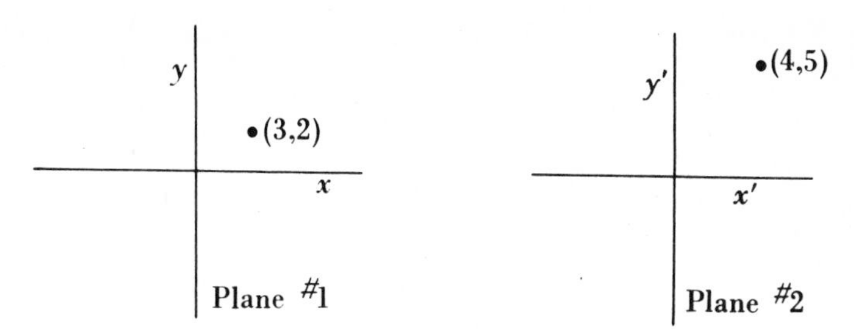

FIGURE 4.8

The point (x',y') is frequently referred to as the *image* of the point (x,y).

In order to obtain a geometrical picture of what a transformation does, it helps to take specific sets of points or specific curves in the first plane and to see what their images are in the second plane.

Suppose we work with the above transformation. To the point (3,2) corresponds the point $(3 + 1, (2 \cdot 2) + 1)$, that is, the point (4,5). What set of points corresponds to the line $y = 2x$? By solving the formulas backward we find readily

$$\begin{cases} x = x' - 1 \\ y = \frac{1}{2}(y' - 1); \end{cases}$$

therefore for all (x,y) on the line $y = 2x$, we have

$$\tfrac{1}{2}(y' - 1) = 2(x' - 1)$$

$$y' - 1 = 4x' - 4 \qquad \text{or} \qquad y' = 4x' - 3.$$

Thus, the set of points $y' = 4x' - 3$ corresponds to the line $y = 2x$ (Figure 4.9).

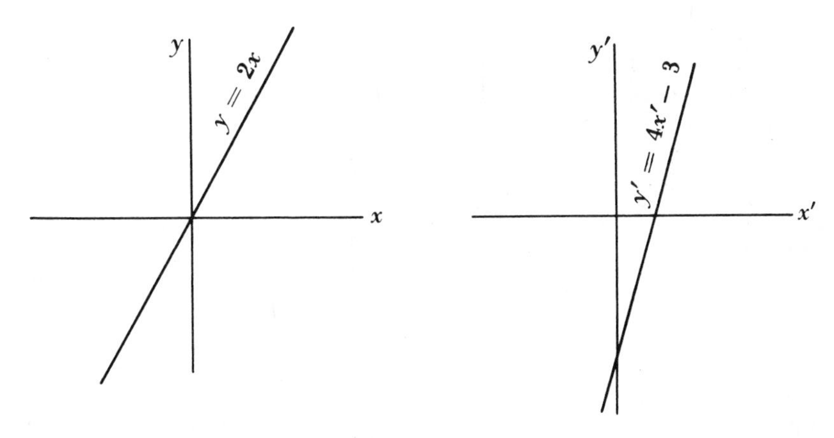

FIGURE 4.9

What is the image of the circle $x^2 + y^2 = 1$ under the transformation

$$\begin{cases} x' = x + y \\ y' = x - y? \end{cases}$$

Since

$$\begin{cases} x = \frac{1}{2}(x' + y') \\ y = \frac{1}{2}(x' - y'), \end{cases}$$

we have

$$(\tfrac{1}{2}(x' + y'))^2 + (\tfrac{1}{2}(x' - y'))^2 = 1$$

or,

$$\tfrac{1}{4}(x'^2 + 2x'y' + y'^2) + \tfrac{1}{4}(x'^2 - 2x'y' + y'^2) = 1.$$

Simplifying, $x'^2 + y'^2 = 2$.

The images (x',y') satisfy the equation of a circle whose center is (0,0) and whose radius is $\sqrt{2}$ (Figure 4.10).

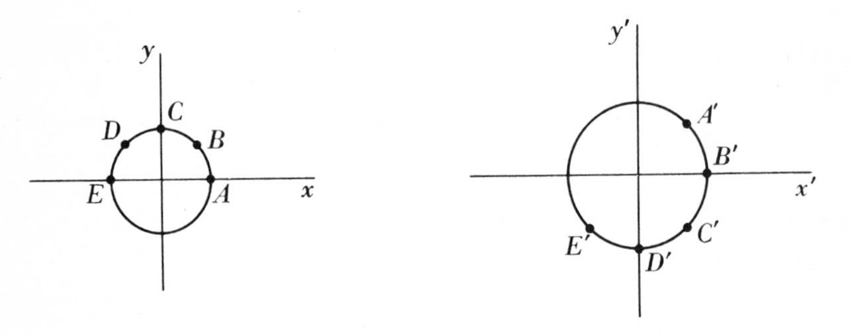

FIGURE 4.10

Some individual images of points on the original circle are tabulated:

	x	y
A	1	0
B	$\frac{1}{2}\sqrt{2}$	$\frac{1}{2}\sqrt{2}$
C	0	1
D	$-\frac{1}{2}\sqrt{2}$	$\frac{1}{2}\sqrt{2}$
E	-1	0

$x - y$ plane

	x'	y'
A'	1	1
B'	$\sqrt{2}$	0
C'	1	-1
D'	0	$-\sqrt{2}$
E'	-1	-1

$x' - y'$ plane

There is another way of regarding a transformation of the plane that has many virtues. It does not employ two planes, but only one. Take a sheet of paper and put a rectangular coordinate system in it. Now sprinkle a good many grains of sand on the sheet. The position of each grain can be described with respect to the coordinate system. Blow over the paper lightly. Each grain will assume a different position, and this new position can also be described with respect to the coordinate system. Let the original coordinates of a grain of sand be (x,y) and the new coordinates (x',y'). A transformation of the plane relates all new locations to the old locations. It may be regarded as a motion of the points of the plane.

PROBLEMS

1. Under the transformation

$$\begin{cases} x' = 2x + 3 \\ y' = x + y + 1, \end{cases}$$

find the images of (0,0), (1,0), and (2,7).

2. Find the image of the line $x = 0$ and the line $y = 0$ under the transformation in Problem 1.

3. Under the transformation of the plane

$$\begin{cases} x' = 2xy \\ y' = x^2 - y^2, \end{cases}$$

find the images of (0,0), (1,0), and (2,4). What point (or points) has the image (2,0)?

4. In Problem 3, solve for x and y in terms of x' and y'.

5. Under the transformation of the plane

$$\begin{cases} x' = \dfrac{x}{x^2 + y^2} \\ y' = \dfrac{y}{x^2 + y^2} \end{cases}$$

find the images of (1,1), (2,0), and $(-1,-4)$.

6. In Problem 5, solve for x and y in terms of x' and y'.

7. In Problem 5, find the image of the circle $x^2 + y^2 = 1$.

4.3 The Simple Transformations

We now undertake a detailed study of five simple transformations of the plane. These transformations arise so frequently that it is important to learn their properties.

TRANSLATIONS: In a translation of the plane each point is moved a fixed distance parallel to the x axis and then another fixed distance parallel to the y axis (Figure 4.11). This is a one-to-one mapping of the whole plane onto itself. Each figure in the plane retains its size, its shape, and its angular placement with respect to the x and y axis.

If (x,y) are the coordinates of a point P and (x',y') are the coordinates of the point P', to which P is moved by the translation, then the translation is expressed by the equations

$$\begin{cases} x' = x + h \\ y' = y + k. \end{cases}$$

The numbers h and k are the fixed distances that measure the shift along the x and y axes respectively (Figure 4.12).

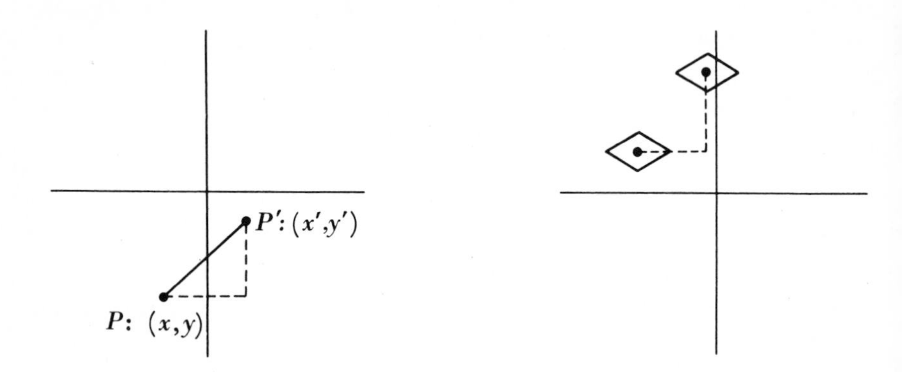

FIGURE 4.11

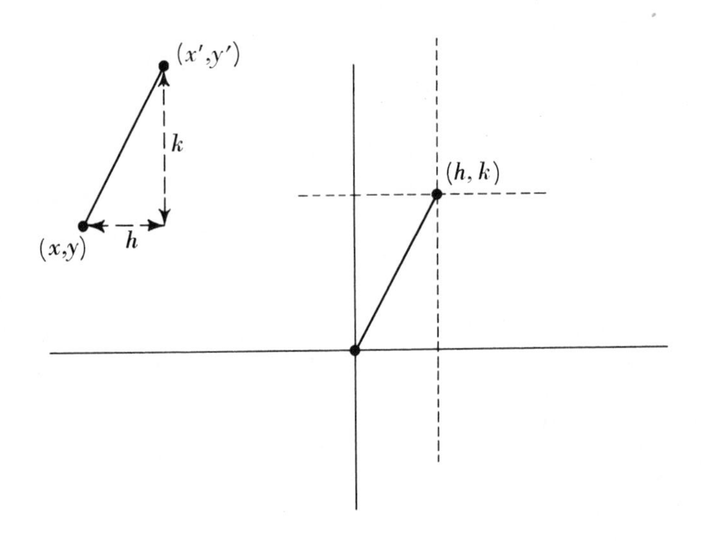

FIGURE 4.12

The equations of translation may be written in a matrix form that is equivalent to the two equations above:

$$\begin{pmatrix} x' \\ y' \end{pmatrix} = \begin{pmatrix} x \\ y \end{pmatrix} + \begin{pmatrix} h \\ k \end{pmatrix}.$$

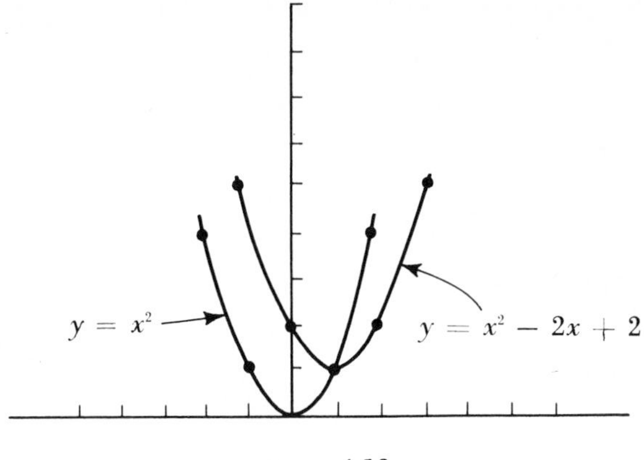

FIGURE 4.13

Example 1: The parabola $y = x^2$ is moved one unit to the right and one unit up (Figure 4.13). Find its new equation.

Here we have

$$\begin{cases} x' = x + 1 \\ y' = y + 1. \end{cases}$$

Hence, $x = x' - 1$, $y = y' - 1$.

By substituting this information in the original equation, we have

$$y' - 1 = (x' - 1)^2.$$

By simplifying,

$$y' = x'^2 - 2x' + 2.$$

If we wish to drop the primes, we may do so, and write the new equation as

$$y = x^2 - 2x + 2.$$

Example 2: A point P with original coordinates (x,y) moves at the rate of v units per second in a direction that makes an angle θ with the x axis (Figure 4.14). Find its coordinates after t seconds. In t seconds, the point has moved a distance vt units in the given direction.

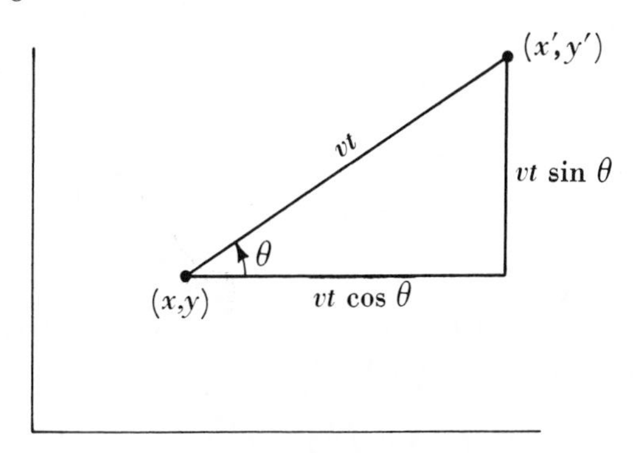

FIGURE 4.14

Thus, it has moved $vt \cos \theta$ units along the x axis and $vt \sin \theta$ units along the y axis. Its new coordinates (x',y') therefore satisfy

$$\begin{cases} x' = x + vt \cos \theta \\ y' = y + vt \sin \theta. \end{cases}$$

PROBLEMS

1. Interpret the equations $\begin{cases} x' = x + 6 \\ y' = y - 3 \end{cases}$ as a translation.

2. Interpret $\begin{pmatrix} x' \\ y' \end{pmatrix} = \begin{pmatrix} x \\ y \end{pmatrix} + \begin{pmatrix} 0 \\ -3 \end{pmatrix}$ as a translation.

3. The circle $x^2 + y^2 = 1$ is translated so that its center is at (1,2). Find the new equation.

4. The circle $x^2 + y^2 + 2y = 3$ is translated so that its center is at the point (2,1). Find the new equation.

5. A straight edge lying along $Ax + By + C = 0$ is translated by $\begin{cases} x' = x + h \\ y' = y + k. \end{cases}$ Find its new equation.

6. Two particles start at the origin and move in straight lines with velocities v_1 and v_2. The first moves at an angle of θ_1 with the positive x-axis while the second moves at an angle of θ_2. Find their distance apart after t seconds.

7. The circle $x^2 + y^2 = 1$ is translated with the velocity 1 unit per second. Its center moves along the line $y = x$. Find the equation after t seconds.

ROTATIONS: We shall consider a rotation in which each point turns about the origin through a fixed number of degrees θ (Figures 4.15 and 4.16). (We agree to measure angles in the counterclockwise sense.)

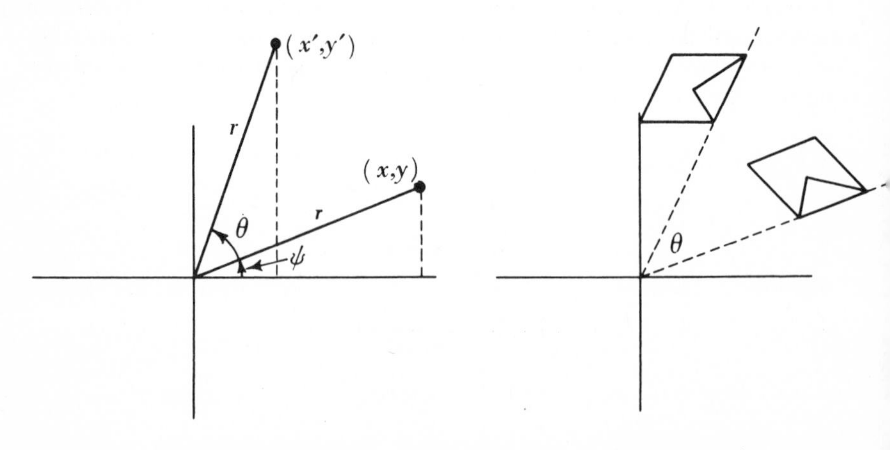

FIGURE 4.15 FIGURE 4.16

This is a one-to-one mapping of the whole plane onto itself. Each point maintains its distance from the origin. Each figure retains its size and its shape, but its orientation is altered.

The equations of a rotation are determined as follows. Upon referring to Figure 4.15, we have

$$\begin{cases} x = r\cos\Psi \\ y = r\sin\Psi \end{cases}$$

and

$$\begin{cases} x' = r\cos(\theta+\Psi) = r\cos\theta\cos\Psi - r\sin\theta\sin\Psi \\ y' = r\sin(\theta+\Psi) = r\sin\theta\cos\Psi + r\cos\theta\sin\Psi. \end{cases}$$

The last equalities follow from the addition formula for the sine and cosine.* Hence,

$$\begin{cases} x' = x\cos\theta - y\sin\theta \\ y' = x\sin\theta + y\cos\theta. \end{cases}$$

These equations of rotation can be written in the matrix form:

$$\begin{pmatrix} x' \\ y' \end{pmatrix} = \begin{pmatrix} \cos\theta & -\sin\theta \\ \sin\theta & \cos\theta \end{pmatrix} \begin{pmatrix} x \\ y \end{pmatrix}.$$

Four special rotations about the origin are worthy of particular notice.

(a) Rotation through 0°: $\theta = 0°$.

$$\begin{cases} x' = x \\ y' = y. \end{cases}$$

This is the identity transformation. Nothing happens.

(b) Rotation through 90°: $\theta = 90°$.

$$\begin{cases} x' = -y \\ y' = x. \end{cases}$$

(c) Rotation through 180°: $\theta = 180°$.

$$\begin{cases} x' = -x \\ y' = -y. \end{cases}$$

(d) Rotation through 270°: $\theta = 270°$.

$$\begin{cases} x' = y \\ y' = -x. \end{cases}$$

Example 1: The line $y = x$ is rotated about the origin through 90°. Find the equation of the new line. We have

$$\begin{cases} x' = -y \\ y' = x. \end{cases}$$

---

* $\text{Sin}\,(A+B) = \sin A\cos B + \cos A\sin B$
$\text{Cos}\,(A+B) = \cos A\cos B - \sin A\sin B.$

Since $y = x$ on the line in question, we have $-x' = y'$ or $x' + y' = 0$. This is the equation of the new line. We may drop the primes and write $x + y = 0$.

Example 2: The points of the plane are rotating at the rate of ω degrees per second. What is the location of the point (x,y) after t seconds? After t seconds, it has rotated through ωt degrees. Hence the point (x,y) is located at (x',y') where

$$\begin{pmatrix} x' \\ y' \end{pmatrix} = \begin{pmatrix} \cos \omega t & -\sin \omega t \\ \sin \omega t & \cos \omega t \end{pmatrix} \begin{pmatrix} x \\ y \end{pmatrix}.$$

It should be intuitively clear that under a rotation, points in the plane preserve their mutual distances. If a proof is wanted, we can give one as follows. Let $P_1:(x_1,y_1)$, $P_2:(x_2,y_2)$. P_1 is rotated to $P_1':(x_1',y_1')$. P_2 is rotated to $P_2':(x_2',y_2')$. Let the distance from P_1 to P_2 be d, and the distance from P_1' to P_2' be D. Then,

$$d^2 = (x_2 - x_1)^2 + (y_2 - y_1)^2,\ D^2 = (x_2' - x_1')^2 + (y_2' - y_1')^2.$$

In matrix notation,

$$(D^2) = (x_2' - x_1',\ y_2' - y_1') \begin{pmatrix} (x_2' - x_1') \\ (y_2' - y_1') \end{pmatrix}.$$

But

$$\begin{pmatrix} (x_2' - x_1') \\ (y_2' - y_1') \end{pmatrix} = \begin{pmatrix} \cos \theta & -\sin \theta \\ \sin \theta & \cos \theta \end{pmatrix} \begin{pmatrix} (x_2 - x_1) \\ (y_2 - y_1) \end{pmatrix}.$$

Hence,

$$(D^2) = (x_2 - x_1,\ y_2 - y_1) \begin{pmatrix} \cos \theta & \sin \theta \\ -\sin \theta & \cos \theta \end{pmatrix} \begin{pmatrix} \cos \theta & -\sin \theta \\ \sin \theta & \cos \theta \end{pmatrix} \begin{pmatrix} (x_2 - x_1) \\ (y_2 - y_1) \end{pmatrix}.$$

The product of the inner two matrices is I and hence,

$$(D^2) = (x_2 - x_1,\ y_2 - y_1) \begin{pmatrix} (x_2 - x_1) \\ (y_2 - y_1) \end{pmatrix} = (d^2).$$

The matrix $\begin{pmatrix} \cos \theta & -\sin \theta \\ \sin \theta & \cos \theta \end{pmatrix}$ is an example of an *orthogonal matrix.* A matrix A is orthogonal if $AA' = I$. The reader should check this matrix equation in the present case.

PROBLEMS

1. Write the equations of rotations about the origin through 0°, 90°, 180°, 270° in matrix form.

2. Write the equations of transformation for a rotation about the origin through 45°.

3. The point (1,1) is rotated about the origin through 45°. Find its image.

4. The circle $x^2 + y^2 = 1$ is rotated about the origin through θ degrees. Find the equation of the new circle.

5. The plane has been rotated about the origin through 180°. Where did the point $(-2,6)$ come from?

6. The curve $x^2 - y^2 = 1$ is rotated about the origin through 45°. Find the equation of the new curve.

7. The ellipse $x^2 + 2y^2 = 1$ is rotated about the origin through 90°. Find the equation of the new curve.

8. The line $y = 0$ is rotated about the origin through θ degrees. Find the equation of the new curve.

9. If $\begin{pmatrix} a & b \\ c & d \end{pmatrix}$ is an orthogonal matrix, prove that

$$a^2 + c^2 = 1,\ c^2 + d^2 = 1,\ ac + bd = 0$$
$$a^2 + b^2 = 1,\ b^2 + d^2 = 1,\ ab + cd = 0.$$

10. A triangle with vertices at $(-1,0)$, $(1,0)$ and $(0,1)$ is rotated about the origin counterclockwise through 45°. Prove directly that the area of the rotated figure equals the area of the original figure.

11. Two sheets of the same kind of graph paper lie on top of one another. A pin is stuck through the origins on each sheet and the sheets are rotated. If the point $(1,0)$ of the top sheet lies above the point $(\frac{5}{13}, \frac{12}{13})$ of the bottom sheet, above what point of the bottom sheet does the point $(2,3)$ of the top sheet lie?

12. Show that if $A = (a_{ij})$ is orthogonal $(AA' = I)$ then the solution to the system of equations

$$\begin{cases} a_{11}x_1 + \cdots + a_{1n}x_n = b_1 \\ \vdots \\ a_{n1}x_1 + \cdots + a_{nn}x_n = b_n \end{cases}$$

is given by

$$\begin{cases} x_1 = a_{11}b_1 + \cdots + a_{n1}b_n \\ \vdots \\ x_n = a_{1n}b_1 + \cdots + a_{nn}b_n. \end{cases}$$

REFLECTIONS: This transformation is suggested by what happens when one looks into a plane mirror. To obtain a reflection in a line ℓ each point P in the plane is transformed as follows: From P drop a perpendicular to ℓ (Figure 4.17). Continue this perpendicular an equal distance on the other side of ℓ. This leads to the point P' called the "mirror image" of P. If P happens to be on the line ℓ then it is considered to be its own image.

A reflection is a one-to-one transformation of the whole plane onto itself. Each figure in the plane retains its size and its shape. But reflection changes one aspect of figures and this is suggested by the familiar phenomenon of looking into a mirror and seeing your right hand paired with the image of

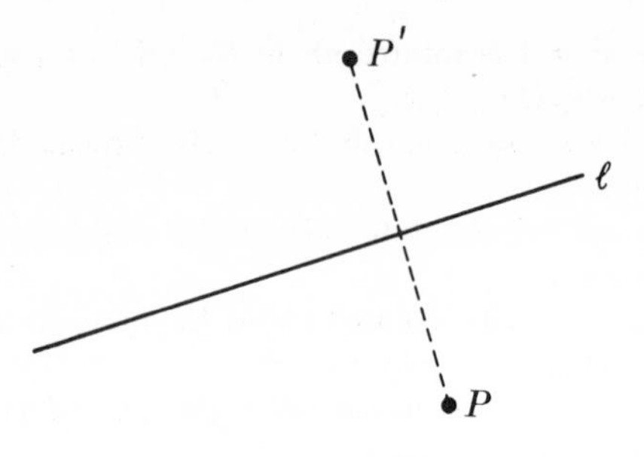

FIGURE 4.17

your right hand and your left paired with the image of your left hand. If you were confronted by a real twin, the opposite would be true: your right hand would be paired with his left hand, et cetera.

Here is a more mathematical description of this phenomenon.

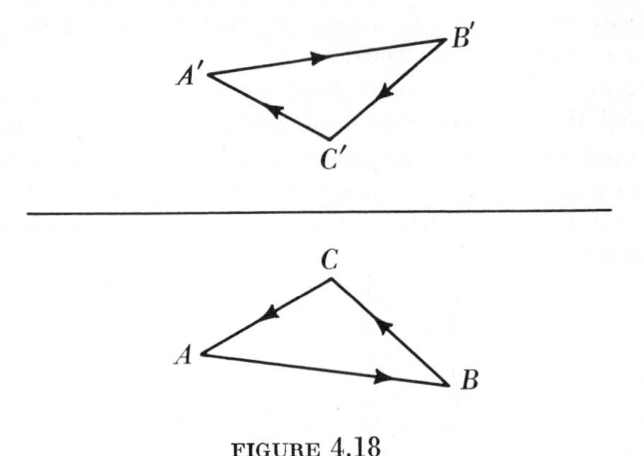

FIGURE 4.18

Let ℓ be a mirror, and let the triangle ABC be in front of it (Figure 4.18). Suppose that its reflection is $A'B'C'$. Trace the sides of the triangle from A to B to C to A, placing an arrow head to indicate the direction of motion. The image of ABC is traced out from A' to B' to C' to A'. Place arrow heads on $A'B'C'$ to indicate the direction of this motion. It will be observed that whereas ABC is traced out in the counterclockwise sense, $A'B'C'$ is traced out in the clockwise sense.

We will take as a standard reflection, the reflection in the 45° line $y = x$.

It can be seen from Figure 4.19 that the equations of a reflection in the line $y = x$ are

$$\begin{cases} x' = y \\ y' = x. \end{cases}$$

In matrix form, this is

$$\begin{pmatrix} x' \\ y' \end{pmatrix} = \begin{pmatrix} 0 & 1 \\ 1 & 0 \end{pmatrix} \begin{pmatrix} x \\ y \end{pmatrix}.$$

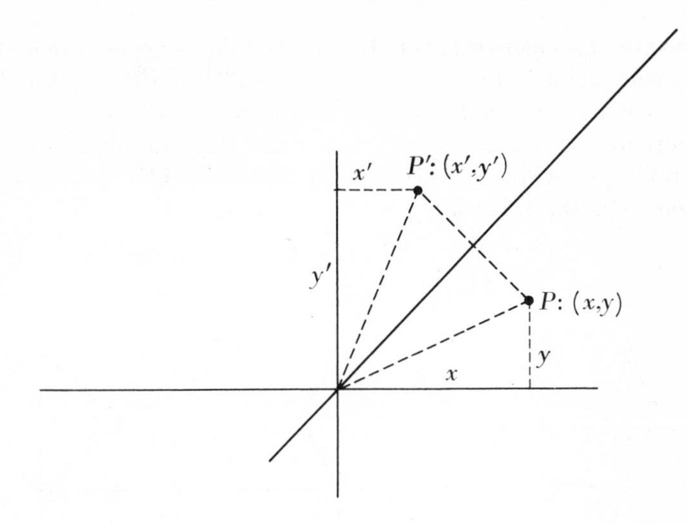

FIGURE 4.19 *Reflection in the 45° Line*

Reflection in $y = x$ is equivalent to an interchange of the variables x and y. This is an elementary row transformation of Type I (compare Chapter 3, Section 2).

Example 1: The line $3x + 7y = 5$ is reflected in the line $y = x$. What is the row equation? Since $x = y'$ and $y = x'$, we have $3y' + 7x' = 5$. Upon dropping the primes and rearranging terms, $7x + 3y = 5$.

Example 2: If the equation of a certain curve is $y = f(x)$, then the equation $x = f(y)$ represents its reflection in the line $y = x$. Try this out with a few functions such as $y = x^3$, et cetera.

PROBLEMS

1. What is the image of $(7, -3)$ under a reflection in $y = x$? What is the image of $(-4, -4)$?
2. The curve $y = x^2$ is reflected in the line $y = x$. Find the new equation.
3. The curve $xy = 1$ is reflected in the line $y = x$. Find the new equation.
4. What is unusual about the answer to Problem 3? Find other curves with this property.
5. Find the equations for a reflection in the x axis.
6. Find the equations for a reflection in the y axis.
7. Find matrix representations for the transformations of Problems 5 and 6.
8. Find the equations for a reflection in the line $y = -x$.
9. Let ℓ_1 and ℓ_2 be two different lines in the plane. Reflect a triangle ABC in ℓ_1 yielding $A'B'C'$. Reflect $A'B'C'$ in ℓ_2 yielding $A''B''C''$. If ABC is traced out clockwise, what about $A'B'C'$ and $A''B''C''$? What happens when a reflection in another line ℓ_3 is carried out?

EXPANSIONS OR CONTRACTIONS: In an expansion or contraction along the x axis, each point in the plane is moved parallel to the x axis and in such a way that its distance from the y axis is multiplied by a number k. The transformation is an expansion if $k > 1$ and is a contraction if $0 < k < 1$. For brevity, we will call either type an expansion. The equations of an expansion along the x axis are

$$\begin{cases} x' = kx \\ y' = y. \end{cases}$$

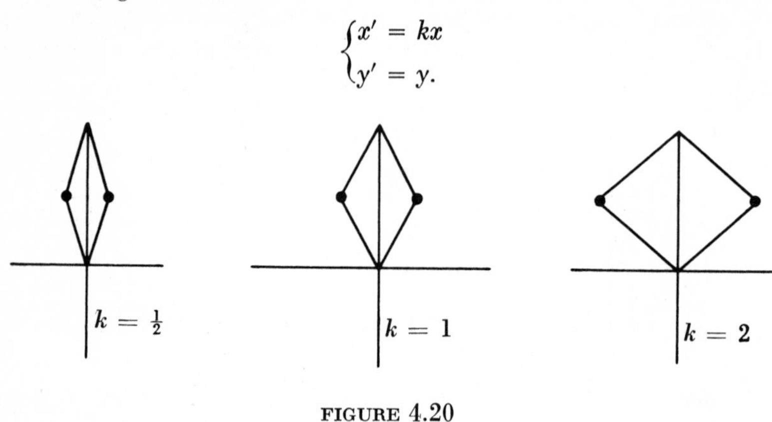

FIGURE 4.20

In matrix form this is

$$\begin{pmatrix} x' \\ y' \end{pmatrix} = \begin{pmatrix} k & 0 \\ 0 & 1 \end{pmatrix} \begin{pmatrix} x \\ y \end{pmatrix}.$$

An expansion is a one-to-one transformation of the whole plane onto itself. It changes size and shape (Figure 4.20). To study this more precisely, let S be a square whose side has length h and which is placed as in Figure

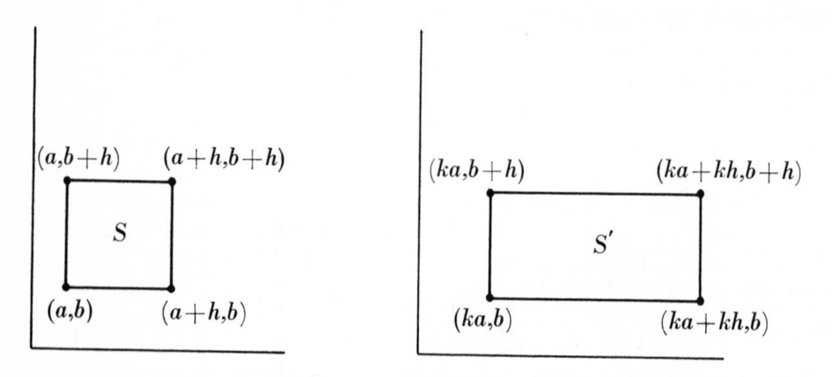

FIGURE 4.21 *Expansion of Square along x-Axis*

4.21. The image of the square is a rectangle S' with respective sides parallel to those of the square. The length of the sides of S' are kh and h. The area of S is h^2 whereas the area of S' is kh^2, so that the area of the image is k times the area of the original figure. In general, an expansion multiplies the area of any shape by k. This can be established by decomposing the original figure into tiny squares.

Each tiny square will be transformed into a rectangle and its area will be multiplied by k (Figure 4.22). Hence, neglecting those squares that are not contained entirely in the figure, we see that the whole figure is itself multiplied in area by k. This proof is carried out rigorously in the integral calculus.

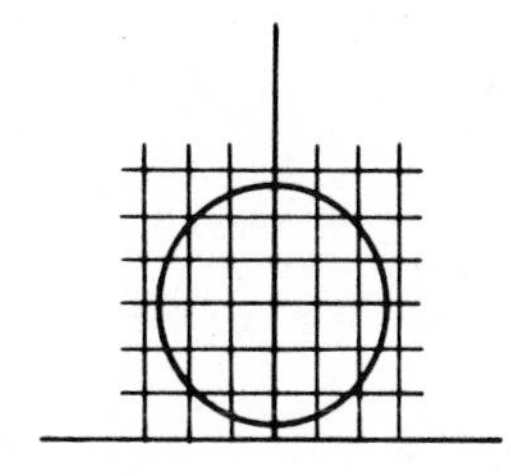
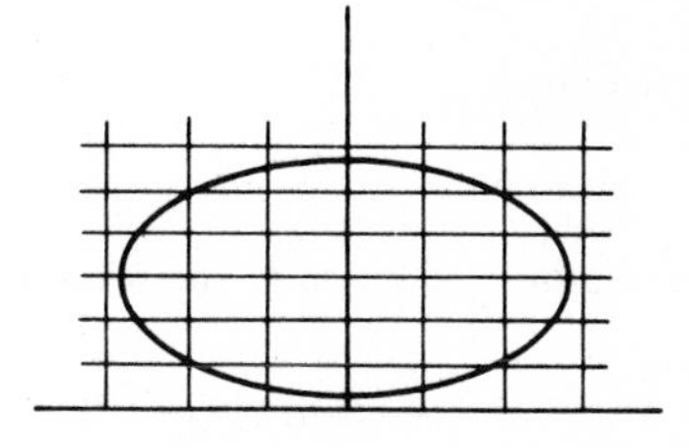

FIGURE 4.22

The equations of an expansion along the y axis are given by

$$\begin{cases} x' = x \\ y' = ky \end{cases}$$

or in matrix form

$$\begin{pmatrix} x' \\ y' \end{pmatrix} = \begin{pmatrix} 1 & 0 \\ 0 & k \end{pmatrix} \begin{pmatrix} x \\ y \end{pmatrix}.$$

Similar remarks apply to this transformation.

Expansions correspond to elementary row transformations of Type II (Chapter 3, Section 2).

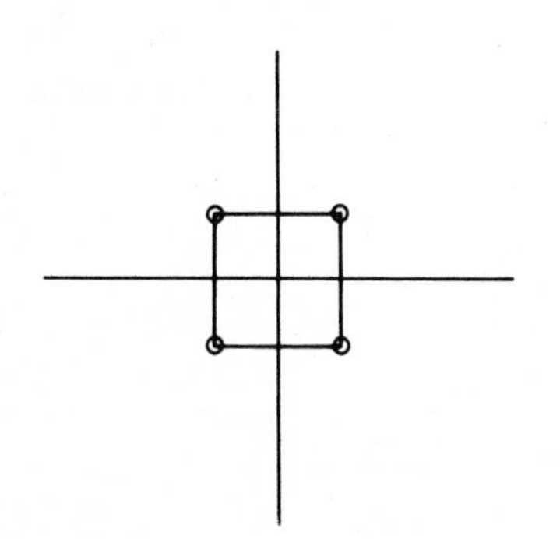
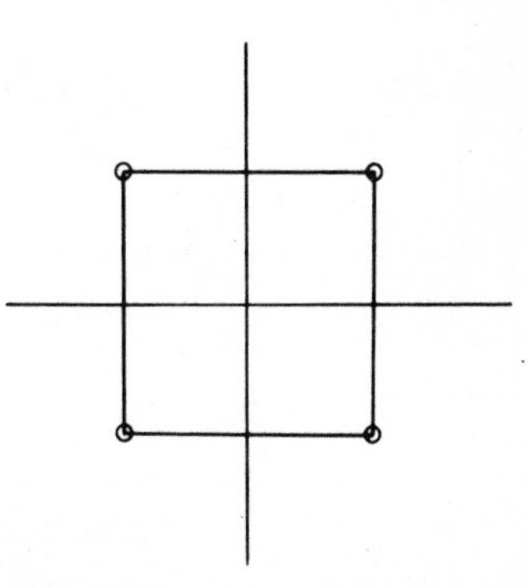

FIGURE 4.23

If expansions with the same factor k occur simultaneously along both axes, we have a *similarity transformation* (Figure 4.23). A similarity transformation changes size but not shape. Its equations are

$$\begin{cases} x' = kx \\ y' = ky \end{cases}$$

or in matrix form,

$$\begin{pmatrix} x' \\ y' \end{pmatrix} = \begin{pmatrix} k & 0 \\ 0 & k \end{pmatrix} \begin{pmatrix} x \\ y \end{pmatrix}.$$

Areas are multiplied by the factor k^2.

Example: The circle $x^2 + y^2 = r^2$ is subject to the expansion $x' = kx$, $y' = y$. Find the equation of the transformed curve. Since $x = \frac{x'}{k}$, $y = y'$, we have $\left(\frac{x'}{k}\right)^2 + (y')^2 = r^2$ or, dropping the primes and rewriting this,

$$\frac{x^2}{k^2r^2} + \frac{y^2}{r^2} = 1.$$

As is well known, this is the equation of an ellipse with semi-axes kr and r. Thus, stretching a circle along one axis transforms it into an ellipse. If the circle is regarded as a special ellipse with both semi-axes equal to r, then the transformation multiplies one semi-axis by k and leaves the other alone.

There is a further consequence. As we have just seen, the area of the ellipse must be k times the area of the circle. Since the area of the circle is πr^2, the area of the ellipse is $k\pi r^2 = \pi(kr)r$. Thus the area of an ellipse is π times the product of its semi-axes.

PROBLEMS

1. The line $3x + 4y = 5$ is transformed by

$$\begin{cases} x' = 2x \\ y' = y. \end{cases}$$

Find the equation of the new curve.

2. The parabola $y = x^2$ is transformed by means of

$$\begin{cases} x' = 3x \\ y' = y. \end{cases}$$

Find the equation of the new curve.

3. Determine the area of the ellipse $\frac{x^2}{4} + \frac{y^2}{9} = 1$.

4. Find the image of the triangle with vertices at (0,0), (1,0), and (0,1) under

$$\begin{cases} x' = kx \\ y' = y. \end{cases}$$

Show directly that the triangle is transformed into a second triangle whose area is k times the original area.

5. What happens to the circle $x^2 + y^2 = r^2$ under the transformation

$$\begin{cases} x' = kx \\ y' = my? \end{cases}$$

6. Describe the transformation

$$\begin{cases} x' = -2x \\ y' = y \end{cases}$$

geometrically. How does it differ from the transformation

$$\begin{cases} x' = 2x \\ y' = y? \end{cases}$$

7. Cut a wide elastic band and secure one end with a thumbtack. Mark a number of points along the band. Now stretch the band and compare the new locations of the points with the old ones. Would you say that the transformation is, mathematically, an expansion?

SHEARS: A shear along the x-axis is a transformation in which each point of the plane is moved parallel to the x-axis by an amount that is proportional to its distance from the x-axis. The constant of proportionality will be designated by k. A shear is given by the equations

$$\begin{cases} x' = x + ky \\ y' = y \end{cases}$$

or in matrix form,

$$\begin{pmatrix} x' \\ y' \end{pmatrix} = \begin{pmatrix} 1 & k \\ 0 & 1 \end{pmatrix} \begin{pmatrix} x \\ y \end{pmatrix}.$$

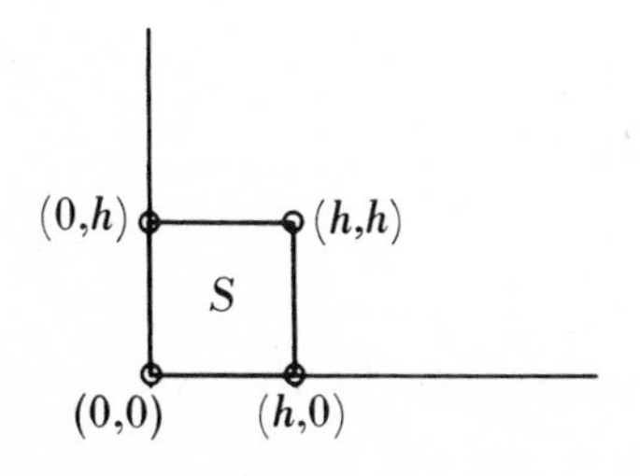

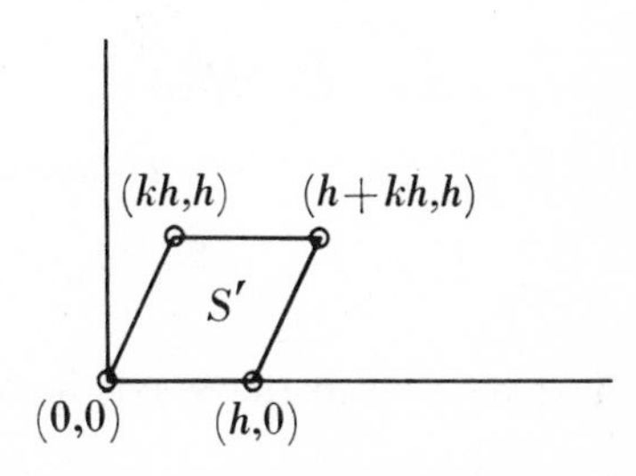

FIGURE 4.24

A shear is a one-to-one transformation of the whole plane onto itself. It transforms squares into parallelograms.

Let S denote the square of side h in Figure 4.24. Now

$$\begin{aligned}(0,0) &\rightarrow (0,0)\\ (h,0) &\rightarrow (h,0)\\ (0,h) &\rightarrow (kh,h)\\ (h,h) &\rightarrow (h + kh,h).\end{aligned}$$

The image of the square S is the parallelogram S'. The area of S' equals the area of S and, in general, though a shear changes the shape of a figure, it does not alter its area (Figure 4.25).

A Camel

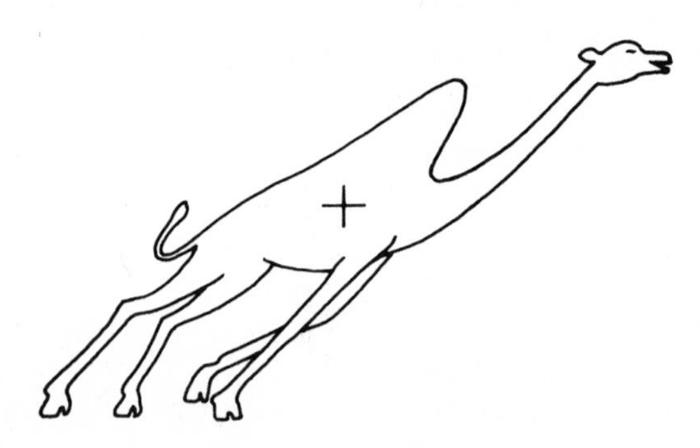

A Camel, Sheared

FIGURE 4.25

A shear parallel to the y axis is given, analogously, by the equations

$$\begin{cases} x' = x \\ y' = kx + y \end{cases}$$

or in matrix form,

$$\begin{pmatrix} x' \\ y' \end{pmatrix} = \begin{pmatrix} 1 & 0 \\ k & 1 \end{pmatrix} \begin{pmatrix} x \\ y \end{pmatrix}.$$

A shear is an elementary row transformation of Type III (Chapter 3, Section 2).

Example: What happens to the straight line $y = 2x$ under the shear

$$\begin{cases} x' = x \\ y' = \frac{1}{2}x + y? \end{cases}$$

Since $y = y' - \frac{1}{2}x'$, the line is transformed into $y' - \frac{1}{2}x' = 2x'$ or, $y' = \frac{5}{2}x'$. By dropping the primes, we have $y = \frac{5}{2}x$.

PROBLEMS

1. To see shear in action, pencil your name on the edges of a fat telephone book. Push on the top so that the pages slide over one another. Observe the distortion of the letters.
2. A triangle T has vertices at $(-1,0)$, $(1,0)$, and $(0,1)$. What happens to T under the shear

$$\begin{cases} x' = x + 2y \\ y' = y? \end{cases}$$

Can T be sheared into a right angled triangle?
3. What happens to the curve $y = x^2$ under the shear

$$\begin{cases} x' = x + \frac{1}{2}y \\ y' = y? \end{cases}$$

4. What is the image of the square whose vertices are at $(\pm 1, \pm 1)$ under the shear

$$\begin{cases} x' = x \\ y' = 2x + y? \end{cases}$$

5. What happens to the circle $x^2 + y^2 = 1$ under the shear of Problem 4? Find the new equation and plot the curve.
6. In Problem 2, verify that the area of the sheared triangle equals that of the original triangle.
7. In Problem 4, verify that the area of the sheared square equals that of the original square.

4.4 Matrices as Transformations of the Plane

Products of Transformations. We have fallen, more or less naturally, into an interpretation of certain special 2×2 matrices as a transformation of the plane. In the next two sections, we shall provide all 2×2 matrices with such an interpretation. What makes this interpretation most impressive—and useful—is that matrix multiplication also falls naturally into this explanation.

As part of our study of simple transformations, we have rotated the plane, sheared the plane, et cetera. In many instances we may want to carry out several of these operations, one followed by another. We may want to shear the plane and then rotate the result. Or we may want to rotate and then reflect. How can this be done with formulas? The method will become clear when we consider a numerical example.

Example: Each point in the plane is rotated counterclockwise through an angle of $\theta°$. Each point of the plane is then reflected in the line $y = x$. Express this compound operation by a single set of equations.

Follow the itinerary of a typical point (x,y).

After it has been rotated through $\theta°$, it becomes the point (x',y') where

$$\begin{cases} x' = x \cos \theta - y \sin \theta \\ y' = x \sin \theta + y \cos \theta. \end{cases}$$

The point (x',y') is then reflected in the line $y = x$. It becomes the point (x'',y'') where

$$\begin{cases} x'' = y' \\ y'' = x'. \end{cases}$$

Combining these, by substitution, we obtain as the final transformation,

$$\begin{cases} x'' = x \sin \theta + y \cos \theta \\ y'' = x \cos \theta - y \sin \theta. \end{cases} \tag{1}$$

In the language of matrices:

$$\begin{pmatrix} x' \\ y' \end{pmatrix} = \begin{pmatrix} \cos \theta & -\sin \theta \\ \sin \theta & \cos \theta \end{pmatrix} \begin{pmatrix} x \\ y \end{pmatrix}$$

and

$$\begin{pmatrix} x'' \\ y'' \end{pmatrix} = \begin{pmatrix} 0 & 1 \\ 1 & 0 \end{pmatrix} \begin{pmatrix} x' \\ y' \end{pmatrix}.$$

Therefore,

$$\begin{pmatrix} x'' \\ y'' \end{pmatrix} = \begin{pmatrix} 0 & 1 \\ 1 & 0 \end{pmatrix} \begin{pmatrix} \cos \theta & -\sin \theta \\ \sin \theta & \cos \theta \end{pmatrix} \begin{pmatrix} x \\ y \end{pmatrix}.$$

The reader should now expand this matrix equation and verify that it leads to the set of equations labelled (1).

We see once again, as we have already seen in Section 9 of Chapter 2, that successive linear changes of variable—or successive transformations of the plane—can be carried out by means of matrix multiplication. In order to display the unity of ideas here, we speak of the *product* of two or more *transformations* and mean by it the transformation that results when each of the individual transformations has been carried out successively.

Example: The shear

$$\begin{cases} x' = x + 3y \\ y' = y \end{cases}$$

is followed by the shear

$$\begin{cases} x'' = x' \\ y'' = 2x' + y'. \end{cases}$$

Find the combined result, or the product of the transformations. The product of the respective matrices is

$$\begin{pmatrix} 1 & 0 \\ 2 & 1 \end{pmatrix}\begin{pmatrix} 1 & 3 \\ 0 & 1 \end{pmatrix} = \begin{pmatrix} 1 & 3 \\ 2 & 7 \end{pmatrix},$$

so that

$$\begin{pmatrix} x'' \\ y'' \end{pmatrix} = \begin{pmatrix} 1 & 3 \\ 2 & 7 \end{pmatrix}\begin{pmatrix} x \\ y \end{pmatrix}$$

is the equation of the combined transformation.

It would be convenient to symbolize the first shear by S_1 and the second shear by S_2. By this notation, we shall mean either the shears considered as a geometrical object or the respective matrices that represent each transformation:

$$S_1 = \begin{pmatrix} 1 & 3 \\ 0 & 1 \end{pmatrix}, \qquad S_2 = \begin{pmatrix} 1 & 0 \\ 2 & 1 \end{pmatrix}.$$

The compound transformation (or the product of the transformations) will be designated by S_2S_1. The order of the factors is in accordance with the order of the matrix factors in the above matrix product. The notation S_2S_1 means: first carry out the transformation S_1, then follow it up with the transformation S_2. Here is one instance in which the English language is read from right to left instead of from left to right.

The transformation S_1S_2 means first carry out S_2 and follow it up by S_1. The matrix of this product is

$$\begin{pmatrix} 1 & 3 \\ 0 & 1 \end{pmatrix}\begin{pmatrix} 1 & 0 \\ 2 & 1 \end{pmatrix} = \begin{pmatrix} 7 & 3 \\ 2 & 1 \end{pmatrix}.$$

If we compare this with the previous result we see that

$$S_1S_2 \neq S_2S_1.$$

The conclusion to be drawn is that transformations of the plane are not necessarily commutative. The order in which they are performed may be crucial. This fact runs parallel with the noncommutativity of matrix multiplication and either may be considered to be an explanation of the other.

Example: The plane is rotated counterclockwise through $A°$. This is followed by a rotation through $B°$. Discuss these transformations from the matrix point of view.

The matrix product—in the proper order—is

$$\begin{pmatrix} \cos B & -\sin B \\ \sin B & \cos B \end{pmatrix} \begin{pmatrix} \cos A & -\sin A \\ \sin A & \cos A \end{pmatrix}$$

$$= \begin{pmatrix} \cos A \cos B - \sin A \sin B & -(\sin A \cos B + \cos A \sin B) \\ \sin A \cos B + \cos A \sin B & \cos A \cos B - \sin A \sin B \end{pmatrix}$$

$$= \begin{pmatrix} \cos (A+B) & -\sin (A+B) \\ \sin (A+B) & \cos (A+B) \end{pmatrix}.$$

This last matrix equation is a result of the well-known identities for $\sin (A + B)$ and $\cos (A + B)$. The matrix product represents a rotation through $(A + B)°$ and this agrees with what we would have concluded geometrically.

PROBLEMS

1. The plane is first expanded by $\begin{pmatrix} 3 & 0 \\ 0 & 1 \end{pmatrix}$, contracted by $\begin{pmatrix} 1 & 0 \\ 0 & \frac{1}{2} \end{pmatrix}$, and finally sheared by $\begin{pmatrix} 1 & 3 \\ 0 & 1 \end{pmatrix}$. Find the equations for the combined transformation.

2. Find the equations for the operations of Problem 1 carried out in the reverse order.

3. If $S_1 = \begin{pmatrix} 2 & 0 \\ 0 & 1 \end{pmatrix}$, $S_2 = \begin{pmatrix} 1 & 3 \\ 0 & 1 \end{pmatrix}$, $S_3 = \begin{pmatrix} 1 & 0 \\ 3 & 1 \end{pmatrix}$, compute $S_1S_2S_3$, $S_2S_1S_3$, and $S_3S_2S_1$. Interpret as transformations.

4. If $S_2 = \begin{pmatrix} 0 & 1 \\ 1 & 0 \end{pmatrix}$, compute S^2. Interpret geometrically. Compute S^3.

5. Determine $\begin{pmatrix} 0 & 1 \\ 1 & 0 \end{pmatrix}^n$. Consider separately n even and n odd.

6. Determine $\begin{pmatrix} k & 0 \\ 0 & 1 \end{pmatrix}^n$.

7. Determine $\begin{pmatrix} 1 & 0 \\ 0 & k \end{pmatrix}^n$.

8. Show that $\begin{pmatrix} 1 & k \\ 0 & 1 \end{pmatrix}^n = \begin{pmatrix} 1 & nk \\ 0 & 1 \end{pmatrix}$. Here is one situation in which multiplication behaves like addition. Explain.

9. Show that $\begin{pmatrix} \cos\theta & -\sin\theta \\ \sin\theta & \cos\theta \end{pmatrix}^n = \begin{pmatrix} \cos n\theta & -\sin n\theta \\ \sin n\theta & \cos n\theta \end{pmatrix}$. Give a geometrical proof.

10. The plane is transformed by the same transformation

$$\begin{cases} x' = \frac{1}{2}x + \frac{1}{2}y \\ y' = -\frac{1}{2}x + \frac{1}{2}y \end{cases}$$

four times. Find the consecutive images of the point (1,1).

11. The plane is transformed by the same transformation

$$\begin{cases} x' = 2x + y \\ y' = -x + y \end{cases}$$

four times. Find the consecutive images of the point (1,1).

12. Prove that a reflection in the x axis followed by a reflection in the y axis is equivalent to a rotation through 180°.

13. A "reflection in the origin" is defined by the equations

$$\begin{cases} x' = -x \\ y' = -y. \end{cases}$$

Show that a reflection in the origin is equivalent to the product of reflections in the axes.

14. Take the square with vertices at (0,0), (0,1), (1,1), (1,0). Rotate it counterclockwise through 45°. Expand it along the y axis by a factor of 2. Rotate it clockwise through an angle whose tangent is 2. What is the compound transformation?

15. The transformation $x' = x - vt$, $y' = y$, $z' = z$, $t' = t$ is known in physics as the *Galileo transformation*. The quantity v (velocity) is a constant. Write the Galileo transformation in matrix form.

16. Find the product of two Galileo transformations, the first with a velocity v_1 and the second with a velocity v_2.

Inverse Transformations. If S is a one-to-one transformation of the plane onto itself, it may be thought of as moving the points of the plane to other locations in the plane. The *inverse transformation*, which will be designated by S^{-1}, moves these points back where they came from. Since we have assumed that the transformation S is one to one, there is no difficulty in determining where a given point came from.

For example, if S is a counterclockwise rotation of the plane through an angle of $\theta°$, its inverse, S^{-1} would be a clockwise rotation of the plane through an angle of $\theta°$. This is sometimes called a rotation through an angle of $-\theta°$.

If S were an expansion along the x axis with an expansion factor 2, S^{-1} would be a contraction along the x axis with a contraction factor $\frac{1}{2}$.

It should be clear from these examples that if the plane is transformed by S and this operation is immediately followed by the inverse of S, the net effect of the combined transformations is to leave each point unchanged. (Each point is moved to another location and then moved back again.) This fact can be expressed in the following way:

$$S^{-1}S = I.$$

The symbol I represents the identity transformation, that is, the transformation that leaves everything unchanged.

It is also true, and a moment's consideration of the above examples leads one to it, that the inverse of S^{-1} is precisely S; and this means, equally, that we must have

$$SS^{-1} = I.$$

Since S may be thought of as a geometric transformation or as a matrix,

Table of Simple Transformations of the Plane

MATRIX	TRANSFORMATION	INVERSE TRANSFORMATION	INVERSE MATRIX
$\begin{pmatrix} 1 & 0 \\ 0 & 1 \end{pmatrix}$	Identity	Identity	$\begin{pmatrix} 1 & 0 \\ 0 & 1 \end{pmatrix}$
$\begin{pmatrix} 0 & 1 \\ 1 & 0 \end{pmatrix}$	Reflection in the line $y = x$	Reflection in the line $y = x$	$\begin{pmatrix} 0 & 1 \\ 1 & 0 \end{pmatrix}$
$\begin{pmatrix} k & 0 \\ 0 & 1 \end{pmatrix}$	Expansion along the x axis with constant k	Expansion along the x axis with constant $1/k$	$\begin{pmatrix} 1/k & 0 \\ 0 & 1 \end{pmatrix}$
$\begin{pmatrix} 1 & 0 \\ 0 & k \end{pmatrix}$	Expansion along the y axis with constant k	Expansion along the y axis with constant $1/k$	$\begin{pmatrix} 1 & 0 \\ 0 & 1/k \end{pmatrix}$
$\begin{pmatrix} 1 & k \\ 0 & 1 \end{pmatrix}$	Shear along the x axis with constant k	Shear along the x axis with constant $-k$	$\begin{pmatrix} 1 & -k \\ 0 & 1 \end{pmatrix}$
$\begin{pmatrix} 1 & 0 \\ k & 1 \end{pmatrix}$	Shear along the y axis with constant k	Shear along the y axis with constant $-k$	$\begin{pmatrix} 1 & 0 \\ -k & 1 \end{pmatrix}$
$\begin{pmatrix} \cos\theta & -\sin\theta \\ \sin\theta & \cos\theta \end{pmatrix}$	Counterclockwise rotation through angle $\theta°$	Counterclockwise rotation through angle $-\theta°$	$\begin{pmatrix} \cos\theta & \sin\theta \\ -\sin\theta & \cos\theta \end{pmatrix}$

it follows that *the matrix that represents the inverse transformation must be the inverse of the matrix that represents the original transformation.*

The reader should verify for himself that the inverse transformations and their associated matrices listed in the table on page 154 do, in fact, possess all these requirements. It should be noted from them that the inverse of each type of transformation listed is a transformation of the same type. For instance, the inverse of a shear is also a shear.

PROBLEMS

1. Determine the inverse of $\begin{pmatrix}2 & 0\\0 & 1\end{pmatrix}\begin{pmatrix}1 & 0\\0 & 2\end{pmatrix}$, and interpret in terms of transformations.

2. Determine the inverse of $\begin{pmatrix}2 & 0\\0 & 1\end{pmatrix}\begin{pmatrix}1 & 0\\0 & 2\end{pmatrix}\begin{pmatrix}\frac{1}{2} & 0\\0 & 1\end{pmatrix}$, and interpret.

3. Do the same for $\begin{pmatrix}2 & 0\\0 & 1\end{pmatrix}\begin{pmatrix}1 & 2\\0 & 1\end{pmatrix}$.

4. Do the same for $\begin{pmatrix}1 & 0\\0 & \frac{1}{2}\end{pmatrix}\begin{pmatrix}1 & 0\\6 & 1\end{pmatrix}\begin{pmatrix}1 & \frac{1}{2}\\0 & 1\end{pmatrix}\begin{pmatrix}2 & 0\\0 & 1\end{pmatrix}$.

5. Find the inverse of the similarity transformation

$$\begin{cases}x' = kx\\y' = ky.\end{cases}$$

6. Find the inverse of the transformation

$$\begin{cases}x' = mx\\y' = ny.\end{cases}$$

7. Find the inverse of the Galileo transformation given on page 153.

The interpretation of matrices as transformations in space also can be used to shed light on the matrix formula $(BA)^{-1} = A^{-1}B^{-1}$. The factors in the inverse occur in the reverse order. Why the reverse order? Here is one explanation that involves an absent-minded professor of mathematics who momentarily thought that $(BA)^{-1} = B^{-1}A^{-1}$.

Let A = act of putting on a shirt
B = act of putting on a coat.
Then BA = act of putting on a shirt and then a coat.

Now, A^{-1} = act of taking off the shirt
B^{-1} = act of taking off the coat.
Also, $(BA)^{-1}$ = act of taking off both shirt and coat
But $B^{-1}A^{-1}$ has the professor taking off his shirt first and then his coat!

$A^{-1}B^{-1}$ tells him to take off his coat first and then his shirt. Hence, $(BA)^{-1} = A^{-1}B^{-1}$.

The equations of certain complicated transformations may occasionally be obtained more conveniently by breaking up the transformation into a succession of simple transformations. Suppose it is desired to obtain the equations that express the reflection of the plane in a line ℓ that passes through the origin and makes an angle of $\theta°$ with the x axis.

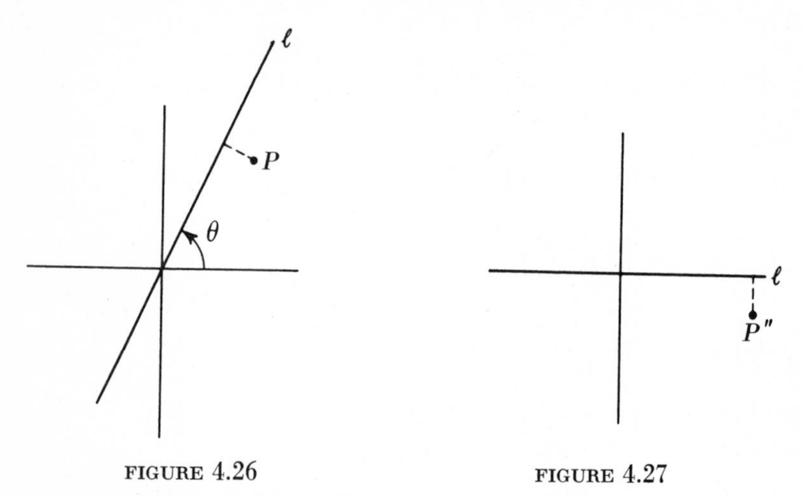

FIGURE 4.26 FIGURE 4.27

We could, of course, obtain them from scratch, using a bit of trigonometry. But we can also consider the transformation as the product of the following three transformations:

S_1: A rotation backwards through $\theta°$. This takes P into P″ (Figures 4.26 and 4.27).

S_2: A reflection in the x axis. This takes P'' into P''' (Figure 4.28).

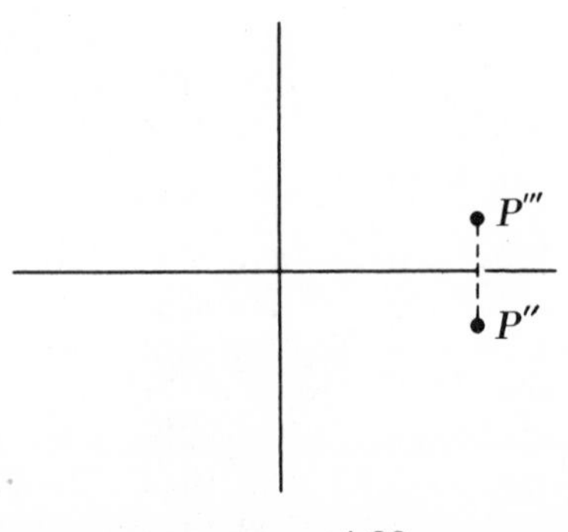

FIGURE 4.28

S_3: A rotation forward through $\theta°$. This takes P'' back to P and P''' into the required point P' (Figure 4.29).

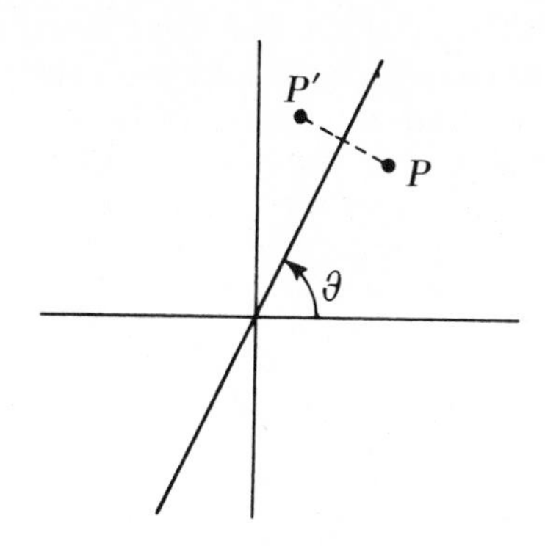

FIGURE 4.29

Recall that the matrix representation of the reflection in the x axis is $\begin{pmatrix}1 & 0\\ 0 & -1\end{pmatrix}$. The combined transformation $S_3S_2S_1$, therefore, is

$$\begin{pmatrix}\cos\theta & -\sin\theta\\ \sin\theta & \cos\theta\end{pmatrix}\begin{pmatrix}1 & 0\\ 0 & -1\end{pmatrix}\begin{pmatrix}\cos\theta & \sin\theta\\ -\sin\theta & \cos\theta\end{pmatrix}$$
$$= \begin{pmatrix}\cos\theta & \sin\theta\\ \sin\theta & -\cos\theta\end{pmatrix}\begin{pmatrix}\cos\theta & \sin\theta\\ -\sin\theta & \cos\theta\end{pmatrix}$$
$$= \begin{pmatrix}\cos^2\theta-\sin^2\theta, & 2\sin\theta\cos\theta\\ 2\sin\theta\cos\theta, & \sin^2\theta-\cos^2\theta\end{pmatrix}$$
$$= \begin{pmatrix}\cos 2\theta & \sin 2\theta\\ \sin 2\theta & -\cos 2\theta\end{pmatrix}.$$

If we designate the coordinates of P' by (x',y'), we have

$$\begin{cases}x' = (\cos 2\theta)x + (\sin 2\theta)y\\ y' = (\sin 2\theta)x - (\cos 2\theta)y.\end{cases}$$

These are the required equations.

PROBLEMS

1. The plane is reflected in the 60° line through the origin. Find the equations of the transformation.

2. Verify the formula for reflections in the special cases $\theta = 45°, \theta = 90°, \theta = 180°$.

3. Find $\begin{pmatrix}\cos 2\theta & \sin 2\theta\\ \sin 2\theta & -\cos 2\theta\end{pmatrix}^2$ and interpret in terms of transformations.

4. Find the inverse of $\begin{pmatrix} \cos 2\theta & \sin 2\theta \\ \sin 2\theta & -\cos 2\theta \end{pmatrix}$ and interpret geometrically.

5. The circle $x^2 + y^2 = 1$ is reflected in a line ℓ that passes through the origin and makes an angle θ with the x axis. Find the new equation. Carry out the work algebraically and verify the obvious answer.

6. Find the equations of an expansion with constant k along an axis that passes through the origin and makes an angle of $\theta°$ with the x axis.

7. Subject the circle $x^2 + y^2 = 1$ to the transformation in Problem 6 and determine the new equation. Use $k = 2$, $\theta = 45°$.

8. Subject Figure 4.30 to the following transformations. Draw graphs.

(a) Translate it two units to the right.

(b) Subject it to

$$\begin{cases} x' = \frac{1}{2}x \\ y' = y. \end{cases}$$

(c) Subject it to

$$\begin{cases} x' = x \\ y' = 2y. \end{cases}$$

(d) Rotate it counterclockwise through 90°.

(e) Reflect it in the line $x = 0$.

(f) Reflect it in the line $y = 0$.

(g) Subject it to the transformation

$$\begin{cases} x' = x \\ y' = \frac{1}{2}x + y. \end{cases}$$

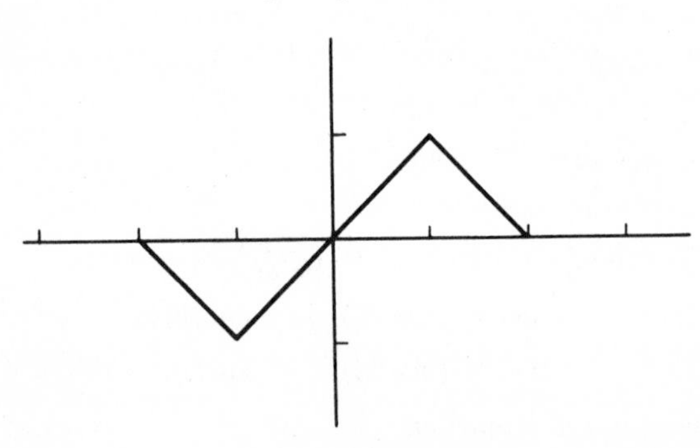

FIGURE 4.30

4.5 Linear Homogeneous Transformations of the Plane

The transformation

$$S: \begin{cases} x' = ax + by \\ y' = cx + dy, \end{cases}$$

or in matrix form,

$$\begin{pmatrix} x' \\ y' \end{pmatrix} = \begin{pmatrix} a & b \\ c & d \end{pmatrix} \begin{pmatrix} x \\ y \end{pmatrix}$$

is known as a *linear homogeneous* transformation of the plane. The word "homogeneous" is very often omitted from this description. In three dimensions (or three variables) the equations of such a transformation would be

$$\begin{pmatrix} x' \\ y' \\ z' \end{pmatrix} = \begin{pmatrix} a & b & c \\ d & e & f \\ g & h & k \end{pmatrix} \begin{pmatrix} x \\ y \\ z \end{pmatrix}.$$

Linear homogeneous transformations are of great importance in many portions of pure and applied mathematics. In the theory of elasticity, for example, if an elastic body undergoes a slight deformation under a stress, and each point (x,y,z) of the body has been displaced to a new point $(x',y,'z')$, then the relationship between these points can be given quite accurately by a transformation of this type. (To visualize such a transformation, try squeezing an orange between two plates.)

We have interpreted certain special transformations geometrically. Our object in this section is to give a geometrical interpretation which is of wider scope.

We assume that the matrix $A = \begin{pmatrix} a & b \\ c & d \end{pmatrix}$ is nonsingular. This is equivalent to the assumption that $ad - bc \neq 0$. Under this assumption, x and y can be solved uniquely in terms of x' and y', so that the transformation is a one-to-one mapping of the plane onto itself.

Theorem: *Any nonsingular linear homogeneous transformation of the plane can be regarded as the net result of expansions along axes, shears, and reflections in the line* y = x.

PROOF: As we know from page 105, any nonsingular matrix can be reduced to the unit matrix by a sequence of elementary row operations. This means that we can find a sequence of elementary row operations $E_1, E_2, \ldots, E_p$ such that $E_pE_{p-1} \cdots E_2E_1A = I$. Each elementary matrix E_i is one of the following types

$$\begin{pmatrix} 0 & 1 \\ 1 & 0 \end{pmatrix}, \quad \begin{pmatrix} k & 0 \\ 0 & 1 \end{pmatrix}, \quad \begin{pmatrix} 1 & 0 \\ 0 & k \end{pmatrix}, \quad \begin{pmatrix} 1 & k \\ 0 & 1 \end{pmatrix}, \quad \begin{pmatrix} 1 & 0 \\ k & 1 \end{pmatrix}.$$

(The k's, naturally, may be different.) The first matrix interchanges the rows (elementary transformation of Type I). The second and third matrices multiply rows by a constant (Type II).

The last two matrices add a multiple of one row to the other row (Type III).

By solving for A, we obtain

$$A = E_1^{-1}E_2^{-1} \ldots E_{p-1}^{-1}E_p^{-1}.$$

Since the inverse of an elementary matrix is an elementary matrix of the same type, (that is, the inverse of an expansion is an expansion, the inverse of a shear is a shear, et cetera), we have succeeded in expressing A as the product of matrices of the required type.

A similar theorem is valid for $n \times n$ matrices and allows us to give a geometric interpretation of linear homogeneous transformations in higher dimensional spaces. In fact, the geometry of n dimensional space is largely equivalent to matrix algebra!

Let us see how this factorization works out in a numerical example. We shall interpret the transformation

$$\begin{cases} x' = 3x + y \\ y' = 2x + 4y \end{cases}$$

as a product of elementary transformations. The matrix is $\begin{pmatrix} 3 & 1 \\ 2 & 4 \end{pmatrix}$ and since $(3 \cdot 4) - (1 \cdot 2) \neq 0$, it is nonsingular. We follow the Gauss-Jordan elimination scheme.

1. Divide first row by 3. This is effected by multiplying by

$$\begin{pmatrix} \frac{1}{3} & 0 \\ 0 & 1 \end{pmatrix}: \quad \begin{pmatrix} \frac{1}{3} & 0 \\ 0 & 1 \end{pmatrix}\begin{pmatrix} 3 & 1 \\ 2 & 4 \end{pmatrix} = \begin{pmatrix} 1 & \frac{1}{3} \\ 2 & 4 \end{pmatrix}.$$

2. Multiply first row by 2 and subtract this multiple from the second row. This is effected by multiplying by

$$\begin{pmatrix} 1 & 0 \\ -2 & 1 \end{pmatrix}: \quad \begin{pmatrix} 1 & 0 \\ -2 & 1 \end{pmatrix}\begin{pmatrix} 1 & \frac{1}{3} \\ 2 & 4 \end{pmatrix} = \begin{pmatrix} 1 & \frac{1}{3} \\ 0 & \frac{10}{3} \end{pmatrix}.$$

3. Divide the second row by $\frac{10}{3}$. This is effected by multiplying by

$$\begin{pmatrix} 1 & 0 \\ 0 & \frac{3}{10} \end{pmatrix}: \quad \begin{pmatrix} 1 & 0 \\ 0 & \frac{3}{10} \end{pmatrix}\begin{pmatrix} 1 & \frac{1}{3} \\ 0 & \frac{10}{3} \end{pmatrix} = \begin{pmatrix} 1 & \frac{1}{3} \\ 0 & 1 \end{pmatrix}.$$

4. Multiply the second row by $\frac{1}{3}$ and subtract this multiple from the first row. This is accomplished by multiplying by

$$\begin{pmatrix} 1 & -\frac{1}{3} \\ 0 & 1 \end{pmatrix}: \quad \begin{pmatrix} 1 & -\frac{1}{3} \\ 0 & 1 \end{pmatrix}\begin{pmatrix} 1 & \frac{1}{3} \\ 0 & 1 \end{pmatrix} = \begin{pmatrix} 1 & 0 \\ 0 & 1 \end{pmatrix}.$$

Hence, compounding these matrices, we have

$$\begin{pmatrix}1 & -\frac{1}{3}\\ 0 & 1\end{pmatrix}\begin{pmatrix}1 & 0\\ 0 & \frac{3}{10}\end{pmatrix}\begin{pmatrix}1 & 0\\ -2 & 1\end{pmatrix}\begin{pmatrix}\frac{1}{3} & 0\\ 0 & 1\end{pmatrix}\begin{pmatrix}3 & 1\\ 2 & 4\end{pmatrix} = \begin{pmatrix}1 & 0\\ 0 & 1\end{pmatrix}.$$

Hence,

$$\begin{pmatrix}3 & 1\\ 2 & 4\end{pmatrix} = \begin{pmatrix}\frac{1}{3} & 0\\ 0 & 1\end{pmatrix}^{-1}\begin{pmatrix}1 & 0\\ -2 & 1\end{pmatrix}^{-1}\begin{pmatrix}1 & 0\\ 0 & \frac{3}{10}\end{pmatrix}^{-1}\begin{pmatrix}1 & -\frac{1}{3}\\ 0 & 1\end{pmatrix}^{-1}$$

$$= \begin{pmatrix}3 & 0\\ 0 & 1\end{pmatrix}\begin{pmatrix}1 & 0\\ 2 & 1\end{pmatrix}\begin{pmatrix}1 & 0\\ 0 & \frac{10}{3}\end{pmatrix}\begin{pmatrix}1 & \frac{1}{3}\\ 0 & 1\end{pmatrix}.$$

Finally,

$$\begin{pmatrix}x'\\ y'\end{pmatrix} = \begin{pmatrix}3 & 0\\ 0 & 1\end{pmatrix}\begin{pmatrix}1 & 0\\ 2 & 1\end{pmatrix}\begin{pmatrix}1 & 0\\ 0 & \frac{10}{3}\end{pmatrix}\begin{pmatrix}1 & \frac{1}{3}\\ 0 & 1\end{pmatrix}\begin{pmatrix}x\\ y\end{pmatrix}.$$

The transformation of this example can be achieved by (1) a shear along the x axis with constant $\frac{1}{3}$; (2) an expansion along the y axis with constant $\frac{10}{3}$; (3) a shear along the y axis with constant 2; and (4) an expansion along the x axis with constant 3. No reflections enter this particular transformation.

PROBLEMS

Express the following transformations as the product of elementary transformations and interpret geometrically.

1. $\begin{cases} x' = 2x - 5y \\ y' = 3x + y. \end{cases}$

2. $\begin{cases} x' = 7x + 8y \\ y' = 6x + 7y. \end{cases}$

3. $\begin{cases} x' = 12x \\ y' = 10y. \end{cases}$

4. $\begin{cases} x' = 2y \\ y' = 3x + 4y. \end{cases}$

5. $\begin{cases} x' = -3x + 4y \\ y' = 2x. \end{cases}$

6. Express $\begin{pmatrix}\cos\theta & -\sin\theta\\ \sin\theta & \cos\theta\end{pmatrix}$ as a product of elementary matrices, and interpret geometrically.

4.6 What Does It Do

By now we have gathered quite a few facts about individual linear transformations. A few more general facts are in order.

We shall suppose that we have a linear homogeneous transformation,

$$S: \begin{cases} x' = ax + by \\ y' = cx + dy \end{cases} \quad \text{or} \quad \begin{pmatrix} x' \\ y' \end{pmatrix} = \begin{pmatrix} a & b \\ c & d \end{pmatrix} \begin{pmatrix} x \\ y \end{pmatrix},$$

whose matrix $\begin{pmatrix} a & b \\ c & d \end{pmatrix}$ has an inverse $\begin{pmatrix} \alpha & \beta \\ \gamma & \delta \end{pmatrix}$:

$\begin{pmatrix} a & b \\ c & d \end{pmatrix} \begin{pmatrix} \alpha & \beta \\ \gamma & \delta \end{pmatrix} = \begin{pmatrix} 1 & 0 \\ 0 & 1 \end{pmatrix}$. This means that we can solve for x and y in terms of x' and y':

$$\begin{pmatrix} x \\ y \end{pmatrix} = \begin{pmatrix} \alpha & \beta \\ \gamma & \delta \end{pmatrix} \begin{pmatrix} x' \\ y' \end{pmatrix}.$$

Theorem: *Under a nonsingular linear transformation,*

(a) The image of the origin is the origin.

(b) The image of a straight line is a straight line.

(c) The image of a triangle is a triangle.

(d) The images of parallel straight lines are parallel straight lines.

PROOF: (a) If $x = 0$, $y = 0$, then substitution in equations S yield $x' = 0$, $y' = 0$.

(b) A straight line has the equation

$$Ax + By + C = 0 \tag{1}$$

for certain coefficients A, B, C. Both A and B cannot be 0. In matrix form, this equation can be written as

$$(A \quad B)\begin{pmatrix} x \\ y \end{pmatrix} = (-C). \tag{2}$$

If a point (x,y) satisfies this relationship, its image, (x',y'), satisfies

$$(A \quad B)\begin{pmatrix} \alpha & \beta \\ \gamma & \delta \end{pmatrix}\begin{pmatrix} x' \\ y' \end{pmatrix} = (-C). \tag{3}$$

That is, $$(A\alpha + B\gamma,\ A\beta + B\delta)\begin{pmatrix} x' \\ y' \end{pmatrix} = (-C).$$

By expanding this, we see that x' and y' satisfy a first degree equation. The coefficients of x' and y' in this equation are $A\alpha + B\gamma$, $A\beta + B\delta$ and cannot both equal zero. For since

$$(A\alpha + B\gamma,\ A\beta + B\delta) = (A \quad B)\begin{pmatrix} \alpha & \beta \\ \gamma & \delta \end{pmatrix},$$

it follows that

$$(A \quad B) = (A\alpha + B\gamma,\ A\beta + B\delta)\begin{pmatrix} a & b \\ c & d \end{pmatrix}.$$

If both $A\alpha + B\gamma$ and $A\beta + B\delta$ were zero, then both A and B would be zero, and this is impossible. The numbers x' and y' therefore satisfy a proper first degree equation and lie on a line (3).

It is true, moreover, that every point (x',y') on the line (3) comes from a point that lies on the line (1). For (x',y') comes from (x,y) where

$$\begin{pmatrix} x \\ y \end{pmatrix} = \begin{pmatrix} \alpha & \beta \\ \gamma & \delta \end{pmatrix}\begin{pmatrix} x' \\ y' \end{pmatrix}.$$

Now

$$(A \quad B)\begin{pmatrix} x \\ y \end{pmatrix} = (A \quad B)\begin{pmatrix} \alpha & \beta \\ \gamma & \delta \end{pmatrix}\begin{pmatrix} x' \\ y' \end{pmatrix} = (-C).$$

Hence (x,y) satisfies Equation (2). This is equivalent to Equation (1).

(c) The images of P_1P_2, P_2P_3, P_3P_1 must be three line segments $P_1'P_2'$, $P_2'P_3'$, $P_3'P_1'$ (Figure 4.31). To show that $P_1'P_2'P_3'$ is a genuine triangle and not a degenerate one, we must show that the points P_1', P_2', P_3' do not lie on a straight line. Suppose, for instance, that P_3 lay on the line $P_1'P_2'$. Since the inverse transfor-

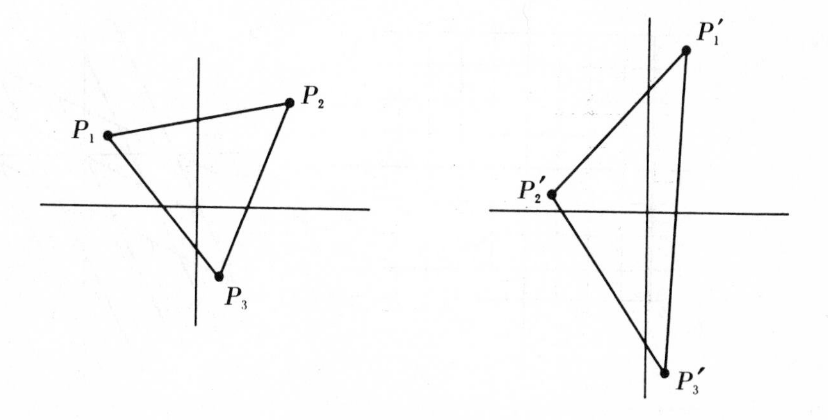

FIGURE 4.31

mation is also nonsingular, all the points on the line $P_1'P_2'$ come from points on the line P_1P_2. But the inverse image of P_3' is P_3 and this we know does not lie on P_1P_2. The assumption that P_3' lies on $P_1'P_2'$ must therefore have been false.

(d) The images of parallel lines are parallel lines. To prove this, let the two lines have equations

$$A_1x + B_1y + C_1 = 0 \tag{1}$$

$$A_2x + B_2y + C_2 = 0. \tag{2}$$

They are parallel if and only if $A_1B_2 = A_2B_1$. The image of line (1) is

$$(A_1\alpha + B_1\gamma,\ A_1\beta + B_1\delta)\begin{pmatrix} x' \\ y' \end{pmatrix} = (-C_1). \tag{3}$$

The image of line (2) is

$$(A_2\alpha + B_2\gamma,\ A_2\beta + B_2\delta)\begin{pmatrix} x' \\ y' \end{pmatrix} = (-C_2). \tag{4}$$

Now $(A_1\alpha + B_1\gamma)(A_2\beta + B_2\delta) = (A_2\alpha + B_2\gamma)(A_1\beta + B_1\delta)$. This is true since $A_1B_2 = A_2B_1$. (Expand, and you will see.) Hence, the images are parallel lines.

A further consequence is that the image of a square is a parallelogram. Figure 4.32 shows the image of the coordinate grid under the transformation

$$\begin{cases} x' = 2x + y \\ y' = x + 2y. \end{cases}$$

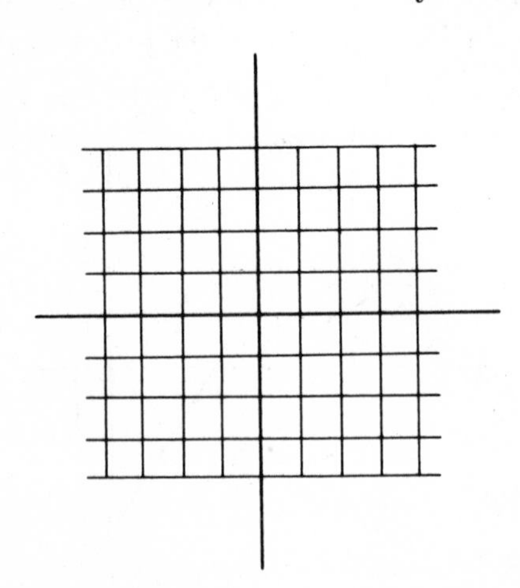

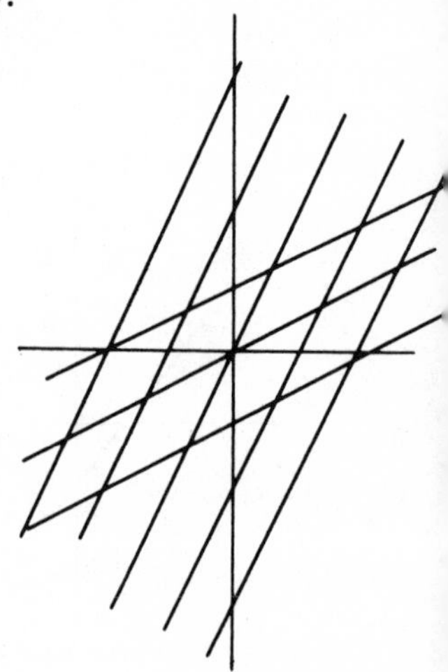

FIGURE 4.32

4.7 Degenerate Linear Transformations

What happens when we allow the matrix of the transformation to be singular? This is the so called *degenerate* case.

Let us study, first of all, the transformation

$$(1) \qquad \begin{cases} x' = 2x + y \\ y' = 4x + 2y. \end{cases}$$

The matrix $\begin{pmatrix} 2 & 1 \\ 4 & 2 \end{pmatrix}$ is singular inasmuch as $2 \cdot 4 - 1 \cdot 4 = 0$. Notice that $2x' = 4x + 2y = y'$. This means that no matter what values of x and y are selected, x' and y' always stand in the relationship $2x' = y'$. Hence the image of *any* point in the plane lies on the line $y = 2x$. Moreover, the transformation is not one-to-one, and if we like, we can determine all the points (x,y) whose image is a given point on this line. Take, for example, $(1,2)$. We have $\begin{pmatrix} 1 \\ 2 \end{pmatrix} = \begin{pmatrix} 2 & 1 \\ 4 & 2 \end{pmatrix} \begin{pmatrix} x \\ y \end{pmatrix}$ or $1 = 2x + y$ and $2 = 4x + 2y$. This last equation is redundant; it gives us no further information. Hence, *any* point on the line $2x + y = 1$ has $(1,2)$ as its image.

What points (x,y) have the origin as their image? To determine this, set $\begin{pmatrix} 0 \\ 0 \end{pmatrix} = \begin{pmatrix} 2 & 1 \\ 4 & 2 \end{pmatrix} \begin{pmatrix} x \\ y \end{pmatrix}$, or $2x + y = 0$, $4x + 2y = 0$. The second equation here is redundant; it adds no further information. Hence, every point on the line $y = -2x$ is sent into the origin.

The set of points of the plane that are sent to the origin is called the *null space* of the transformation.

The transformation (1) collapses the whole plane into the line $y = 2x$. Under this transformation plane figures are squashed into segments of this line.

Consider the transformation

$$\begin{cases} x' = 0x + 0y \\ y' = 0x + 0y. \end{cases}$$

This is badly degenerate. It transforms the whole plane into the single point $(0,0)$.

PROBLEMS

1. A triangle has vertices at $(1,1)$, $(0,1)$, and $(1,0)$. The plane is transformed by

$$\begin{cases} x' = 2x + y \\ y' = 4x + 2y. \end{cases}$$

Describe what happens to the triangle.

2. Describe the action of the transformations whose matrices are as follows:

$$\text{(a)} \begin{pmatrix} 2 & 0 \\ 1 & 0 \end{pmatrix} \quad \text{(b)} \begin{pmatrix} 1 & 0 \\ 0 & 0 \end{pmatrix} \quad \text{(c)} \begin{pmatrix} 2 & 3 \\ 2 & 3 \end{pmatrix} \quad \text{(d)} \begin{pmatrix} 0 & 0 \\ -1 & 7 \end{pmatrix}.$$

3. In transformation 2(a), find all the points whose image is (0,0).
4. In transformation 2(c), find all the points whose image is (1,1).
5. Find the null space of the transformation 2(d).
6. The circle $x^2 + y^2 = 1$ is transformed by 2(d). What happens to it?

4.8 Projections

A projection is a special degenerate transformation that occurs with considerable frequency. Here is a description of projection onto the x axis. From a point (x,y), a perpendicular is dropped to the x axis intersecting the x axis at $(x,0)$. The projection maps the point $P : (x,y)$ onto the point $P' : (x,0)$ (Figure 4.33). If the point (x,y) is already on the x axis, it is agreed that it is to go into itself. Hence, the equation of the projection is

$$\begin{cases} x' = x \\ y' = 0 \end{cases}$$

or, in matrix form,

$$\begin{pmatrix} x' \\ y' \end{pmatrix} = \begin{pmatrix} 1 & 0 \\ 0 & 0 \end{pmatrix} \begin{pmatrix} x \\ y \end{pmatrix}.$$

The matrix of the transformation, $\begin{pmatrix} 1 & 0 \\ 0 & 0 \end{pmatrix}$, is singular.

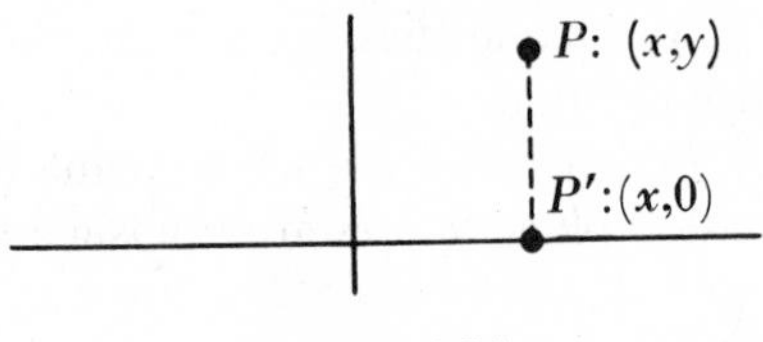

FIGURE 4.33

A line ℓ passes through (0,0) and makes an angle θ with the x axis. Suppose that it is desired to find the equation of a projection onto ℓ. This can be done from scratch geometrically, or we can use matrix multiplication.

(1) Rotate the plane through $-\theta$. The point P goes into P''.

(2) Find the projection of P'' on the x axis. This is P'''.

(3) Rotate back through θ. The point P'' goes back to P and P''' goes back into the required point P' (Figure 4.34). In matrix terms,

$$\begin{pmatrix} x' \\ y' \end{pmatrix} = \begin{pmatrix} \cos\theta & -\sin\theta \\ \sin\theta & \cos\theta \end{pmatrix} \begin{pmatrix} 1 & 0 \\ 0 & 0 \end{pmatrix} \begin{pmatrix} \cos\theta & \sin\theta \\ -\sin\theta & \cos\theta \end{pmatrix} \begin{pmatrix} x \\ y \end{pmatrix},$$

or, simplifying,

$$\begin{pmatrix} x' \\ y' \end{pmatrix} = \begin{pmatrix} \cos^2\theta & \sin\theta\cos\theta \\ \sin\theta\cos\theta & \sin^2\theta \end{pmatrix} \begin{pmatrix} x \\ y \end{pmatrix}.$$

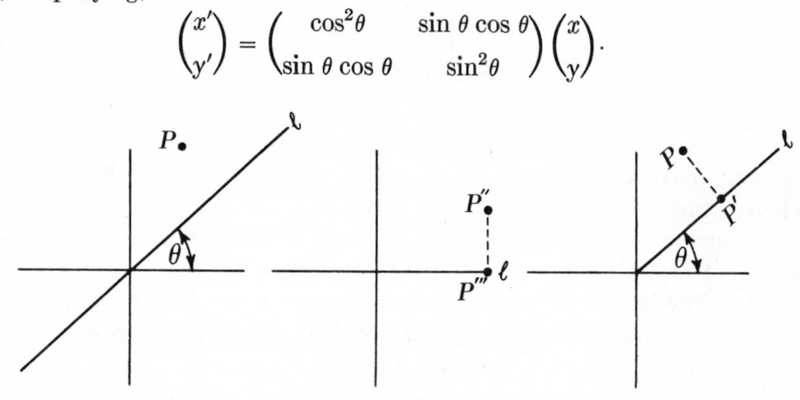

FIGURE 4.34

PROBLEMS

1. Find the equations of the projection of the plane onto the 45° line through the origin.
2. What is the image of (6,2) under this transformation?
3. Find all the points that have this image.
4. If $Q = \begin{pmatrix} \cos^2\theta & \sin\theta\cos\theta \\ \sin\theta\cos\theta & \sin^2\theta \end{pmatrix}$, show that Q is singular.
5. Show that $Q^2 = Q$, and interpret geometrically.
6. Is the product of two projections a projection?
7. Compute $\begin{pmatrix} 1 & 0 \\ 0 & 0 \end{pmatrix}\begin{pmatrix} 0 & 0 \\ 0 & 1 \end{pmatrix}$ and interpret geometrically.
8. A matrix A that satisfies the equation $A^2 = A$ is called *idempotent*. Prove that if an idempotent matrix is nonsingular, it must be the identity.
9. Describe the null space of a projection onto a line ℓ.
10. Prove that the product

$$\begin{pmatrix} \cos^2\theta & \sin\theta\cos\theta \\ \sin\theta\cos\theta & \sin^2\theta \end{pmatrix}\begin{pmatrix} \cos^2\phi & \sin\phi\cos\phi \\ \sin\phi\cos\phi & \sin^2\phi \end{pmatrix}$$

is zero if θ and ϕ differ by an odd multiple of 90°. Interpret geometrically.

4.9 Nonhomogeneous Transformations

A wider class of transformations of the plane are the *nonhomogeneous linear transformations*. The general equations for this kind of transformation are

$$(1) \qquad \begin{cases} x' = ax + by + c \\ y' = dx + ey + f. \end{cases}$$

The translations, whose equations are

$$\begin{cases} x' = x + c \\ y' = y + f, \end{cases}$$

are a special case of this type. The expression "nonhomogeneous" refers to the fact that the terms ax, by, dx, ey are of first degree in the variables, whereas the constant terms c and f are not.

The nonhomogeneous transformations are distinguished from the homogeneous transformation in these two respects.

(1) The image of (0,0) in the homogeneous case is always (0,0).

(2) A nonhomogeneous transformation cannot be expressed as the product of a 2×2 matrix and a 2×1 matrix.

Despite this last fact, it is useful to develop a representation of a nonhomogeneous transformation in terms of matrix multiplication. This can be done by using 3×3 matrices. The Equations (1) are completely equivalent to the matrix equation

$$\begin{pmatrix} x' \\ y' \\ 1 \end{pmatrix} = \begin{pmatrix} a & b & c \\ d & e & f \\ 0 & 0 & 1 \end{pmatrix} \begin{pmatrix} x \\ y \\ 1 \end{pmatrix}. \tag{2}$$

This can be verified by multiplying out the matrices.

When the matrix Equation (2) is expanded in terms of ordinary equations, it will be found that there are three equations, two of which are the equations in (1), while the third is the redundant equation $1 = 1$. This matrix representation is related to what are called *homogeneous coordinates* in the plane and is a topic that is developed in considerable detail in projective geometry.

The matrix equation

$$\begin{pmatrix} x' \\ y' \\ 1 \end{pmatrix} = \begin{pmatrix} 1 & 0 & c \\ 0 & 1 & f \\ 0 & 0 & 1 \end{pmatrix} \begin{pmatrix} x \\ y \\ 1 \end{pmatrix}$$

represents a translation.

The matrix equation

$$\begin{pmatrix} x' \\ y' \\ 1 \end{pmatrix} = \begin{pmatrix} \cos\theta & -\sin\theta & 0 \\ \sin\theta & \cos\theta & 0 \\ 0 & 0 & 1 \end{pmatrix} \begin{pmatrix} x \\ y \\ 1 \end{pmatrix}$$

is really a homogeneous transformation written in nonhomogeneous form, and it represents a rotation through $\theta°$.

Nonhomogeneous transformations may be combined either by employing substitution of their ordinary equations or by matrix multiplication of their matrix equation.

Example 1: The translation T_1:

$$\begin{cases} x' = x + a \\ y' = y + b \end{cases}$$

is followed by the translation T_2:

$$\begin{cases} x'' = x' + c \\ y'' = y' + d \end{cases}$$

Find the equation of T_2T_1. By substitution, we have

$$\begin{cases} x'' = (x + a) + c = x + a + c \\ y'' = (y + b) + d = y + b + d. \end{cases}$$

If we employ matrix multiplication as a second method, we have

$$\begin{pmatrix} x'' \\ y'' \\ 1 \end{pmatrix} = \begin{pmatrix} 1 & 0 & c \\ 0 & 1 & d \\ 0 & 0 & 1 \end{pmatrix} \begin{pmatrix} 1 & 0 & a \\ 0 & 1 & b \\ 0 & 0 & 1 \end{pmatrix} \begin{pmatrix} x \\ y \\ 1 \end{pmatrix},$$

or simplifying,

$$\begin{pmatrix} x'' \\ y'' \\ 1 \end{pmatrix} = \begin{pmatrix} 1 & 0 & a + c \\ 0 & 1 & b + d \\ 0 & 0 & 1 \end{pmatrix} \begin{pmatrix} x \\ y \\ 1 \end{pmatrix}.$$

Example 2: The translation T:

$$\begin{cases} x' = x + a \\ y' = y + b \end{cases}$$

is followed by the rotation R:

$$\begin{cases} x'' = x' \cos \theta - y' \sin \theta \\ y'' = x' \sin \theta + y' \cos \theta \end{cases}$$

Compute RT.

RT has the matrix

$$\begin{pmatrix} 1 & 0 & a \\ 0 & 1 & b \\ 0 & 0 & 1 \end{pmatrix} \begin{pmatrix} \cos \theta & -\sin \theta & 0 \\ \sin \theta & \cos \theta & 0 \\ 0 & 0 & 1 \end{pmatrix}$$

$$= \begin{pmatrix} \cos \theta & -\sin \theta & a \\ \sin \theta & \cos \theta & b \\ 0 & 0 & 1 \end{pmatrix}.$$

Transformations of this kind are known as *rigid motions of the plane.* Under rigid motions figures preserve their shape, sizes, and orientations.

PROBLEMS

1. Compute

$$\begin{pmatrix} 1 & k & 0 \\ 0 & 1 & 0 \\ 0 & 0 & 1 \end{pmatrix} \begin{pmatrix} 1 & 0 & a \\ 0 & 1 & b \\ 0 & 0 & 1 \end{pmatrix}$$

and interpret geometrically.

2. Compute

$$\begin{pmatrix} a & b & c \\ d & e & f \\ 0 & 0 & 1 \end{pmatrix}^2$$

and interpret geometrically.

3. A translation of one unit to the right and one unit up is followed by a counterclockwise rotation through 90°. Use matrices to find the compound transformation.

4. If S_1 is one shear along the x axis and S_2 is a second shear along the x axis, show that $S_1S_2 = S_2S_1$.

5. Carry out a systematic program of determining whether one simple transformation commutes with a second simple transformation; for example do translations commute with translations? Do expansions commute with reflections?

6. Typesetters paradise. Which of the following "words" can be obtained from EXIT by rotations and reflections?

EXI⊥ ƎXIT ƎXI⊥ TIXE ⊥IXE

TIXƎ ⊥IXƎ

7. Two pieces of the same graph paper lie on top of one another. Show that it is possible for the pair of points (2,1), (3,8) to lie on top of the pair of points (6,−2), (11,3).

8. In Problem 7, on top of what point does (0,0) lie?

CHAPTER 5

Determinants

5.1 What is a Determinant

Every square matrix has a number associated with it known as the *determinant* of the matrix. The determinant is intimately related to the various interpretations and applications of matrices. The determinant of a square matrix A will be designated by det A. Determinants are also designated by placing vertical lines at the sides of the matrix. Thus:

$$|A| \qquad \text{or} \qquad \begin{vmatrix} 1 & 2 \\ 3 & 1 \end{vmatrix}.$$

Determinants are defined only for matrices that are square.

Definition: *The determinant of a* 1×1 *matrix* $\mathrm{A} = (\mathrm{a})$ *is the number* a *itself:*

$$\det(\mathrm{A}) = |\mathrm{a}| = \mathrm{a}. \tag{1}$$

The determinant of a 2×2 *matrix* $\mathrm{A} = \begin{pmatrix} \mathrm{a}_1 & \mathrm{a}_2 \\ \mathrm{b}_1 & \mathrm{b}_2 \end{pmatrix}$ *is the quantity* $\mathrm{a}_1\mathrm{b}_2 - \mathrm{a}_2\mathrm{b}_1$:

$$\det \mathrm{A} = \begin{vmatrix} \mathrm{a}_1 & \mathrm{a}_2 \\ \mathrm{b}_1 & \mathrm{b}_2 \end{vmatrix} = \mathrm{a}_1\mathrm{b}_2 - \mathrm{a}_2\mathrm{b}_1. \tag{2}$$

The determinant of a 3×3 *matrix*

$$\mathrm{A} = \begin{pmatrix} \mathrm{a}_1 & \mathrm{a}_2 & \mathrm{a}_3 \\ \mathrm{b}_1 & \mathrm{b}_2 & \mathrm{b}_3 \\ \mathrm{c}_1 & \mathrm{c}_2 & \mathrm{c}_3 \end{pmatrix} \text{ is the quantity}$$

$$(3)\ \det A = \begin{vmatrix} a_1 & a_2 & a_3 \\ b_1 & b_2 & b_3 \\ c_1 & c_2 & c_3 \end{vmatrix} = a_1b_2c_3 - a_1b_3c_2 + a_2b_3c_1 - a_2b_1c_3 + a_3b_1c_2 - a_3b_2c_1.$$

Although a determinant, strictly speaking, is a single number, the word "determinant" is occasionally used to refer to the matrix that gave rise to it. Thus, we might refer to the element 7 in the determinant $\begin{vmatrix} 1 & 7 \\ 8 & 0 \end{vmatrix}$ meaning, of course, the element 7 in the matrix $\begin{pmatrix} 1 & 7 \\ 8 & 0 \end{pmatrix}$. We shall also speak of 3×3 determinants, or a third order determinant, meaning the determinants arising from 3×3 matrices.

These definitions will do as a starter, and actually, will suffice for all the applications that will be made of determinants in this book. The above definition of a third order determinant is a fairly cumbersome one and fairly difficult to use. Similar definitions of fourth and higher order determinants are possible but lead to conceptual difficulties. In subsequent sections we shall give a more accessible definition of determinants of higher order.

The definition of the second order determinant can be remembered in the following way.

$$\begin{vmatrix} a_1 & a_2 \\ b_1 & b_2 \end{vmatrix} = \begin{array}{l} \text{product of the main diagonal elements} \\ - \text{product of the other diagonal elements} \end{array}$$

Another memory device is this:

$$\begin{vmatrix} a_1 & a_2 \\ b_1 & b_2 \end{vmatrix} = \begin{array}{ccc} + \searrow & & \swarrow - \\ & a_1 \quad a_2 & \\ & \times & \\ & b_1 \quad b_2 & \\ \swarrow & & \searrow \end{array} = a_1b_2 - a_2b_1.$$

When one works with determinants, this rule should always be kept in mind.

It is not expected that the student remember the expansion for 3×3 determinants in the form given. Here is a more convenient device for evaluating 3×3 determinants. It is known as *expansion by the elements of rows or columns.*

Notice that

$$a_1 \begin{vmatrix} b_2 & b_3 \\ c_2 & c_3 \end{vmatrix} - b_1 \begin{vmatrix} a_2 & a_3 \\ c_2 & c_3 \end{vmatrix} + c_1 \begin{vmatrix} a_2 & a_3 \\ b_2 & b_3 \end{vmatrix}$$

$$= a_1(b_2c_3 - b_3c_2) - b_1(a_2c_3 - a_3c_2) + c_1(a_2b_3 - a_3b_2)$$
$$= a_1b_2c_3 - a_1b_3c_2 - a_2b_1c_3 + a_3b_1c_2 + a_2b_3c_1 - a_3b_2c_1$$
$$= \begin{vmatrix} a_1 & a_2 & a_3 \\ b_1 & b_2 & b_3 \\ c_1 & c_2 & c_3 \end{vmatrix}.$$

In this way, the 3×3 determinant can be evaluated as the sum of three 2×2 determinants. The factors in front of the 2×2 determinants are the elements of the first column; corresponding to each element in the first column we form a related 2×2 subdeterminant by crossing out the row and column in which that element stands.

The sum of the products of the elements by the 2×2 determinants thus formed, and each element provided with a proper sign, yields the 3×3 determinant. This is a general rule, and it works for any row or column. The proper sign is given by this checkerboard of signs:

$$\begin{matrix} + & - & + & \cdots \\ - & + & - & \\ + & - & + & \\ \vdots & & & \end{matrix}$$

For example, the sign in the (1,1) position is $+$. To show a further example of how this works, we shall expand a 3×3 determinant by the elements of its second row:

$$\begin{vmatrix} a_1 & a_2 & a_3 \\ b_1 & b_2 & b_3 \\ c_1 & c_2 & c_3 \end{vmatrix} = -b_1 \begin{vmatrix} a_2 & a_3 \\ c_2 & c_3 \end{vmatrix} + b_2 \begin{vmatrix} a_1 & a_3 \\ c_1 & c_3 \end{vmatrix} - b_3 \begin{vmatrix} a_1 & a_2 \\ c_1 & c_2 \end{vmatrix}.$$

The determinant, expanded by the elements of the third row, is

$$\begin{vmatrix} a_1 & a_2 & a_3 \\ b_1 & b_2 & b_3 \\ c_1 & c_2 & c_3 \end{vmatrix} = c_1 \begin{vmatrix} a_2 & a_3 \\ b_2 & b_3 \end{vmatrix} - c_2 \begin{vmatrix} a_1 & a_3 \\ b_1 & b_3 \end{vmatrix} + c_3 \begin{vmatrix} a_1 & a_2 \\ b_1 & b_2 \end{vmatrix}.$$

In these 3×3 cases, not too much labor is involved in showing directly that each of these expansions leads to the same final answer as given by the definition. The reader should satisfy his curiosity about this.

Example 1: $\begin{vmatrix} 2 & 4 \\ 1 & 6 \end{vmatrix} = (2 \times 6) - (4 \times 1) = 8.$

Example 2: $\begin{vmatrix} x & y \\ 3 & 4 \end{vmatrix} = x(4) - y(3) = 4x - 3y.$

Example 3: $\begin{vmatrix} 1 & 2 & 1 \\ 4 & 1 & -4 \\ 0 & 1 & 2 \end{vmatrix}$. Expand by the elements of the first column.

(This is advantageous since there is a zero in this column.) We obtain

$$1\begin{vmatrix} 1 & -4 \\ 1 & 2 \end{vmatrix} - 4\begin{vmatrix} 2 & 1 \\ 1 & 2 \end{vmatrix} + 0\begin{vmatrix} 2 & 1 \\ 1 & -4 \end{vmatrix} = (2+4) - 4(4-1) + 0 = -6.$$

PROBLEMS

1. Show that $\begin{vmatrix} 6 & 3 \\ 9 & 4 \end{vmatrix} = -3,\quad \begin{vmatrix} 2 & -1 \\ 0 & 3 \end{vmatrix} = 6.$

$$\begin{vmatrix} x & y \\ -1 & 1 \end{vmatrix} = x + y,\quad \begin{vmatrix} 1 & 2 \\ 4 & 8 \end{vmatrix} = 0,\quad \begin{vmatrix} x & x+1 \\ x+2 & x+3 \end{vmatrix} = -2.$$

2. Show that $\begin{vmatrix} 1 & 2 \\ 3 & 4 \end{vmatrix} \cdot \begin{vmatrix} 5 & 6 \\ 7 & 8 \end{vmatrix} = 4.$

3. Evaluate $\begin{vmatrix} 2x & 4y \\ x & 3y \end{vmatrix},\quad \begin{vmatrix} x & 6 \\ 1 & x \end{vmatrix},\quad \begin{vmatrix} a & 0 \\ 0 & b \end{vmatrix},$

$$\begin{vmatrix} a & 0 & 0 \\ 0 & b & 0 \\ 0 & 0 & c \end{vmatrix}, \quad \text{and} \quad \begin{vmatrix} 1 & 6 & 3 \\ 0 & 0 & 2 \\ 0 & 0 & 4 \end{vmatrix}.$$

4. Show that $\begin{vmatrix} 1 & 2 & 4 \\ 0 & 1 & 1 \\ 1 & 1 & 1 \end{vmatrix} = -2,\quad \begin{vmatrix} 1 & 1 & 0 \\ 0 & 1 & 1 \\ 0 & 0 & 1 \end{vmatrix} = 1,$ and

$$\begin{vmatrix} 1 & 0 & 2 \\ 1 & 2 & 5 \\ 6 & 8 & 0 \end{vmatrix} = -48.$$

5. There are 2^4 2×2 matrices where elements are either 0 or 1. How many of the determinants of these matrices are 0?

6. Take all 2×2 matrices A and set up the transformation $A \rightarrow \det A$. What is the range of this mapping? Is the mapping one to one?

7. $\begin{vmatrix} a & b & c \\ b & c & a \\ c & a & b \end{vmatrix} = ?$

8. Evaluate $\begin{vmatrix} 1+e & 1 \\ 1 & 1+f \end{vmatrix}$.

9. Compute $\begin{vmatrix} t & 0 \\ 1 & t \end{vmatrix}$ and $\begin{vmatrix} t & 0 & 0 \\ 1 & t & 0 \\ 1 & 1 & t \end{vmatrix}$.

10. Compute $\begin{vmatrix} t & 1 \\ 0 & t \end{vmatrix}$ and $\begin{vmatrix} t & 1 & 0 \\ 0 & t & 1 \\ 0 & 0 & t \end{vmatrix}$.

11. Compute $\begin{vmatrix} 1 & t & t^2 \\ t & t^2 & 1 \\ t^2 & t & 1 \end{vmatrix}$ and $\begin{vmatrix} a & b & c \\ b & c & a \\ a+b & b & c \end{vmatrix}$.

12. Solve for x: $\begin{vmatrix} x & 2 \\ 1 & 3 \end{vmatrix} = 2,\quad \begin{vmatrix} x & 2 \\ 1 & 3 \end{vmatrix} = 0,\quad \begin{vmatrix} x & 1 \\ 0 & x \end{vmatrix} = 4,$

$$\begin{vmatrix} x-1 & 1 \\ 1 & x-1 \end{vmatrix} = 0,\qquad \begin{vmatrix} x & 1 & 1 \\ 0 & x & 1 \\ 0 & 0 & x \end{vmatrix} = 8.$$

13. Show that $\begin{vmatrix} a & b \\ c & d \end{vmatrix} + \begin{vmatrix} b & q \\ p & c \end{vmatrix} + \begin{vmatrix} p & d \\ a & q \end{vmatrix} = 0.$

14. Evaluate

$$\begin{vmatrix} 1 & a & b \\ a^{-1} & 1 & a^{-1}b \\ b^{-1} & ab^{-1} & 1 \end{vmatrix},\qquad \begin{vmatrix} 1 & a^{-1} & a^{-2} \\ a & 1 & a^{-1} \\ a^2 & a & 1 \end{vmatrix},\qquad \text{and}\qquad \begin{vmatrix} 0 & b & c \\ -b & 0 & c-b \\ -c & b-c & 0 \end{vmatrix}.$$

15. Evaluate $\dfrac{1}{h}\left(\begin{vmatrix} a+h & b+h \\ c+h & d+h \end{vmatrix} - \begin{vmatrix} a & b \\ c & d \end{vmatrix}\right)$.

16. Evaluate $\dfrac{1}{h^2}\left(\begin{vmatrix} a+2h & b+2h \\ c+2h & d+2h \end{vmatrix} - 2\begin{vmatrix} a+h & b+h \\ c+h & d+h \end{vmatrix} + \begin{vmatrix} a & b \\ c & d \end{vmatrix}\right)$.

17. Verify that

$$\begin{vmatrix} 1 & a & a^2 \\ 1 & b & b^2 \\ 1 & c & c^2 \end{vmatrix} = (a-b)(b-c)(c-a).$$

18. Evaluate $\begin{vmatrix} 1 & a & a^2 \\ 0 & 1 & 2a \\ 1 & b & b^2 \end{vmatrix}$.

19. Evaluate $\begin{vmatrix} 1 & a & a^2 \\ 0 & 1 & 2a \\ 0 & 0 & 2 \end{vmatrix}$.

20. Evaluate

$$\begin{vmatrix} 0 & 1 & 0 \\ 1 & 0 & 0 \\ 0 & 0 & 1 \end{vmatrix}, \quad \begin{vmatrix} 1 & 0 & 0 \\ 0 & 0 & 1 \\ 0 & 1 & 0 \end{vmatrix}, \quad \begin{vmatrix} k & 0 & 0 \\ 0 & 1 & 0 \\ 0 & 0 & 1 \end{vmatrix}, \quad \begin{vmatrix} 1 & 0 & 0 \\ 0 & 1 & 0 \\ 0 & 0 & k \end{vmatrix},$$

$$\begin{vmatrix} 1 & k & 0 \\ 0 & 1 & 0 \\ 0 & 0 & 1 \end{vmatrix}, \quad \begin{vmatrix} 1 & 0 & 0 \\ 0 & 1 & 0 \\ k & 0 & 1 \end{vmatrix}.$$

The following seven properties of 2×2 and 3×3 determinants should be noted particularly. The proofs of these statements are simple—one merely invokes the definitions given—and should be written out as an exercise. They are valid for $n \times n$ determinants.

(1) $\det A = \det A'$.

(2) If B results from A by interchanging a pair of rows or columns, $\det B = -\det A$.

(3)* If B results from A by multiplying the elements of a row or column by a factor k then $\det B = k \det A$.

(4) If two rows (or columns) of A are identical or proportional, then $\det A = 0$.

(5) If a row (or a column) of A is identically 0, (that is, all the elements are zero), then $\det A = 0$.

(6) If the ith row (or column) of B equals the ith row (or column) of A plus a multiple of the jth row (or column) of A, and otherwise B and A are identical, then $\det B = \det A$. (Here i must $\neq j$).

(7) If I is the identity matrix, then $\det I = 1$.

Some numerical examples will illustrate these principles:

Property (1) $\begin{vmatrix} 1 & 2 & 1 \\ 3 & 1 & 2 \\ 0 & 1 & -4 \end{vmatrix} = \begin{vmatrix} 1 & 3 & 0 \\ 2 & 1 & 1 \\ 1 & 2 & -4 \end{vmatrix}$.

*The reader should contrast this with the multiplication of a matrix by a scalar.

Property (2) $$\begin{vmatrix} 2 & 1 & 3 \\ 3 & 4 & 2 \\ 7 & 8 & 9 \end{vmatrix} = -\begin{vmatrix} 3 & 4 & 2 \\ 2 & 1 & 3 \\ 7 & 8 & 9 \end{vmatrix}.$$

Property (3) $$\begin{vmatrix} 2x & 2y & 2z \\ 1 & 6 & 5 \\ 0 & 1 & 3 \end{vmatrix} = 2\begin{vmatrix} x & y & z \\ 1 & 6 & 5 \\ 0 & 1 & 3 \end{vmatrix}.$$

Property (4) $$\begin{vmatrix} 19 & 4 & 4 \\ 1 & 1 & 1 \\ 6 & 3 & 3 \end{vmatrix} = 0, \qquad \begin{vmatrix} 19 & 4 & 8 \\ 1 & 1 & 2 \\ 6 & 3 & 6 \end{vmatrix} = 0.$$

Note that $2\begin{pmatrix} 4 \\ 1 \\ 3 \end{pmatrix} = \begin{pmatrix} 8 \\ 2 \\ 6 \end{pmatrix}$, so that these columns are proportional.

Property (5) $$\begin{vmatrix} x & y & z \\ 0 & 0 & 0 \\ 2 & 9 & 5 \end{vmatrix} = 0.$$

Property (6) $$\begin{vmatrix} 1 & 6 & 3 \\ 2 & 0 & 2 \\ 5 & 1 & 2 \end{vmatrix} = \begin{vmatrix} 5 & 6 & 7 \\ 2 & 0 & 2 \\ 5 & 1 & 2 \end{vmatrix}.$$

Note that $(1,6,3) + 2(2,0,2) = (5,6,7)$.

Occasionally it is convenient to evaluate a determinant by making use of Property (6) to reduce a row or column to as many zeros as possible and then to expand by the elements of that row or column.

Here is how it works:

Given:

$$D = \begin{vmatrix} 1 & 1 & 6 \\ 2 & 1 & 3 \\ 4 & 2 & 2 \end{vmatrix}.$$

Subtract first row from second row. This yields

$$D = \begin{vmatrix} 1 & 1 & 6 \\ 1 & 0 & -3 \\ 4 & 2 & 2 \end{vmatrix}.$$

Multiply first row by -2 and add to third row. This yields

$$D = \begin{vmatrix} 1 & 1 & 6 \\ 1 & 0 & -3 \\ 2 & 0 & -10 \end{vmatrix}.$$

Expand by the elements of the second column. This yields

$$D = -1\begin{vmatrix} 1 & -3 \\ 2 & -10 \end{vmatrix} + 0\begin{vmatrix} * & * \\ * & * \end{vmatrix} - 0\begin{vmatrix} * & * \\ * & * \end{vmatrix}$$
$$= -1(-10 - (-3)(2)) = 4.$$

The elements of the last two determinants have not been written down explicitly, since they are irrevelant to the final answer.

Here is a proof of Property (6) in the 2×2 case.

$$\text{Let } A = \begin{pmatrix} a_1 & a_2 \\ b_1 & b_2 \end{pmatrix} \quad \text{and} \quad B = \begin{pmatrix} a_1 + kb_1 & a_2 + kb_2 \\ b_1 & b_2 \end{pmatrix}.$$

Note that the first row of B equals the first row of A plus a multiple of the second row of A. That is, $(a_1 + kb_1,\ a_2 + kb_2) = (a_1,a_2) + k\,(b_1,b_2)$. Now from the definition on page 171,

$$\det A = a_1b_2 - a_2b_1.$$

Similarly,

$$\begin{aligned}\det B &= (a_1 + kb_1)b_2 - (a_2 + kb_2)b_1 \\ &= a_1b_2 + kb_1b_2 - a_2b_1 - kb_2b_1 \\ &= a_1b_2 - a_2b_1.\end{aligned}$$

Hence,

$$\det A = \det B.$$

PROBLEMS

1. Evaluate the following determinants by the device just explained.

$$\begin{vmatrix} 1 & 2 & 6 \\ 3 & 0 & 1 \\ 1 & 1 & 2 \end{vmatrix}, \quad \begin{vmatrix} 2 & 1 & 2 \\ 4 & 1 & 3 \\ 6 & 3 & 1 \end{vmatrix}, \quad \begin{vmatrix} 2 & 2 & 1 \\ 1 & 2 & 2 \\ 2 & 1 & 2 \end{vmatrix}.$$

2. Without expanding, show that

$$\begin{vmatrix} a & b & c \\ d & e & f \\ g & h & k \end{vmatrix} = \begin{vmatrix} e & b & h \\ d & a & g \\ f & c & k \end{vmatrix}.$$

3. Prove directly from the definition that

$$\begin{vmatrix} a_1 & a_2 & a_3 \\ b_1 & b_2 & b_3 \\ c_1 & c_2 & c_3 \end{vmatrix} = \begin{vmatrix} a_1 + b_1 & a_2 + b_2 & a_3 + b_3 \\ b_1 & b_2 & b_3 \\ c_1 & c_2 & c_3 \end{vmatrix}.$$

How can this be obtained from Property (6)?

4. What is the relation between

$$\begin{vmatrix} 1 & 2 & 1 \\ 3 & 0 & 2 \\ 1 & 1 & 1 \end{vmatrix}, \quad \begin{vmatrix} k & 2 & 1 \\ 3k & 0 & 2 \\ k & 1 & 1 \end{vmatrix}, \quad \begin{vmatrix} k & 2k & 1 \\ 3k & 0 & 2 \\ k & k & 1 \end{vmatrix}, \quad \text{and} \quad \begin{vmatrix} k & 2k & k \\ 3k & 0 & 2k \\ k & k & k \end{vmatrix}.$$

5. Prove several of the statements on page 176 for 3×3 determinants.

5.2 Determinants, Cofactors, and Inverses

Our object in this section is to exhibit an explicit formula for the inverse of a 3×3 matrix. In order to do this and prove the result, we shall first develop the expansions of a determinant in terms of the elements of rows or columns a bit more carefully.

Definition: *Given an* $n \times n$ *matrix* $A = (a_{ij})$, *the* minor *of the element* a_{ij} *is the* $(n-1) \times (n-1)$ *matrix that results when the* ith *row and the* jth *column of* A *are deleted. The minor of the element* a_{ij} will *be designated by* M_{ij} (Figure 5.1).

Examples:

$$\text{If } A = \begin{pmatrix} a_{11} & a_{12} \\ a_{21} & a_{22} \end{pmatrix} \quad \text{then} \quad \begin{aligned} M_{12} &= (a_{21}), \\ M_{11} &= (a_{22}). \end{aligned}$$

$$\text{If } A = \begin{pmatrix} 3 & 0 & 6 \\ 9 & 1 & 1 \\ 2 & 0 & -5 \end{pmatrix} \quad \text{then} \quad M_{22} = \begin{pmatrix} 3 & 6 \\ 2 & -5 \end{pmatrix},$$

$$M_{12} = \begin{pmatrix} 9 & 1 \\ 2 & -5 \end{pmatrix}.$$

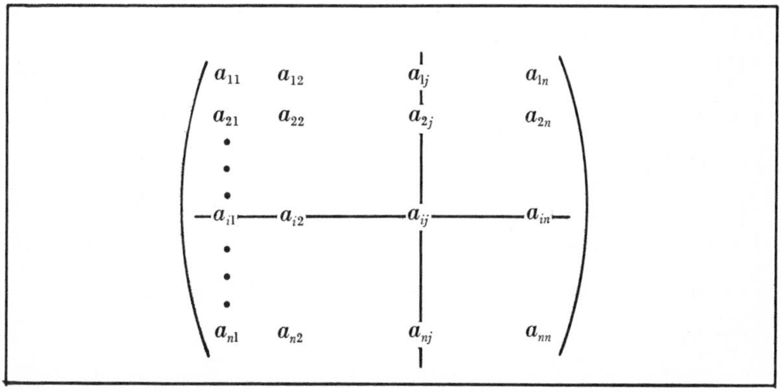

$$\begin{pmatrix} a_{11} & a_{12} & a_{1j} & a_{1n} \\ a_{21} & a_{22} & a_{2j} & a_{2n} \\ \vdots & & & \\ a_{i1} & a_{i2} & a_{ij} & a_{in} \\ \vdots & & & \\ a_{n1} & a_{n2} & a_{nj} & a_{nn} \end{pmatrix}$$

FIGURE 5.1 *Formation of the Minor* M_{ij}

Definition: *Given an* n × n *matrix* A = (a_{ij}), *the* cofactor, C_{ij} *of the element* a_{ij} *is defined by**

$$C_{ij} = (-1)^{i+j}\,|M_{ij}|\,.$$

A bit of computation shows that the expression $(-1)^{i+j}$ reproduces the checkerboard pattern of +'s and −'s:

$$\begin{matrix} +1 & -1 & 1 & \cdots \\ -1 & 1 & -1 & \\ \vdots & & & \end{matrix}$$

Hence, the cofactor of an element is the determinant of the minor of the element together with a sign according to where the element fits in the checkerboard pattern of +'s and −'s.

Examples:

If $A = \begin{pmatrix} a_{11} & a_{12} \\ a_{21} & a_{22} \end{pmatrix}$ then $C_{12} = (-1)^{1+2}\,|a_{21}| = -a_{21}.$

If $A = \begin{pmatrix} 3 & 0 & 6 \\ 9 & 1 & 1 \\ 2 & 0 & -5 \end{pmatrix}$ then $C_{22} = (-1)^{2+2}\begin{vmatrix} 3 & 6 \\ 2 & -5 \end{vmatrix} = -27.$

The expansion of a 3 × 3 determinant according to the elements of a row or column can be formulated in this way.

$$\text{If } \Delta = \begin{vmatrix} a_{11} & a_{12} & a_{13} \\ a_{21} & a_{22} & a_{23} \\ a_{31} & a_{32} & a_{33} \end{vmatrix},$$

then	Expansion by the elements of the
$\Delta = a_{11}C_{11} + a_{12}C_{12} + a_{13}C_{13}$	first row
$\Delta = a_{21}C_{21} + a_{22}C_{22} + a_{23}C_{23}$	second row
$\Delta = a_{31}C_{31} + a_{32}C_{32} + a_{33}C_{33}$	third row.
and	Expansion by the elements of the
$\Delta = a_{11}C_{11} + a_{21}C_{21} + a_{31}C_{31}$	first column
$\Delta = a_{12}C_{12} + a_{22}C_{22} + a_{32}C_{32}$	second column
$\Delta = a_{13}C_{13} + a_{23}C_{23} + a_{33}C_{33}$	third column.

*The vertical bars here designate the determinant.

Several other algebraic identities that relate elements and cofactors are important. Start with the determinant

$$D = \begin{vmatrix} a_{11} & a_{12} & a_{13} \\ a_{11} & a_{12} & a_{13} \\ a_{31} & a_{32} & a_{33} \end{vmatrix}.$$

We have deliberately selected the first two rows identical and hence $D = 0$.

Now the cofactors of the elements of the second row of the determinants Δ and D are identical; hence, expanding D by the elements of the second row,

$$D = a_{11}C_{21} + a_{12}C_{22} + a_{13}C_{23} = 0.$$

By a similar trick we can show that

$$a_{11}C_{31} + a_{12}C_{32} + a_{13}C_{33} = 0.$$

(What determinant should we start with?)

In general, the sums of the products of the elements of a row (or column) by the cofactors of the elements of a *different* row (or column) is zero.

Theorem: *The matrix*

$$\mathrm{A} = \begin{pmatrix} \mathrm{a}_{11} & \mathrm{a}_{12} & \mathrm{a}_{13} \\ \mathrm{a}_{21} & \mathrm{a}_{22} & \mathrm{a}_{23} \\ \mathrm{a}_{31} & \mathrm{a}_{32} & \mathrm{a}_{33} \end{pmatrix}$$

has an inverse if and only if

$$\Delta = \begin{vmatrix} \mathrm{a}_{11} & \mathrm{a}_{12} & \mathrm{a}_{13} \\ \mathrm{a}_{21} & \mathrm{a}_{22} & \mathrm{a}_{23} \\ \mathrm{a}_{31} & \mathrm{a}_{32} & \mathrm{a}_{33} \end{vmatrix} \neq 0.$$

If $\Delta \neq 0$, the inverse is given explicitly by

$$\mathrm{A}^{-1} = \frac{1}{\Delta}\begin{pmatrix} \mathrm{C}_{11} & \mathrm{C}_{21} & \mathrm{C}_{31} \\ \mathrm{C}_{12} & \mathrm{C}_{22} & \mathrm{C}_{32} \\ \mathrm{C}_{13} & \mathrm{C}_{23} & \mathrm{C}_{33} \end{pmatrix}.$$

The quantities C_{ij} are the cofactors of a_{ij}.

PROOF: By assuming that $\Delta \neq 0$, we can form the matrix designated by A^{-1}. Now compute the products AA^{-1} and $A^{-1}A$. By using the relations between elements and cofactors just developed, we can show that $AA^{-1} = I$ and $A^{-1}A = I$. (Verify this.)

If $\Delta = 0$, we must prove that A has no inverse. A proof can be given similar to that on page 93 and will be omitted.

The inverse of A can be written in the somewhat more explicit form

$$A^{-1} = \frac{1}{\Delta}\begin{pmatrix} \begin{vmatrix} a_{22} & a_{23} \\ a_{32} & a_{33} \end{vmatrix} & -\begin{vmatrix} a_{12} & a_{13} \\ a_{32} & a_{33} \end{vmatrix} & \begin{vmatrix} a_{12} & a_{13} \\ a_{22} & a_{23} \end{vmatrix} \\ -\begin{vmatrix} a_{21} & a_{23} \\ a_{31} & a_{33} \end{vmatrix} & \begin{vmatrix} a_{11} & a_{13} \\ a_{31} & a_{33} \end{vmatrix} & -\begin{vmatrix} a_{11} & a_{13} \\ a_{21} & a_{23} \end{vmatrix} \\ \begin{vmatrix} a_{21} & a_{22} \\ a_{31} & a_{32} \end{vmatrix} & -\begin{vmatrix} a_{11} & a_{12} \\ a_{31} & a_{32} \end{vmatrix} & \begin{vmatrix} a_{11} & a_{12} \\ a_{21} & a_{22} \end{vmatrix} \end{pmatrix}.$$

A similar pattern is followed by the inverses of matrices of higher order. The general formula for the inverse of a matrix is

$$A^{-1} = \frac{1}{|A|}(C_{ij})' = \frac{1}{|A|}(C_{ji}).$$

For 3×3 matrices, the explicit formula just given is occasionally useful numerically.

PROBLEMS

1. Write the minors of the elements of the third row of

$$\begin{pmatrix} 1 & 6 & 3 \\ x & 2 & 4 \\ 1 & 2 & 9 \end{pmatrix}.$$

Write the minors of the elements of the second column.

2. Determine the cofactors of these elements.

3. Go over the proof of the theorem on page 181 and write out the product AA^{-1} and the product $A^{-1}A$ explicitly.

4. Show how the explicit inverse of a 2×2 matrix can be expressed in terms of cofactors.

5. Use the formula on page 182 and compute A^{-1} if

$$A = \begin{pmatrix} 1 & 2 & 4 \\ 2 & 0 & 2 \\ 1 & 1 & 3 \end{pmatrix}; \quad \text{if } A = \begin{pmatrix} 1 & 0 & 0 \\ 2 & 0 & 4 \\ 5 & 1 & 7 \end{pmatrix}.$$

6. Use this formula to show that the inverse of a symmetric 3×3 matrix is also symmetric.

7. Use this formula to show that the inverse of I is I.

5.3 Pushing the Postulates: An Alternate Approach to Determinants

Recall, first of all, the definition of elementary row transformations.

Type I: Interchange of two rows.

Type II: Multiplication of any row by a nonzero constant.

Type III: Addition of a multiple of the jth row to the ith row, $j \neq i$.

The following rules of operation (which involve only row transformations) are sufficient to define and evaluate determinants of all orders.

Rule 1. If a matrix B is obtained from a matrix A by means of an elementary row transformation of Type I then $\det B = -\det A$.

Rule 2.* If a matrix B is obtained from a matrix A by means of an elementary row transformation of Type II, then $\det B = k(\det A)$.

Rule 3. If a matrix B is obtained from a matrix A by means of an elementary row transformation of Type III, then $\det B = \det A$.

Rule 4. $\det (I) = 1$.

To see how these rules can be applied systematically to evaluate determinants, we take as an example

$$\Delta = \begin{vmatrix} 3 & 4 & 5 \\ 2 & -1 & 8 \\ 5 & -2 & 7 \end{vmatrix},$$

which is the determinant of the system of equations in Section 1 of Chapter 3. By a sequence of elementary row transformations, we can reduce the matrix to the unit matrix. Since the determinant of the unit matrix is 1, (by Rule 4), this will enable us to determine the value of Δ. The reduction can be carried out systematically as in the Gauss-Jordan elimination method. It can also be carried out on a more informal basis. In the work below, we omit some of the row interchanges that bring the largest element into crucial position; although these may be advisable for large problems on a computing machine, they are not needed for small computations.

Step 1. Divide the first row by 3. By Rule 2,

$$\frac{\Delta}{3} = \begin{vmatrix} 1 & \frac{4}{3} & \frac{5}{3} \\ 2 & -1 & 8 \\ 5 & -2 & 7 \end{vmatrix}.$$

*The reader should contrast this with the multiplication of a matrix by a scalar.

Step 2. Multiply the first row by -2 and add it, element by element, to the second row. By Rule 3,

$$\frac{\Delta}{3} = \begin{vmatrix} 1 & \frac{4}{3} & \frac{5}{3} \\ 0 & -\frac{11}{3} & \frac{14}{3} \\ 5 & -2 & 7 \end{vmatrix}.$$

Step 3. Multiply the first row by -5 and add it to the third row. By Rule 3,

$$\frac{\Delta}{3} = \begin{vmatrix} 1 & \frac{4}{3} & \frac{5}{3} \\ 0 & -\frac{11}{3} & \frac{14}{3} \\ 0 & -\frac{26}{3} & -\frac{4}{3} \end{vmatrix}.$$

Step 4. Divide the second row by $-\frac{11}{3}$. By Rule 2,

$$-\frac{\Delta}{11} = \begin{vmatrix} 1 & \frac{4}{3} & \frac{5}{3} \\ 0 & 1 & -\frac{14}{11} \\ 0 & -\frac{26}{3} & -\frac{4}{3} \end{vmatrix}.$$

Step 5. Multiply the second row by $-\frac{4}{3}$ and add it to the first row. By Rule 3,

$$-\frac{\Delta}{11} = \begin{vmatrix} 1 & 0 & \frac{111}{33} \\ 0 & 1 & -\frac{14}{11} \\ 0 & -\frac{26}{3} & -\frac{4}{3} \end{vmatrix}.$$

Step 6. Multiply the second row by $\frac{26}{3}$ and add it to the third row. By Rule 3,

$$-\frac{\Delta}{11} = \begin{vmatrix} 1 & 0 & \frac{111}{33} \\ 0 & 1 & -\frac{14}{11} \\ 0 & 0 & -\frac{408}{33} \end{vmatrix}.$$

Step 7. Divide the third row by $-\frac{408}{33}$. By Rule 2,

$$\frac{3}{408}\Delta = \begin{vmatrix} 1 & 0 & \frac{111}{33} \\ 0 & 1 & -\frac{14}{11} \\ 0 & 0 & 1 \end{vmatrix}.$$

Step 8. Multiply the third row by $-\frac{111}{33}$ and add it to the first row. By Rule 3,

$$\frac{3}{408}\Delta = \begin{vmatrix} 1 & 0 & 0 \\ 0 & 1 & -\frac{14}{11} \\ 0 & 0 & 1 \end{vmatrix}.$$

Step 9. Multiply the third row by $\frac{14}{11}$ and add it to the second row. By Rule 3,

$$\tfrac{3}{408}\Delta = \begin{vmatrix} 1 & 0 & 0 \\ 0 & 1 & 0 \\ 0 & 0 & 1 \end{vmatrix}.$$

Step 10. By Rule 4,

$$\tfrac{3}{408}\Delta = 1,$$

hence,

$$\Delta = \tfrac{408}{3} = 136.$$

Although this method is not recommended for simple computation, it is important theoretically.

As we know from a previous discussion, there are two possibilities as far as reduction is concerned. If the matrix we start with is nonsingular, then it can be reduced to the unit matrix—just as we have done in this numerical example. But what if the matrix is singular? We cannot reduce it to the unit matrix, but only to an upper triangular matrix that has one or more zeros on its main diagonal.

In this case, an appropriate sequence of elementary row transformations can be found which will produce a matrix with a row of zeros. Rule 2 will now imply that the value of its determinant is zero, and hence, the value of the original determinant must be zero.

To see how this works, suppose we deduce the value of

$$\Delta = \begin{vmatrix} 1 & 2 & 3 \\ 0 & 0 & 6 \\ 0 & 0 & 4 \end{vmatrix}$$

from Rules 1–4. The matrix is upper triangular and has one zero on the main diagonal.

Multiply the second row by $-\frac{4}{6}$ and add it to the third row. By Rule 3, we obtain

$$\Delta = \begin{vmatrix} 1 & 2 & 3 \\ 0 & 0 & 6 \\ 0 & 0 & 0 \end{vmatrix}.$$

Since $(0,0,0) = 2(0,0,0)$, by Rule 2,

$$2\Delta = \begin{vmatrix} 1 & 2 & 3 \\ 0 & 0 & 6 \\ 0 & 0 & 0 \end{vmatrix} = \Delta.$$

Hence, $2\Delta = \Delta$ and therefore $\Delta = 0$.

PROBLEMS

1. Evaluate the following determinants by making use of Rules 1–4.

$$\begin{vmatrix} 0 & 1 \\ 1 & 0 \end{vmatrix}, \quad \begin{vmatrix} 2 & 6 \\ -5 & 4 \end{vmatrix}, \quad \begin{vmatrix} 1 & 7 \\ 1 & 7 \end{vmatrix}, \quad \begin{vmatrix} 1 & 2 & 4 \\ 2 & 1 & 3 \\ 1 & 0 & 6 \end{vmatrix}, \quad \begin{vmatrix} 2 & 3 \\ 4 & 5 \end{vmatrix},$$

$$\begin{vmatrix} 1 & 6 \\ 2 & 0 \end{vmatrix}, \quad \begin{vmatrix} \frac{1}{2} & \frac{1}{3} \\ \frac{1}{3} & \frac{1}{4} \end{vmatrix}, \quad \begin{vmatrix} 1 & 1 & 2 \\ 0 & 2 & 1 \\ 0 & 0 & 3 \end{vmatrix}, \quad \begin{vmatrix} 2 & 0 & 2 \\ 3 & 0 & 1 \\ 1 & 1 & 1 \end{vmatrix}.$$

2. In evaluating determinants by the method of this section, the only time the coefficient of Δ changes is when we divide a row by a constant. Hence conclude that the value of the determinant is the product of the pivots in the Gauss-Jordan elimination method. Try this out in the example on page 183.

To develop a complete and consistent theory of $n \times n$ determinants, we might adopt one of several programs:

(1) Give an explicit formula which defines an $n \times n$ determinant in terms of its elements.

(2) Give an inductive definition of a determinant by expansion in terms of elements of a row or column. This reduces an $n \times n$ determinant to a sum of n $(n-1) \times (n-1)$ determinants, and these in turn, can be reduced further.

(3) Give an inductive definition of a determinant in terms of elementary row operations.

Program (1) would consist of showing that the various expansions and rules hold in general.

Programs (2) and (3) would consist of showing that various options met with in expanding the elements of a row or column or in applying row operations all lead to the same result, and lead to an explicit formula in terms of the elements that coincides with that given in (1).

In this chapter, we have had a taste of all three approaches. Each approach has its strengths and weaknesses from the practical or from the aesthetic point of view.

The proofs of the theorems, as given, are complete for determinants up to order 3×3, and are suggestive in the higher order cases. For a thorough program in determinant theory, the reader should consult an advanced text.

5.4 Determinants, Matrices, and Multiplication

The fundamental law that relates determinants, matrices, and multiplication is that the determinant of the product of two matrices is equal to the product of the determinants.

Theorem: *If* A *and* B *are two* n × n *matrices, then*

$$\det(AB) = (\det A) \times (\det B),$$

or, using alternative symbols,

$$|AB| = |A|\,|B|.$$

Let's try this out.

If $A = \begin{pmatrix} 1 & 3 \\ 2 & 1 \end{pmatrix}$ and $B = \begin{pmatrix} 2 & 0 \\ 1 & 4 \end{pmatrix}$, then $AB = \begin{pmatrix} 5 & 12 \\ 5 & 4 \end{pmatrix}$.

Now $\begin{vmatrix} 1 & 3 \\ 2 & 1 \end{vmatrix} = -5, \quad \begin{vmatrix} 2 & 0 \\ 1 & 4 \end{vmatrix} = 8.$

But $\begin{vmatrix} 5 & 12 \\ 5 & 4 \end{vmatrix} = -40$, so that $|A| \cdot |B| = |AB|$.

In the case of 2 × 2 matrices, this theorem can be proved without too much difficulty. For, let

$$A = \begin{pmatrix} a & b \\ c & d \end{pmatrix} \quad \text{and} \quad B = \begin{pmatrix} m & n \\ p & q \end{pmatrix}.$$

Then, $|A| = ad - bc$ and $|B| = mq - np$.

Now $AB = \begin{pmatrix} am + bp & an + bq \\ cm + dp & cn + dq \end{pmatrix}$

so that
$$\begin{aligned} |AB| &= (am + bp)(cn + dq) - (an + bq)(cm + dp) \\ &= amcn + amdq + bpcn + bpdq - ancm - andp - bqcm - bqdp \\ &= amdq - andp - bqcm + bpcn \\ &= (ad - bc)(mq - np). \end{aligned}$$

Hence $|A| \cdot |B| = |AB|$.

To carry out a similar proof in the 3 × 3 case is possible, but it would require quite a bit of paper work and checking. To carry it out in the case of higher order determinants would be a difficult and certainly an unenlightening task. Other methods of proof must be developed.

PROBLEMS

Check the law of multiplication of determinants in the following cases.

1. $A = \begin{pmatrix} 3 & 1 \\ 2 & 1 \end{pmatrix}, \quad B = \begin{pmatrix} 1 & -4 \\ 2 & 6 \end{pmatrix}.$

2. $A = \begin{pmatrix} 2 & 9 & 1 \\ 6 & 0 & 3 \\ 1 & 1 & 0 \end{pmatrix}, \quad B = \begin{pmatrix} 1 & 0 & 0 \\ 0 & 1 & 0 \\ 0 & 0 & 2 \end{pmatrix}.$

3. $A = \begin{pmatrix} x & y \\ 2 & 1 \end{pmatrix}, \quad B = \begin{pmatrix} 2 & 0 \\ 1 & 1 \end{pmatrix}.$

4. $A = (6), \quad B = (-2).$

5. $A = \begin{pmatrix} x & 0 & 0 \\ 0 & x & 1 \\ 0 & 1 & x \end{pmatrix}, \quad B = \begin{pmatrix} 0 & 1 & 1 \\ 1 & 0 & 1 \\ 1 & 0 & 0 \end{pmatrix}.$

6. $A = \begin{pmatrix} \cos\theta & -\sin\theta \\ \sin\theta & \cos\theta \end{pmatrix}, \quad B = \begin{pmatrix} \cos\Psi & -\sin\Psi \\ \sin\Psi & \cos\Psi \end{pmatrix}.$

7. $A = \begin{pmatrix} a-x & b \\ b & c-x \end{pmatrix}, \quad B = \begin{pmatrix} a-x & b \\ b & c-x \end{pmatrix}.$

8. Prove that $|A|^2 = |A^2|$.

9. Express as a single determinant

$$\begin{vmatrix} 0 & a & b \\ a & 0 & c \\ b & c & 0 \end{vmatrix}^2.$$

10. By calculating the determinant of $\begin{pmatrix} a & b \\ c & d \end{pmatrix}\begin{pmatrix} a & c \\ b & d \end{pmatrix}$ in two ways, obtain the identity $(ad - bc)^2 + (ac + bd)^2 = (a^2 + b^2)(c^2 + d^2)$.

11. Show that $|AB| = |BA|$, and that this is true even though AB may not equal BA.

Theorem: *If* E *is an elementary matrix and* A *is any matrix (of the same order) then*

$$\det EA = (\det E)(\det A).$$

PROOF: The elementary matrices are those that effect elementary row transformations. For example, working with 3×3 matrices,

$$\begin{pmatrix} 0 & 1 & 0 \\ 1 & 0 & 0 \\ 0 & 0 & 1 \end{pmatrix}$$

is an elementary matrix of Type I: it interchanges the first and second rows;

$$\begin{pmatrix} 1 & 0 & 0 \\ 0 & k & 0 \\ 0 & 0 & 1 \end{pmatrix}$$

is an elementary matrix of Type II: it multiplies the second row by k;

$$\begin{pmatrix} 1 & k & 0 \\ 0 & 1 & 0 \\ 0 & 0 & 1 \end{pmatrix}$$

is an elementary matrix of Type III: it multiplies the second row by k and adds it to the first row.

Now if A is any 3×3 matrix,

$$\det\left[\begin{pmatrix} 0 & 1 & 0 \\ 1 & 0 & 0 \\ 0 & 0 & 1 \end{pmatrix} A\right] = -\det A.$$ This is by Rule 1 on page 183.

$$\det\left[\begin{pmatrix} 1 & 0 & 0 \\ 0 & k & 0 \\ 0 & 0 & 1 \end{pmatrix} A\right] = k \det A.$$ This is by Rule 2.

$$\det\left[\begin{pmatrix} 1 & k & 0 \\ 0 & 1 & 0 \\ 0 & 0 & 1 \end{pmatrix} A\right] = \det A.$$ This is by Rule 3.

Now

$$\det\begin{pmatrix} 0 & 1 & 0 \\ 1 & 0 & 0 \\ 0 & 0 & 1 \end{pmatrix} = -1.$$

This can be proved directly from the definition. The same value is obtained for all matrices of Type I. Similarly,

$$\det\begin{pmatrix} 1 & 0 & 0 \\ 0 & k & 0 \\ 0 & 0 & 1 \end{pmatrix} = k, \qquad \text{and} \qquad \det\begin{pmatrix} 1 & k & 0 \\ 0 & 1 & 0 \\ 0 & 0 & 1 \end{pmatrix} = 1.$$

Thus, for example,

$$\det\left[\begin{pmatrix} 0 & 1 & 0 \\ 1 & 0 & 0 \\ 0 & 0 & 1 \end{pmatrix} A\right] = \det\begin{pmatrix} 0 & 1 & 0 \\ 1 & 0 & 0 \\ 0 & 0 & 1 \end{pmatrix} \det A,$$

and similar equations hold for the elementary matrices of the other types. Hence, if E is an elementary matrix,

$$\det(EA) = (\det E)(\det A).$$

Corollary: If $E_1, E_2, \ldots, E_p$ are elementary matrices, and if A is any matrix, then

$$\det (E_1E_2 \cdots E_pA) = (\det E_1)(\det E_2) \cdots (\det E_p) \det A.$$

PROOF: $\det (E_1E_2 \cdots E_pA) = \det (E_1(E_2 \cdots E_pA))$. By the theorem, $\det (E_1(E_2 \cdots E_pA)) = \det E_1 \det (E_2 \cdots E_pA)$. Similarly,

$$\det (E_2 \cdots E_pA) = \det E_2 \det (E_3 \cdots E_pA).$$

We can keep up this process, and finally arrive at the stated equality.

Theorem: *If* A *is nonsingular then* $\det \mathrm{A} \neq 0$.
If A *is singular then* $\det \mathrm{A} = 0$.

PROOF: If A is nonsingular then we can find elementary matrices $E_1, E_2, \ldots, E_p$ such that

$$A = E_1E_2 \cdots E_p.$$

Now by the corollary, $\det A = \det E_1 \det E_2 \cdots \det E_p$. But the determinants of elementary matrices are not zero and hence their product is not zero.

If A is singular, we can find elementary matrices $E_1, E_2, \ldots, E_p$ such that $E_pE_{p-1} \cdots E_2E_1A = T$. The matrix T

(1) is upper triangular;
(2) has zeros and ones on its main diagonal and has at least one zero there;
(3) has zeros above the main diagonal element in any column where the main diagonal element is 1.

Under these circumstances, there will be at least one row of T which is completely zero and hence $\det T = 0$. Now, application of the corollary above yields

$$\det E_p \det E_{p-1} \cdots \det A = \det T = 0.$$

Since none of the numbers $\det E_1, \det E_2, \ldots, \det E_p$ is zero, it follows that $\det A = 0$.

We can now prove:

Theorem: *If* A *and* B *are two* $\mathrm{n} \times \mathrm{n}$ *matrices, then*

$$\det (\mathrm{AB}) = \det \mathrm{A} \det \mathrm{B}.$$

PROOF: Case 1. A is a nonsingular matrix. In this case, we can find elementary matrices $E_1, E_2, \ldots, E_p$, which reduce A to the identity: $E_pE_{p-1} \cdots E_2E_1A = I$. Hence, $A = E_1^{-1}E_2^{-1} \cdots E_p^{-1}$ where these inverses are themselves elementary matrices. By the corollary just proved,

$$\det A = (\det E_1^{-1})(\det E_2^{-1}) \cdots \det (E_p^{-1}).$$

Now

$$\det (AB) = \det (E_1^{-1}E_2^{-1} \cdots E_p^{-1}B),$$

and again by the corollary,

$$\begin{aligned}\det (E_1^{-1}E_2^{-1} \cdots E_p^{-1}B) &= (\det E_1^{-1})(\det E_2^{-1}) \cdots (\det E_p^{-1})(\det B)\\ &= (\det A)(\det B).\end{aligned}$$

Case 2. A is a singular matrix. Then $\det A = 0$. In this case, according to the theorem on page 106, we can find elementary matrices $E_1, E_2, \ldots, E_p$ which reduce A to a matrix T which

(1) is upper triangular;
(2) has zeros and 1's on its main diagonal and has at least one zero there;
(3) has zeros above the main diagonal element in any column where the main diagonal element is 1.

In symbols, $E_pE_{p-1} \cdots E_2E_1A = T$. Under these circumstances, there will be at least one row of T which consists completely of zeros.

Now, $A = E_1^{-1}E_2^{-1} \cdots E_{p-1}^{-1}E_p^{-1}T$ so that $AB = E_1^{-1}E_2^{-1} \cdots E_{p-1}^{-1}E_p^{-1}TB$. Hence, since E_1^{-1}, E_2^{-1}, et cetera, are elementary matrices, applying the corollary on page 190, yields

$$\det AB = (\det E_1^{-1})(\det E_2^{-1}) \cdots (\det E_p^{-1}) \det TB.$$

Since T has at least one row of zeros, it follows that TB will also have at least one row of zeros. From Rule 2 on page 183 with $k = 0$, it follows that $\det TB = 0$. Hence, $\det AB = 0$. But $(\det A)(\det B) = 0$ since $\det A = 0$. Therefore $\det AB = \det AB = (\det A)(\det B)$.

Theorem: *A product AB has an inverse if and only if both factors A and B have inverses.*

PROOF: We have already proved that if both A and B have inverses so does AB (see page 95).

Suppose, conversely, that AB has an inverse. Then $\det (AB) \neq 0$. Since $\det (AB) = (\det A)(\det B)$, it follows that $\det A \neq 0$ and $\det B \neq 0$. Hence both A and B have inverses.

5.5 Additional Algebra of Determinants

An obvious extension of the multiplication rule for determinants is this:

If $A_1, A_2, \ldots, A_n$ are square matrices of the same order, then $\det(A_1A_2 \cdots A_n) = (\det A_1)(\det A_2) \cdots (\det A_n)$.

In other words, *the determinant of the product of any number of matrices equals the product of the individual determinants.* The proof, with three matrices would go as follows:

$$\begin{aligned}\det (A_1A_2A_3) &= \det ((A_1A_2)A_3)\\ &= \det (A_1A_2) \det A_3\\ &= \det A_1 \det A_2 \det A_3.\end{aligned}$$

The proof is similar for any number of factors.

Theorem: *If* A *is a nonsingular* $n \times n$ *matrix whose inverse is* A^{-1} *then*

$$\det (A^{-1}) = \frac{1}{\det A}.$$

That is to say, the determinant of an inverse of a matrix is equal to the reciprocal of the determinant of the matrix.

PROOF: $AA^{-1} = I$. Hence by the last theorem on page 190,

$$(\det A)(\det A^{-1}) = \det I.$$

But the determinant of the unit matrix is 1. Hence

$$\det A \det A^{-1} = 1$$

or

$$\det A^{-1} = \frac{1}{\det A}.$$

Since determinants of products have such a "natural" law associated with them, the reader might be tempted to think that determinants of sums also behave in an "obvious" fashion:

$$|A + B| = |A| + |B|.$$

This is not, in general, the case; simple examples suffice to show that it is not. Take, for example,

$$A = \begin{pmatrix} 1 & 2 \\ 3 & 4 \end{pmatrix} \quad \text{and} \quad B = \begin{pmatrix} 1 & 1 \\ 1 & 2 \end{pmatrix}.$$

Then $A + B = \begin{pmatrix} 2 & 3 \\ 4 & 6 \end{pmatrix}$.

Now $|A| = -2 \qquad |B| = 1 \qquad |A + B| = 0.$

Hence $$|A| + |B| \neq |A + B|.$$

But what can be said about the determinant of the sum of two matrices? To see what happens, work with 3×3 matrices, and consider first

$$D = \begin{vmatrix} a_1 + b_1 & c_1 & d_1 \\ a_2 + b_2 & c_2 & d_2 \\ a_3 + b_3 & c_3 & d_3 \end{vmatrix}.$$

Expand this by the elements of the first row:

$$D = (a_1 + b_1)\begin{vmatrix} c_2 & d_2 \\ c_3 & d_3 \end{vmatrix} - (a_2 + b_2)\begin{vmatrix} c_1 & d_1 \\ c_3 & d_3 \end{vmatrix} + (a_3 + b_3)\begin{vmatrix} c_1 & d_1 \\ c_2 & d_2 \end{vmatrix}.$$

It should be clear, by examining this last expression, that

$$D = \begin{vmatrix} a_1 & c_1 & d_1 \\ a_2 & c_2 & d_2 \\ a_3 & c_3 & d_3 \end{vmatrix} + \begin{vmatrix} b_1 & c_1 & d_1 \\ b_2 & c_2 & d_2 \\ b_3 & c_3 & d_3 \end{vmatrix}.$$

In other words, the sums in the first column distribute themselves into two determinants. This is true for any row, or any column. If we had

$$D = \begin{vmatrix} a_1 + b_1 & c_1 + d_1 & e_1 \\ a_2 + b_2 & c_2 + d_2 & e_2 \\ a_3 + b_3 & c_3 + d_3 & e_3 \end{vmatrix},$$

then

$$D = \begin{vmatrix} a_1 & c_1 + d_1 & e_1 \\ a_2 & c_2 + d_2 & e_2 \\ a_3 & c_3 + d_3 & e_3 \end{vmatrix} + \begin{vmatrix} b_1 & c_1 + d_1 & e_1 \\ b_2 & c_2 + d_2 & e_2 \\ b_3 & c_3 + d_3 & e_3 \end{vmatrix}$$

$$= \begin{vmatrix} a_1 & c_1 & e_1 \\ a_2 & c_2 & e_2 \\ a_3 & c_3 & e_3 \end{vmatrix} + \begin{vmatrix} a_1 & d_1 & e_1 \\ a_2 & d_2 & e_2 \\ a_3 & d_3 & e_3 \end{vmatrix} + \begin{vmatrix} b_1 & c_1 & e_1 \\ b_2 & c_2 & e_2 \\ b_3 & c_3 & e_3 \end{vmatrix} + \begin{vmatrix} b_1 & d_1 & e_1 \\ b_2 & d_2 & e_2 \\ b_3 & d_3 & e_3 \end{vmatrix}.$$

Thus, D is equal to the sum of four determinants.

Finally, if

$$D = \left| \begin{pmatrix} a_1 & b_1 & c_1 \\ a_2 & b_2 & c_2 \\ a_3 & b_3 & c_3 \end{pmatrix} + \begin{pmatrix} d_1 & e_1 & f_1 \\ d_2 & e_2 & f_2 \\ d_3 & e_3 & f_3 \end{pmatrix} \right|,$$

then it can be expressed as the sum of eight separate 3×3 determinants.

The general case can be handled similarly. It becomes apparent that there is no very simple formula for the determinant of the sum of two matrices.

PROBLEMS

1. Prove that $|A^n| = |A|^n$; n is an integer $\geqq 1$
2. If A is nonsingular, prove that $|A^{-n}| = |A|^{-n}$.
3. Prove that $\det(A^{-1}BA) = \det B$.
4. Prove that $\det(AB^{-1}CA^{-1}BC^{-1}) = 1$.
5. If

$$D = \begin{pmatrix} a_1 & & & & 0 \\ & a_2 & & & \\ & & \cdot & & \\ & & & \cdot & \\ & & & & \cdot \\ 0 & & & & a_n \end{pmatrix}$$

is a diagonal matrix, prove that $|D| = a_1 a_2 \dots a_n$.

6. Prove that if A is an $n \times n$ matrix, $|cA| = c^n|A|$.
7. If

$$A = \begin{pmatrix} a_{11} & a_{12} \\ a_{21} & a_{22} \end{pmatrix} \qquad B = \begin{pmatrix} b_{11} & b_{12} \\ b_{21} & b_{22} \end{pmatrix},$$

express $|A + B|$ as the sum of four determinants.

8. Determine $\begin{vmatrix} 1+1 & 2+1 \\ 1+2 & 2+2 \end{vmatrix}$ in two ways.
9. Is it true that $|A + B|^2 = |(A + B)^2|$?
10. Is it true that $|A + B|^2 = |A^2 + B^2|$?
11. Is it true that $|A + B|^2 = |A^2 + 2AB + B^2|$?

5.6 The Geometry Behind the Multiplication Rule

There is a very nice geometrical interpretation of the multiplication rule for determinants. This interpretation is important not only in linear algebra, but also in the integral calculus.

We begin our investigations by finding a determinant formula for the area of a triangle in terms of the coordinates of its vertices.

Let the triangle ABC have vertices (x_1,y_1), (x_2,y_2), (x_3,y_3). Then, if the vertices are located in the relative positions of Figure 5.2,

$$\text{area } ABC = \text{area } AFEC + \text{area } CEDB - \text{area } AFDB.$$

The area of a trapezoid equals $1/2$ the product of its altitude by the sum of its parallel sides. Hence,

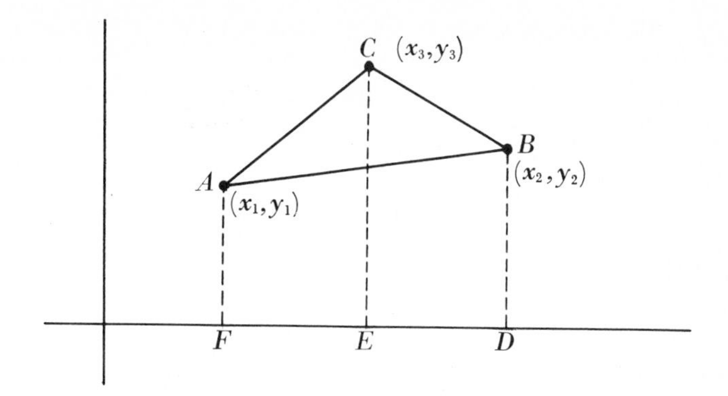

FIGURE 5.2

$$\text{area } AFEC = \tfrac{1}{2}(x_3 - x_1)(y_1 + y_3)$$

$$\text{area } CEDB = \tfrac{1}{2}(x_2 - x_3)(y_2 + y_3)$$

$$\text{area } AFDB = \tfrac{1}{2}(x_2 - x_1)(y_1 + y_2).$$

By combining these quantities,

$$\begin{aligned}\text{area } ABC &= \tfrac{1}{2}[(x_3 - x_1)(y_1 + y_3) + (x_2 - x_3)(y_2 + y_3) \\ &\qquad - (x_2 - x_1)(y_1 + y_2)] \\ &= \tfrac{1}{2}[x_3y_1 + x_3y_3 - x_1y_1 - x_1y_3 + x_2y_2 + x_2y_3 \\ &\qquad - x_3y_2 - x_3y_3 - x_2y_1 - x_2y_2 + x_1y_1 + x_1y_2] \\ &= \tfrac{1}{2}[(x_1y_2 - x_2y_1) - (x_1y_3 - x_3y_1) + (x_2y_3 - x_3y_2)].\end{aligned}$$

This formula can be expressed as a determinant:

$$\text{area } ABC = \tfrac{1}{2}\begin{vmatrix} x_1 & y_1 & 1 \\ x_2 & y_2 & 1 \\ x_3 & y_3 & 1 \end{vmatrix}.$$

This should be verified by expanding the determinant by the elements of the third column.

Notice that the placement of the points ABC in Figure 5.2 is such that when the triangle is traced in the order ABC (or from subscripts 1 to 2 to 3), it is traced in the counterclockwise sense. What happens when the order of the points is not counterclockwise? Take, for example, Figure 5.3.

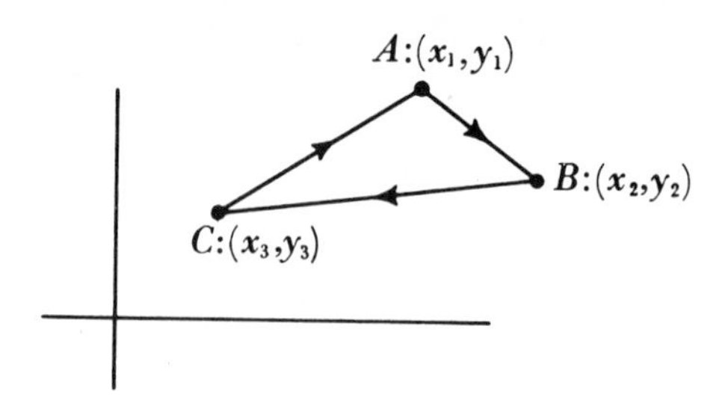

FIGURE 5.3

Since the formula just developed works when the arrangement is counterclockwise,

$$\text{area } ABC = \frac{1}{2}\begin{vmatrix} x_3 & y_3 & 1 \\ x_2 & y_2 & 1 \\ x_1 & y_1 & 1 \end{vmatrix}.$$

That is, we must interchange the role of (x_1,y_1) and (x_3,y_3) in the original formula to get this. This is equivalent to interchanging the first and third rows of the determinant. Similar considerations of the other possible relative positions of A, B, and C lead one to the following theorem.

Theorem: *Let three points* A, B, C *(not on a straight line) have coordinates* (x_1,y_1), (x_2,y_2), (x_3,y_3). *Then the determinant*

$$\frac{1}{2}\begin{vmatrix} x_1 & y_1 & 1 \\ x_2 & y_2 & 1 \\ x_3 & y_3 & 1 \end{vmatrix}$$

equals the area of ABC *if the order* A, B, C *is counterclockwise. The determinant equals minus the area of* ABC *if the order* A, B, C *is clockwise.*

The area of a triangle, taken with the sign + if the triangle is traced counterclockwise and taken with the sign − if the triangle is traced clockwise is called the *signed* or *directed area* of the triangle.

Example 1: In what order are the points $(-2,1)$, $(4,3)$, $(0,0)$?

Since

$$\begin{vmatrix} -2 & 1 & 1 \\ 4 & 3 & 1 \\ 0 & 0 & 1 \end{vmatrix} = -2(3) - 1(4) = -10,$$

the determinant is negative and the order is clockwise. One can conclude this independently by drawing a figure.

Example 2: What is the area of the triangle whose vertices are at (1,1), (2,−1), (−3,0)?

$$\frac{1}{2}\begin{vmatrix} 1 & 1 & 1 \\ 2 & -1 & 1 \\ -3 & 0 & 1 \end{vmatrix} = -\tfrac{3}{2}(1+1) + \tfrac{1}{2}(-1-2) = \tfrac{1}{2}(-6-3) = -\tfrac{9}{2}.$$

The signed area is $-\frac{9}{2}$, so that the area itself is $\frac{9}{2}$.

PROBLEMS

1. Find the area of the triangle whose vertices are (1,1), (2,2), (2,0).
2. Find the area of a triangle whose vertices are (−6,0), (1,1), (3,−4).
3. The vertices of a triangle are (0,4), (−1,1), (2,10). Show that its area is zero and interpret.
4. Find the area of the quadrilateral whose vertices are at (1,4), (1,3), (−2,−2), (2,−2).
5. In what order are the points (7,7), (−1,−1), (4,3)?
6. What inequality must hold between x and y if the points (0,0), (1,1), (x,y) are in counterclockwise order?
7. What inequality must hold between a, b, c, and d if the points (a,b), (0,0), and (c,d) are located in counterclockwise order?
8. The vertices of a triangle are $(0,t)$, $(t,2t)$, $(3t,0)$. Find a formula for the area of the triangle. Is there any value of t for which the area is zero?

A linear homogeneous transformation of the plane is given by

$$\begin{cases} w = ax + by \\ v = cx + dy \end{cases}$$

The matrix of the transformation is $\begin{pmatrix} a & b \\ c & d \end{pmatrix}$ and the determinant of the matrix is $\begin{vmatrix} a & b \\ c & d \end{vmatrix} = ad - bc$. What is the relation between the determinant and the transformation?

Take a triangle T in the x,y plane. Let its vertices have coordinates (x_1,y_1), (x_2,y_2), (x_3,y_3). Suppose that these vertices are in counterclockwise order.

Under the above transformation, the triangle has as its image in the w,v plane a second triangle, U, with vertices (w_1,v_1), (w_2,v_2), (w_3,v_3). These vertices can be obtained from the vertices of T by means of the equations

$$\begin{cases} w_1 = ax_1 + by_1 \\ v_1 = cx_1 + dy_1 \end{cases} \qquad \begin{cases} w_2 = ax_2 + by_2 \\ v_2 = cx_2 + dy_2 \end{cases} \qquad \begin{cases} w_3 = ax_3 + by_3 \\ v_3 = cx_3 + dy_3. \end{cases}$$

The order of these points in the w,v plane may or may not be counterclockwise. (We have drawn them in clockwise order in Figure 5.4.) Now,

$$\text{area of } T = \frac{1}{2}\begin{vmatrix} x_1 & y_1 & 1 \\ x_2 & y_2 & 1 \\ x_3 & y_3 & 1 \end{vmatrix}$$

while

$$\text{signed area of } U = \frac{1}{2}\begin{vmatrix} w_1 & v_1 & 1 \\ w_2 & v_2 & 1 \\ w_3 & v_3 & 1 \end{vmatrix}.$$

But

$$\begin{vmatrix} w_1 & v_1 & 1 \\ w_2 & v_2 & 1 \\ w_3 & v_3 & 1 \end{vmatrix} = \begin{vmatrix} ax_1 + by_1 & cx_1 + dy_1 & 1 \\ ax_2 + by_2 & cx_2 + dy_2 & 1 \\ ax_3 + by_3 & cx_3 + dy_3 & 1 \end{vmatrix}$$

$$= \begin{vmatrix} ax_1 & cx_1 & 1 \\ ax_2 & cx_2 & 1 \\ ax_3 & cx_3 & 1 \end{vmatrix} + \begin{vmatrix} ax_1 & dy_1 & 1 \\ ax_2 & dy_2 & 1 \\ ax_3 & dy_3 & 1 \end{vmatrix}$$

$$+ \begin{vmatrix} by_1 & cx_1 & 1 \\ by_2 & cx_2 & 1 \\ by_3 & cx_3 & 1 \end{vmatrix} + \begin{vmatrix} by_1 & dy_1 & 1 \\ by_2 & dy_2 & 1 \\ by_3 & dy_3 & 1 \end{vmatrix}.$$

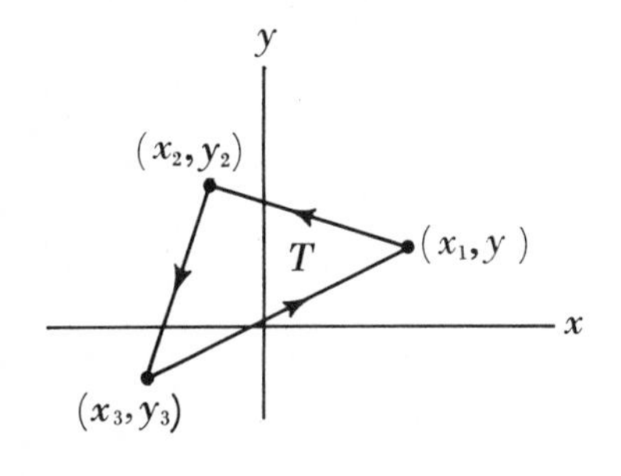

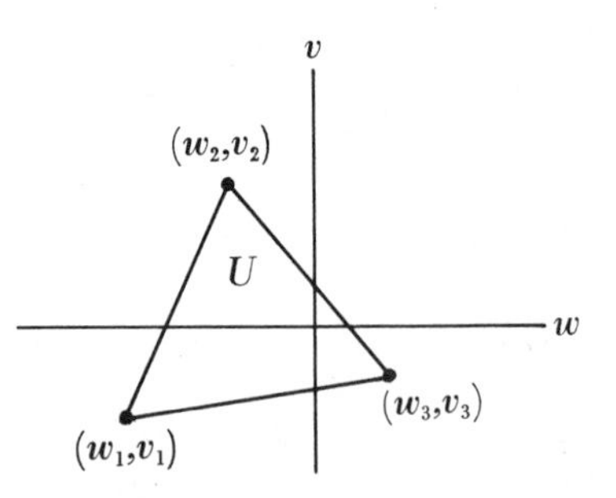

FIGURE 5.4

This equality is a result of the algebraic developments mentioned in Section 5. The first and last determinants equal zero since the first two columns are proportional. The second determinant equals

$$ad\begin{vmatrix} x_1 & y_1 & 1 \\ x_2 & y_2 & 1 \\ x_3 & y_3 & 1 \end{vmatrix},$$

and the third determinant equals

$$bc\begin{vmatrix} y_1 & x_1 & 1 \\ y_2 & x_2 & 1 \\ y_3 & x_3 & 1 \end{vmatrix} \quad \text{or} \quad -bc\begin{vmatrix} x_1 & y_1 & 1 \\ x_2 & y_2 & 1 \\ x_3 & y_3 & 1 \end{vmatrix}.$$

Hence,

$$\text{signed area of } U = \frac{(ad-bc)}{2}\begin{vmatrix} x_1 & y_1 & 1 \\ x_2 & y_2 & 1 \\ x_3 & y_3 & 1 \end{vmatrix}$$

$$= (ad-bc)(\text{area of } T).$$

Thus, finally, as a fundamental equation,

$$\text{signed area of } U = \begin{vmatrix} a & b \\ c & d \end{vmatrix} \cdot \text{area of } T.$$

This preliminary work leads to the following result.

Theorem: *Let*

$$\begin{cases} \mathrm{w} = \mathrm{ax} + \mathrm{by} \\ \mathrm{v} = \mathrm{cx} + \mathrm{dy} \end{cases}$$

or $\begin{pmatrix} \mathrm{w} \\ \mathrm{v} \end{pmatrix} = \mathrm{A}\begin{pmatrix} \mathrm{x} \\ \mathrm{y} \end{pmatrix}$ *where* $\mathrm{A} = \begin{pmatrix} \mathrm{a} & \mathrm{b} \\ \mathrm{c} & \mathrm{d} \end{pmatrix}$,

be a linear transformation of the plane.

(1) *Let* ad − bc = *det* A > *0. If a triangle is traced out in the* x,y *plane in a certain sense, its image will be traced out in the* w,v *plane in the same sense. Furthermore,*

$$\frac{\textit{area of its image}}{\textit{area of a triangle}} = \mathrm{ad} - \mathrm{bc} = \textit{det}\ \mathrm{A}.$$

(2) *Let* ad − bc = *det* A < *0. If a triangle is traced out in the* x,y *plane in a certain sense, its image will be traced out in the* w,v *plane in the opposite sense. In this case,*

$$\frac{\textit{area of its image}}{\textit{area of a triangle}} = -(\mathrm{ad} - \mathrm{bc}) = -\textit{det}\ \mathrm{A}.$$

(3) *Let* ad − bc = *det* A = *0. The transformation is singular and maps a triangle onto a straight line segment or onto a point.*

PROOF: (1). Let a triangle T be traced out in the counterclockwise sense. If $\begin{vmatrix} a & b \\ c & d \end{vmatrix} > 0$, then the signed area of the triangle U is

$\begin{vmatrix} a & b \\ c & d \end{vmatrix} \cdot$area of T. Hence the signed area of U is greater than zero. This means that U, the image of T, is traced out in the counterclockwise sense. If T were traced in the clockwise sense, a similar argument would show that U is also traced out in that sense.

(2) If $\begin{vmatrix} a & b \\ c & d \end{vmatrix} < 0$, then, as in (1), the signed area of U is negative. Hence, U is traced out in the clockwise sense when T is traced out in the counterclockwise sense.

In both (1) and (2), the equation for the ratio of the areas follows from the fundamental equation.

(3) If $\begin{vmatrix} a & b \\ c & d \end{vmatrix} = 0$, then the signed area of U must be zero. The only way this can happen is for the triangle U to degenerate either to a straight line segment or to a point.

We now see that nonsingular linear transformations fall into two broad categories. These are

1. Transformations with matrix A and det $A > 0$. These transformations preserve order in tracing. They are called *sense-preserving transformations*.

2. Transformations with matrix A and det $A < 0$. These reverse order and are called *sense-reversing transformations*.

We can show, furthermore, that although a linear homogeneous transformation may not preserve shape or size, it effects a homogeneous expan-

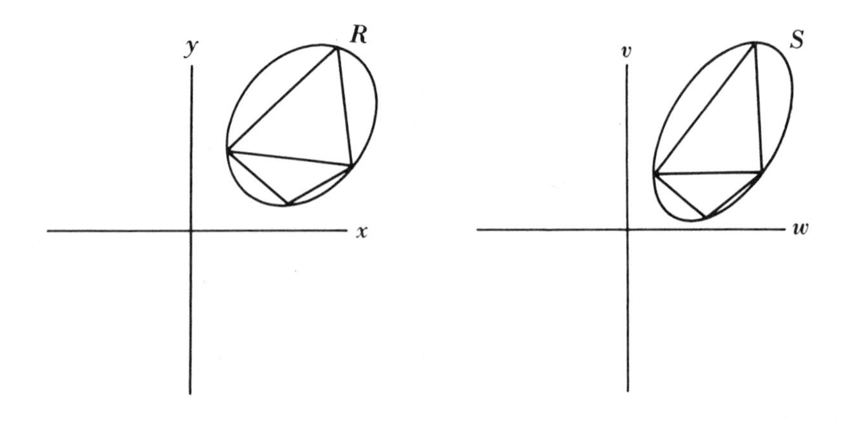

FIGURE 5.5

sion or contraction of area. If R is any region whatsoever in the x,y plane, and S is its image in the w,v plane (Figure 5.5), then

$$\frac{\text{area of the image region}}{\text{area of the region}} = \pm (ad - bc) = \pm \det A.$$

The $+$ sign must be chosen if $\det A > 0$ and the $-$ sign must be chosen if $\det A < 0$.

This can be shown rigorously by dividing the region R into triangles. Each triangle is transformed into an image triangle and the ratio of the area of each image triangle to the original triangle is the constant $\pm (ad - bc)$. This theorem is proved rigorously in integral calculus in the study of double integrals.

The determinant of a transformation, apart from its sign, is the areal expansion ratio of the transformation. With its sign, it is the expansion ratio if the transformation is sense preserving and it is minus the expansion ratio if the transformation is sense reversing.

PROBLEMS

1. Determine whether

$$\begin{cases} w = 2x + 3y \\ v = 3x - 4y \end{cases} \quad \text{and} \quad \begin{cases} w = 6x - 4y \\ v = 3x + 3y \end{cases}$$

are sense preserving or reversing.

2. Determine whether

$$\begin{cases} w = x - 3y \\ v = -x - y \end{cases} \quad \text{and} \quad \begin{cases} w = y \\ v = x \end{cases}$$

are sense preserving or reversing.

3. Prove, using determinants, that reflection in any line is sense reversing.

4. $x' = -x$, $y' = -y$ is a reflection in the origin. Prove, using determinants, that it is sense preserving. Prove it geometrically.

5. The transformation

$$\begin{cases} x' = 3x + 2y \\ y' = 2x + 3y \end{cases}$$

transforms the triangle whose vertices are at (0,0), (1,0), (0,1) into a second triangle. Find, in two ways, the ratio of the areas.

6. The transformation

$$\begin{cases} x' = 5x + 2y \\ y' = 4x + 2y \end{cases}$$

transforms the triangle whose vertices are at (1,1), (−1,2), (0,−2) into a second triangle. Find, in two ways, the ratio of the areas.

7. Give a geometrical interpretation, involving areas, of the identity:

$$\begin{vmatrix} ka & kb \\ kc & kd \end{vmatrix} = k^2 \begin{vmatrix} a & b \\ c & d \end{vmatrix}.$$

8. Find the image of $x^2 + y^2 = 1$ under the transformation

$$\begin{cases} x' = 2x \\ y' = 3y \end{cases}$$

and discuss the areas.

Let us now see what happens when one transformation is followed by another. If the first transformation multiplies areas by two and the second transformation multiplies areas by three, it should be intuitively clear that the result of the two transformations, one after another, is to multiply areas by $2 \times 3 = 6$. It should be clear, moreover, that if the first and second transformations are sense preserving so also is their product. If one is sense preserving and the other is not, the product is not. Finally, if both reverse sense, their product will preserve sense. This information can be put into a small "multiplication table" and can be compared with the multiplication table for signed quantities (Figure 5.6). P stands for sense preserving, R stands for sense reversing.

	P	R
P	P	R
R	R	P

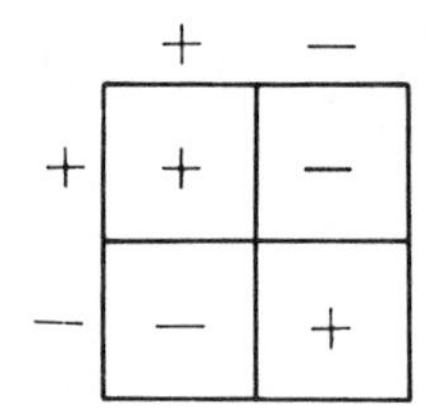

	$+$	$-$
$+$	$+$	$-$
$-$	$-$	$+$

FIGURE 5.6

The multiplication of expansion ratios, with due regard for the preservation or reversing of sense, is the geometry behind the multiplication rule for determinants.

To carry out this argument in a formal way, let A designate the transformation

$$\begin{cases} x' = ax + by \\ y' = cx + dy \end{cases}$$

and B the transformation

$$\begin{cases} x'' = ex' + fy' \\ y'' = gx' + hy'. \end{cases}$$

In the x,y plane, let there be given a triangle T. Its image under A will be called T', and the image of T' under B will be called T''.

Then $\det A = \dfrac{\text{signed area of } T'}{\text{signed area of } T}$, as we have shown.

Moreover, $\det B = \dfrac{\text{signed area of } T''}{\text{signed area of } T'}$.

Hence, multiplying these equations,

$$\det A \det B = \frac{\text{signed area of } T'}{\text{signed area of } T} \cdot \frac{\text{signed area of } T''}{\text{signed area of } T'}$$

$$= \frac{\text{signed area of } T''}{\text{signed area of } T}.$$

But the transformation AB transforms T into T'' and therefore

$\det AB = \dfrac{\text{signed area of } T''}{\text{signed area of } T}$. By comparing equations, we obtain

$$\det AB = \det A \det B.$$

If either A or B is singular (or if both are singular), then at least one of the quantities $\det A$ or $\det B$ is zero. But in this case, AB is also singular, and $\det AB$ is zero. The multiplication law for determinants is valid here also. The zero determinant in the case of singular transformations can be thought of as corresponding to the fact that a triangle is collapsed to a line segment or a point whose "area" is zero.

Third order determinants may be interpreted as a volume of a tetrahedron or as a ratio of two such volumes, and for higher order determinants a similar interpretation is possible.

PROBLEMS

1. Give a geometrical interpretation for the equation

$$\det A^{-1} = \frac{1}{\det A}.$$

2. Prove geometrically as well as by the use of matrices that
   (a) The identity transformation does not change area.
   (b) An expansion along an axis by a factor k multiplies the area by that factor.
   (c) A shear does not change area.
   (d) A reflection does not change area, but changes signed area.

5.7 Determinants and Linear Systems of Equations

We come now (after 5 chapters) to what historically was the starting point of the whole subject of determinants and matrices: the solution of general systems of linear equations. The object is to represent the solution compactly in terms of the coefficients that are involved, and to study the dependence of the solution on the coefficients. The mathematicians of the seventeenth century obtained their results in a direct and unsophisticated way. We shall obtain the same result using matrix multiplication.

The system of equations

$$\begin{cases} a_{11}x + a_{12}y = b_1 \\ a_{21}x + a_{22}y = b_2 \end{cases}$$

is equivalent to

$$\begin{pmatrix} a_{11} & a_{12} \\ a_{21} & a_{22} \end{pmatrix} \begin{pmatrix} x \\ y \end{pmatrix} = \begin{pmatrix} b_1 \\ b_2 \end{pmatrix}.$$

Write this matrix equation as

$$\begin{pmatrix} a_{11} & a_{12} \\ a_{21} & a_{22} \end{pmatrix} \begin{pmatrix} x & 0 \\ y & 1 \end{pmatrix} = \begin{pmatrix} b_1 & a_{12} \\ b_2 & a_{22} \end{pmatrix}.$$

We have added the "dummy" column $\begin{pmatrix} 0 \\ 1 \end{pmatrix}$ and a corresponding column on the right side which makes the equation true. Hence, since the determinant of a product equals the product of the determinants,

$$\begin{vmatrix} a_{11} & a_{12} \\ a_{21} & a_{22} \end{vmatrix} \begin{vmatrix} x & 0 \\ y & 1 \end{vmatrix} = \begin{vmatrix} b_1 & a_{12} \\ b_2 & a_{22} \end{vmatrix}.$$

But $\begin{vmatrix} x & 0 \\ y & 1 \end{vmatrix} = x$, and hence, dividing, we obtain

$$x = \begin{vmatrix} b_1 & a_{12} \\ b_2 & a_{22} \end{vmatrix} \div \begin{vmatrix} a_{11} & a_{12} \\ a_{21} & a_{22} \end{vmatrix}.$$

To obtain y, add a dummy column $\begin{pmatrix} 1 \\ 0 \end{pmatrix}$:

$$\begin{pmatrix} a_{11} & a_{12} \\ a_{21} & a_{22} \end{pmatrix} \begin{pmatrix} 1 & x \\ 0 & y \end{pmatrix} = \begin{pmatrix} a_{11} & b_1 \\ a_{21} & b_2 \end{pmatrix}.$$

Hence, taking determinants,

$$\begin{vmatrix} a_{11} & a_{12} \\ a_{21} & a_{22} \end{vmatrix} \begin{vmatrix} 1 & x \\ 0 & y \end{vmatrix} = \begin{vmatrix} a_{11} & b_1 \\ a_{21} & b_2 \end{vmatrix}.$$

But, $\begin{vmatrix} 1 & x \\ 0 & y \end{vmatrix} = y$, so that

$$y = \begin{vmatrix} a_{11} & b_1 \\ a_{21} & b_2 \end{vmatrix} \div \begin{vmatrix} a_{11} & a_{12} \\ a_{21} & a_{22} \end{vmatrix}.$$

This device will work for $n \times n$ systems of equations. Here is the 3×3 case. Let

$$\begin{pmatrix} a_{11} & a_{12} & a_{13} \\ a_{21} & a_{22} & a_{23} \\ a_{31} & a_{32} & a_{33} \end{pmatrix} \begin{pmatrix} x \\ y \\ z \end{pmatrix} = \begin{pmatrix} b_1 \\ b_2 \\ b_3 \end{pmatrix}.$$

To obtain x, append two dummy columns $\begin{pmatrix} 0 \\ 1 \\ 0 \end{pmatrix}$ and $\begin{pmatrix} 0 \\ 0 \\ 1 \end{pmatrix}$ and complete the matrix equation:

$$\begin{pmatrix} a_{11} & a_{12} & a_{13} \\ a_{21} & a_{22} & a_{23} \\ a_{31} & a_{32} & a_{33} \end{pmatrix} \begin{pmatrix} x & 0 & 0 \\ y & 1 & 0 \\ z & 0 & 1 \end{pmatrix} = \begin{pmatrix} b_1 & a_{12} & a_{13} \\ b_2 & a_{22} & a_{23} \\ b_3 & a_{32} & a_{33} \end{pmatrix}.$$

Hence, by taking determinants and dividing through,

$$x = \begin{vmatrix} b_1 & a_{12} & a_{13} \\ b_2 & a_{22} & a_{23} \\ b_3 & a_{32} & a_{33} \end{vmatrix} \div \begin{vmatrix} a_{11} & a_{12} & a_{13} \\ a_{21} & a_{22} & a_{23} \\ a_{31} & a_{32} & a_{33} \end{vmatrix}.$$

Similarly,

$$y = \begin{vmatrix} a_{11} & b_1 & a_{13} \\ a_{21} & b_2 & a_{23} \\ a_{31} & b_3 & a_{33} \end{vmatrix} \div \begin{vmatrix} a_{11} & a_{12} & a_{13} \\ a_{21} & a_{22} & a_{23} \\ a_{31} & a_{32} & a_{33} \end{vmatrix}$$

$$z = \begin{vmatrix} a_{11} & a_{12} & b_1 \\ a_{21} & a_{22} & b_2 \\ a_{31} & a_{32} & b_3 \end{vmatrix} \div \begin{vmatrix} a_{11} & a_{12} & a_{13} \\ a_{21} & a_{22} & a_{23} \\ a_{31} & a_{32} & a_{33} \end{vmatrix}.$$

These formulas go by the name of *Cramer's Rule.* They are useful theoretically, but when the systems have a large number of unknowns, they are not a good way of obtaining numerical solutions.

Example: Solve, using Cramer's Rule

$$\begin{cases} 3x + 5y = 7 \\ 2x - 6y = 4 \end{cases}$$

$$x = \begin{vmatrix} 7 & 5 \\ 4 & -6 \end{vmatrix} \div \begin{vmatrix} 3 & 5 \\ 2 & -6 \end{vmatrix} = (-42 - 20) \div (-18 - 10) = \tfrac{31}{14}$$

$$y = \begin{vmatrix} 3 & 7 \\ 2 & 4 \end{vmatrix} \div \begin{vmatrix} 3 & 5 \\ 2 & -6 \end{vmatrix} = (12 - 14) \div (-18 - 10) = \tfrac{1}{14}$$

The general Cramer's Rule can be formulated in this way. *If*

$$\mathrm{A} = (\mathrm{a_{ij}}) \text{ is an } \mathrm{n} \times \mathrm{n} \text{ matrix, } \mathrm{X} = \begin{pmatrix} \mathrm{x}_1 \\ \cdot \\ \cdot \\ \cdot \\ \mathrm{x}_\mathrm{n} \end{pmatrix} \quad \text{and} \quad \mathrm{B} = \begin{pmatrix} \mathrm{b}_1 \\ \cdot \\ \cdot \\ \cdot \\ \mathrm{b}_\mathrm{n} \end{pmatrix},$$

the linear system of equation AX = B *is solved by setting* $\mathrm{x_i}$ *equal to the determinant of the matrix found from* A *by replacing its* i*th column by* B *and then dividing this determinant by* det A.

PROBLEMS

Solve using Cramer's Rule

1. $\begin{cases} 3x + 4y = 2 \\ x + y = 0. \end{cases}$

2. $\begin{cases} 9x + 7y = 5 \\ x + 2y = 1. \end{cases}$

3. $\begin{cases} -x + y = 7 \\ x + y = 3. \end{cases}$

4. $\begin{cases} 2x + 3y = 0 \\ x + 4y = 0. \end{cases}$

5. $\begin{cases} 2x + 3y - 5z = 0 \\ x + y + z = 1 \\ x + 3y + z = 3. \end{cases}$

6. $\begin{cases} 2x + 2y - z = 1 \\ x + y - 3z = -7 \\ 3x + y = 4. \end{cases}$

7. $\begin{cases} 4x + y + z = 0 \\ 3x - y + z = -2 \\ x + y + 2z = -1. \end{cases}$

8. $\begin{cases} x + y = 5 \\ x + z = 2 \\ y + z = 5. \end{cases}$

9. $\begin{cases} 2x + 2y + 3z = 3 \\ x + 4y = 0 \\ x + 2y + z = 1. \end{cases}$

10. Solve using Cramer's rule, but do not expand the determinants

$$\begin{cases} x + y + z + w = 3 \\ 2x + y + z - 2w = 4 \\ x - y - z + w = -1 \\ 2x - 3y + 4z + w = 3. \end{cases}$$

11. Prove, using Cramer's rule, that if $AX = 0$ is a system of n equations in n unknowns and if $\det A \neq 0$, then the solution must be $X = 0$.

12. Prove that if a system of linear equations has rational coefficients, then the solution consists of rational numbers.

CHAPTER 6

Vectors and Inner Products

6.1 Column Matrices as Vectors

A column matrix or vector has a geometric interpretation in the plane or in space. We shall limit our presentation to the case of 2×1 matrices and to planes.

Definition: *A geometrical vector is a directed line segment drawn from the origin to a point in the plane.*

Very often a small arrowhead is placed at the end of the line segment to indicate the direction of motion of the pencil as it proceeds from the origin to the point (Figure 6.1).

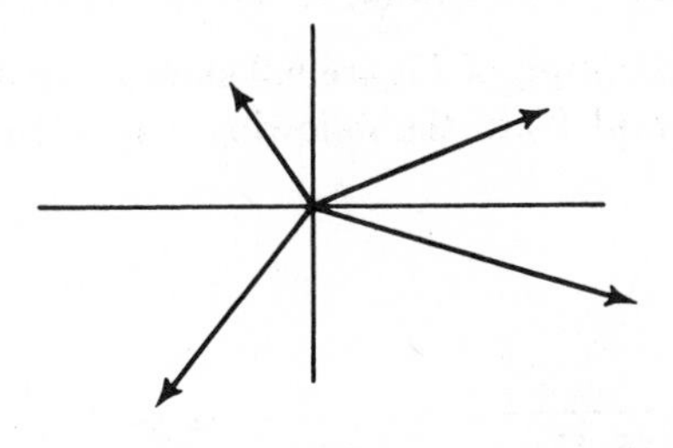

FIGURE 6.1

If a vector terminates at the point whose coordinates are (x, y), this geometrical vector will be the representative of the column matrix (or column vector) $\begin{pmatrix} x \\ y \end{pmatrix}$. A single capital letter, such as V, will be used to designate the geometrical vector as well as to designate the column matrix (Figure 6.2).

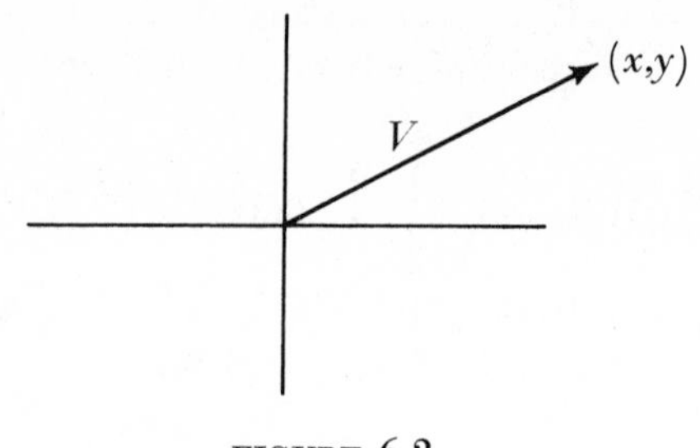

FIGURE 6.2

The zero column vector is $\begin{pmatrix} 0 \\ 0 \end{pmatrix}$ and this will be identified with the origin itself. It can be regarded as a segment of "length" 0.

If we think back to the basic algebraic operations of matrices, we see that two 2×1 matrices can be added or subtracted. Moreover, a 2×1 matrix can be multiplied by a scalar. In each case a 2×1 matrix results. Furthermore, we can form the 1×1 matrix $V_1'V_2$. We shall develop a geometrical interpretation for each of these operations.

ADDITION OF VECTORS: If $V_1 = \begin{pmatrix} x_1 \\ y_1 \end{pmatrix}$ and $V_2 = \begin{pmatrix} x_2 \\ y_2 \end{pmatrix}$, then by the laws of matrix addition, $V_1 + V_2 = \begin{pmatrix} x_1 + x_2 \\ y_1 + y_2 \end{pmatrix}$. Now V_1 has an interpretation as the line segment from (0, 0) to (x_1, y_1) and V_2 has an interpretation as a line segment from (0, 0) to (x_2, y_2). Hence $V_1 + V_2$ has an interpretation as the line segment from (0, 0) to $(x_1 + x_2, y_1 + y_2)$.

A moment's consideration of Figure 6.3 shows that the vector $V_1 + V_2$ is obtained from V_1 and V_2 in the following way. Complete the parallelo-

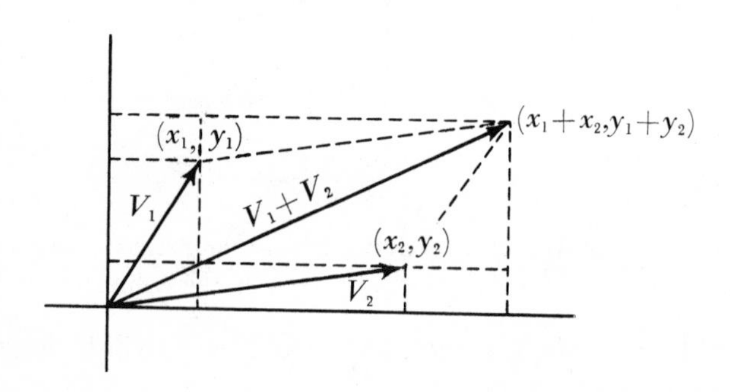

FIGURE 6.3

gram of which V_1 and V_2 are contiguous edges. Then $V_1 + V_2$ is the diagonal of this parallelogram that is located between V_1 and V_2. This is the *parallelogram law for vector addition.*

If V is the column vector $\begin{pmatrix} x \\ y \end{pmatrix}$, the column vector $-V$ is $\begin{pmatrix} -x \\ -y \end{pmatrix}$. The geometrical interpretation of this is that of a line segment extending from the origin to the point $(-x, -y)$ (Figure 6.4).

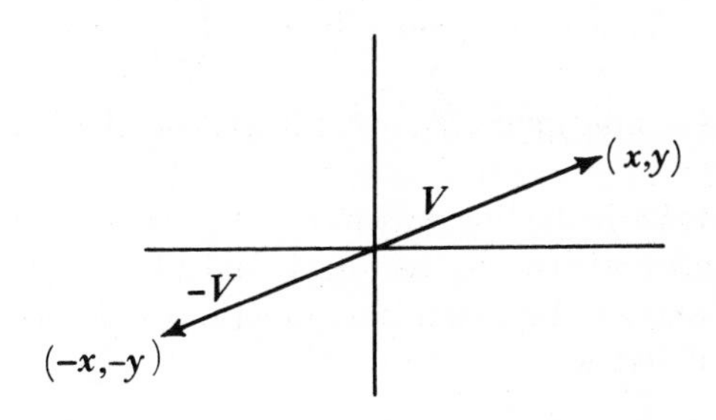

FIGURE 6.4

The transformation from V to $-V$ is known as a *reflection of the plane in the origin.*

SUBTRACTION OF VECTORS: If $V_1 = \begin{pmatrix} x_1 \\ y_1 \end{pmatrix}$ and $V_2 = \begin{pmatrix} x_2 \\ y_2 \end{pmatrix}$ then $V_1 - V_2 = \begin{pmatrix} x_1 - x_2 \\ y_1 - y_2 \end{pmatrix}$. Form the vector $-V_2$. Add V_1 to $-V_2$ by means of the parallelogram law. The geometrical construction for subtraction is given in Figure 6.5.

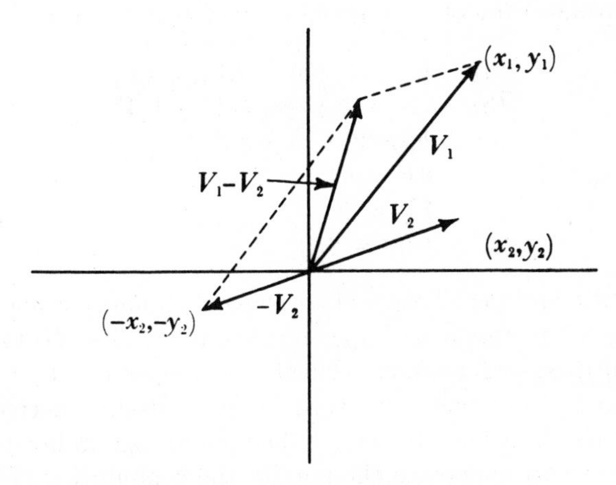

FIGURE 6.5

Vector addition and subtraction obey the following laws.

(a) $V_1 + V_2 = V_2 + V_1$
(b) $V_1 + (V_2 + V_3) = (V_1 + V_2) + V_3$
(c) $V + 0 = V$
(d) $V + (-V) = 0.$

These laws are special cases of the corresponding laws for matrices.

SCALAR MULTIPLICATION OF VECTORS: If $V = \begin{pmatrix} x \\ y \end{pmatrix}$ and k is a scalar then $kV = \begin{pmatrix} kx \\ ky \end{pmatrix}$. Scalar multiplication accordingly has the following geometrical interpretation: kV is the line drawn from the origin to the point (kx, ky). If the constant k is positive, the vectors V and kV overlap one another. If k is negative, V and kV have opposite directions (Figures 6.6 and 6.7). If k is 0, kV is the 0 vector.

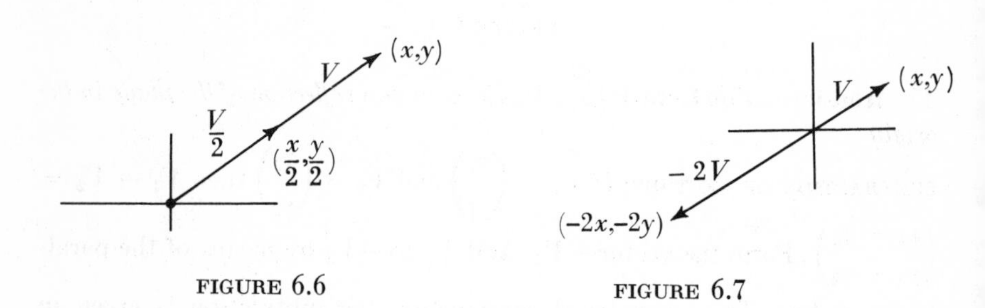

FIGURE 6.6

FIGURE 6.7

Scalar multiplication of vectors obeys the following laws:

(a) $k(V_1 + V_2) = kV_1 + kV_2$
(b) $(k_1 + k_2)V = k_1V + k_2V$
(c) $k_1(k_2V) = k_1k_2(V)$
(d) $0V = 0$
(e) $1V = V$
(f) $(k)0 = 0.$

These laws also are special cases of corresponding laws for matrices.

The notion of vectors is an important one in physics. Vectors represent certain quantities, such as force, velocity, or acceleration that have both a magnitude and a direction. The word "vector" itself is derived from the Latin *vehere* which means "to carry." The parallelogram law for the addition of vectors corresponds to the law for the composition of forces or of velocities. It is convenient for applications in physics and in some parts of geometry to allow a slightly more general geometric interpretation of the notion of vector.

Definition: *A free vector is a directed line segment in the plane. Two free vectors are considered equal if they have the same length and the same direction* (Figure 6.8).

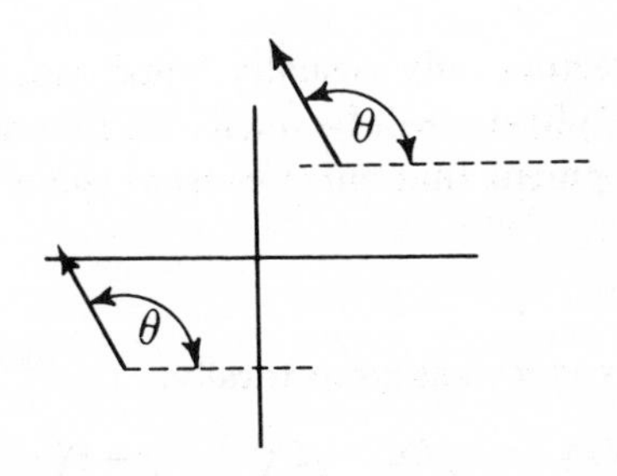

FIGURE 6.8 *Equality of Two Free Vectors*

If one employs free vectors, a simple geometrical construction of continued vector sums can be obtained. This is illustrated in Figure 6.9.

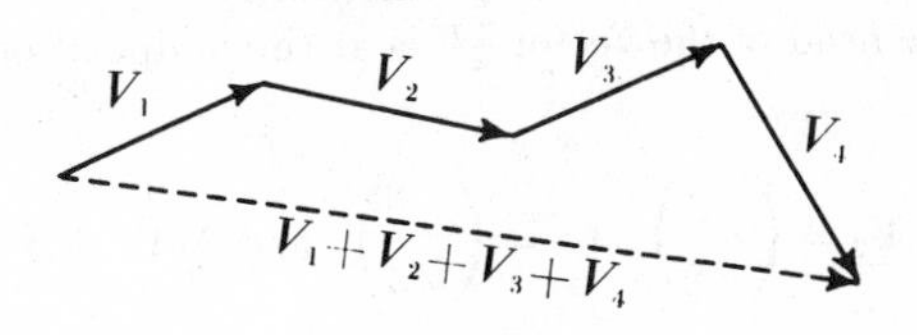

FIGURE 6.9

To add a sequence of vectors, place the tail of each vector at the head of the previous vector. The vector drawn from the tail of the first to the head of the last is the vector sum.

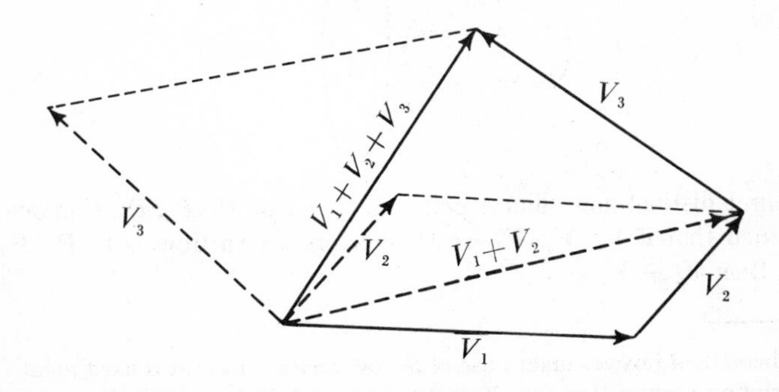

FIGURE 6.10

This "elephant parade" diagram (vectors hanging on to the tail of the one in front) requires justification. Figure 6.10 provides the justification in the case of three vectors V_1, V_2, V_3. In this figure, the broken lines are employed to construct, successively, and by means of the parallelogram law, the sums $V_1 + V_2$ and $(V_1 + V_2) + V_3 = V_1 + V_2 + V_3$. If the broken lines are disregarded, the result can be obtained directly from the solid lines.

We mention free vectors only casually,* and since no applications of vectors to problems of physics will be made, we revert to our original idea of a vector as a line segment that emerges from the origin.

PROBLEMS

1. Find the following vector sums geometrically:

$$\begin{pmatrix}1\\1\end{pmatrix} + \begin{pmatrix}1\\1\end{pmatrix}, \quad \begin{pmatrix}0\\0\end{pmatrix} + \begin{pmatrix}3\\2\end{pmatrix}, \quad \begin{pmatrix}-1\\0\end{pmatrix} + \begin{pmatrix}2\\7\end{pmatrix}.$$

2. Find the following geometrically $\quad 4\begin{pmatrix}-1\\1\end{pmatrix}, \quad -2\begin{pmatrix}-1\\2\end{pmatrix}, \quad 6\begin{pmatrix}-1\\\frac{1}{2}\end{pmatrix}.$

3. $V_1 + V_2 + V_3 = 0$. Illustrate this geometrically.

4. Verify that the head of the vector $\frac{1}{2}V$ is at the midpoint of the line segment that represents V.

5. If $V_1 = \begin{pmatrix}1\\1\end{pmatrix}$, $V_2 = \begin{pmatrix}-1\\2\end{pmatrix}$, $V_3 = \begin{pmatrix}0\\-4\end{pmatrix}$, find $\frac{1}{3}(V_1 + V_2 + V_3)$.

6. If $V_1 = \begin{pmatrix}x_1\\y_1\end{pmatrix}$, $V_2 = \begin{pmatrix}x_2\\y_2\end{pmatrix}$, $\ldots$, $V_n = \begin{pmatrix}x_n\\y_n\end{pmatrix}$, determine $a_1V_1 + a_2V_2 + \ldots + a_nV_n$. Show that this sum equals

$$\begin{pmatrix}x_1 & x_2 & \ldots & x_n\\ y_1 & y_2 & \ldots & y_n\end{pmatrix}\begin{pmatrix}a_1\\a_2\\\cdot\\\cdot\\\cdot\\a_n\end{pmatrix}.$$

7. Given three distinct noncollinear points in the plane P_1, P_2, P_3. Can one find an origin O such that if V_1, V_2, V_3 are the vectors drawn from O to P_1, P_2, P_3 respectively, then $V_1 + V_2 = V_3$?

---

*Indeed, mathematical physics makes use of bound vectors (tails at a fixed point), free vectors, and sliding vectors that are allowed to move parallel to themselves with their tails along a line.

6.2 Components, Magnitude, and Direction

The volumn vector $V = \begin{pmatrix} x \\ y \end{pmatrix}$ can be represented as a directed line segment extending from the origin to the point (x, y) (Figure 6.11).

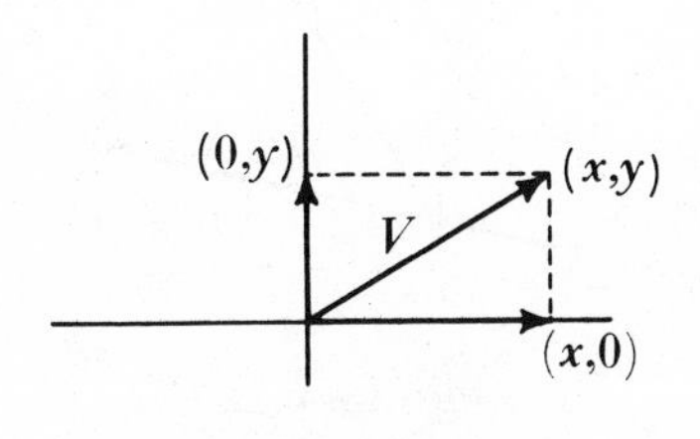

FIGURE 6.11

This vector is the sum of the two vectors $\begin{pmatrix} x \\ 0 \end{pmatrix}$ and $\begin{pmatrix} 0 \\ y \end{pmatrix}$: $\begin{pmatrix} x \\ y \end{pmatrix} = \begin{pmatrix} x \\ 0 \end{pmatrix} + \begin{pmatrix} 0 \\ y \end{pmatrix}$.
The first vector, $\begin{pmatrix} x \\ 0 \end{pmatrix}$, runs along the x axis, whereas the second $\begin{pmatrix} 0 \\ y \end{pmatrix}$ runs along the y axis. The numbers x and y are called the x and y *components* of the vector V.

The length of the geometric vector V can be found from the Theorem of Pythagoras in terms of the x and y components:

$$\text{length of } V = \sqrt{x^2 + y^2}.$$

Notation: The length or *magnitude* of a vector V is frequently indicated by writing $\| V \|$.

If $V = \begin{pmatrix} x \\ y \end{pmatrix}$, then we have the formula

$$\| V \| = \sqrt{x^2 + y^2}.$$

The symbol V should be distinguished from that of $\| V \|$. V is a directed line segment (or a 2×1 matrix). $\| V \|$ is a number that indicates the length of this segment.

Example 1: If $V = \begin{pmatrix} 3 \\ -2 \end{pmatrix}$, then $\| V \| = \sqrt{3^2 + (-2)^2} = \sqrt{13}.$

Example 2: If $V = \begin{pmatrix} 0 \\ 0 \end{pmatrix}$, then $\| V \| = 0.$

Example 3: If V_1 and V_2 are two sides of a triangle, then the length of the third side is $\|V_1 - V_2\|$. This fact should be clear from Figure 6.12.

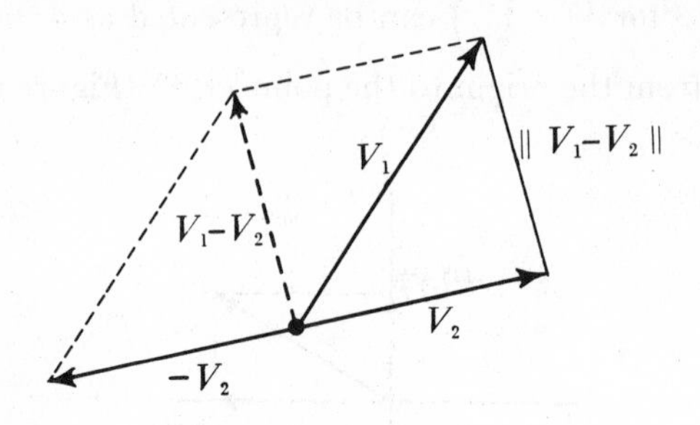

FIGURE 6.12

The expression $\| V_1 - V_2 \|$ is the vector form of the formula for the *distance between two points*. If $V_1 = \begin{pmatrix} x_1 \\ y_1 \end{pmatrix}$, $V_2 = \begin{pmatrix} x_2 \\ y_2 \end{pmatrix}$ then $V_1 - V_2 = \begin{pmatrix} x_1 - x_2 \\ y_1 - y_2 \end{pmatrix}$ and hence $\| V_1 - V_2 \| = ((x_1 - x_2)^2 + (y_1 - y_2)^2)^{\frac{1}{2}}$.

Theorem:
$$\begin{aligned} \| \mathrm{kV} \| &= \mathrm{k} \, \| \mathrm{V} \| \; \textit{if} \; \mathrm{k} \geq 0 \\ &= -\mathrm{k} \, \| \mathrm{V} \| \; \textit{if} \; \mathrm{k} \leq 0. \end{aligned}$$

These two equations are summed up by writing $\| \mathrm{kV} \| = |\mathrm{k}| \, \| \mathrm{V} \|$. *The symbol* $|\mathrm{k}|$ *designates the absolute value of the number* k.

PROOF: If $V = \begin{pmatrix} x \\ y \end{pmatrix}$, $kV = \begin{pmatrix} kx \\ ky \end{pmatrix}$. Now, $\| V \| = \sqrt{x^2 + y^2}$, and

$$\begin{aligned} \| kV \| = \sqrt{(kx)^2 + (ky)^2} &= \sqrt{k^2(x^2 + y^2)} \\ &= k\sqrt{x^2 + y^2} \quad \text{if } k \geq 0. \\ &= -k\sqrt{x^2 + y^2} \quad \text{if } k \leq 0. \end{aligned}$$

Hence,

$$\begin{aligned} k \, \| V \| &= \| kV \| \text{ if } k \geq 0 \\ -k \, \| V \| &= \| kV \| \text{ if } k \leq 0. \end{aligned}$$

This theorem says that when a vector is multiplied by a scalar, the length of the vector is multiplied by the absolute value of the scalar.

Definition: *The direction of a vector* V *is the angle* θ *that* V *makes with the positive* x *axis. The angle is measured in the counterclockwise sense, as indicated in Figure 6.13.*

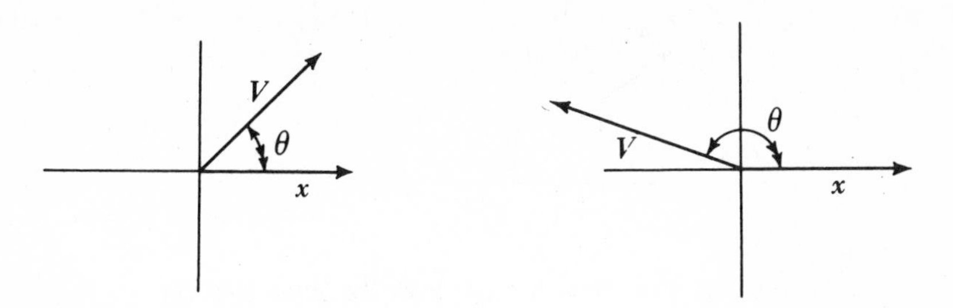

FIGURE 6.13

The notion of direction is undefined for the zero vector $\begin{pmatrix}0\\0\end{pmatrix}$.

The use of the trigonometric functions leads one to the following formulas. If $V = \begin{pmatrix}x\\y\end{pmatrix}$ then

$$\begin{aligned} x &= \| V \| \cos \theta \\ y &= \| V \| \sin \theta \\ \tan \theta &= y/x. \end{aligned}$$

These formulas should be apparent from Figure 6.14.

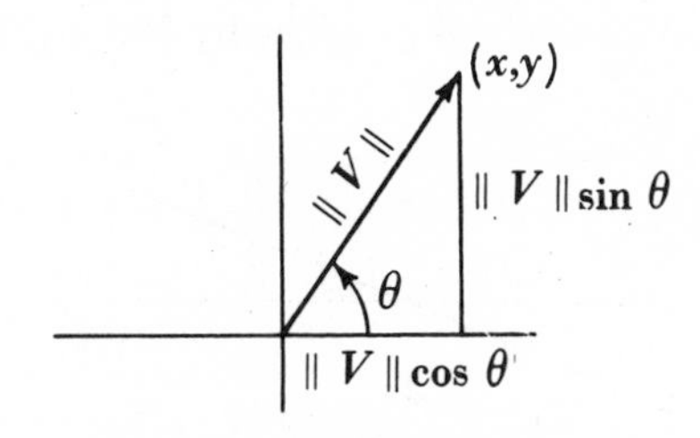

FIGURE 6.14

Example 1: Find the direction of the vector $\begin{pmatrix}2\\1\end{pmatrix}$. We have $\tan \theta = 1/2$. Hence $\theta = 26° \; 34'$ or $206° \; 34'$. But the tip of this vector lies in the first quadrant, so we select $\theta = 26° \; 34'$ as the proper direction.

Example 2: Find the direction of the vector $\begin{pmatrix}5\\-2\end{pmatrix}$. The tip of this vector is in the fourth quadrant. Now, $\tan \theta = -2/5$. Hence $\theta = 338° \; 12'$.

Two vectors $V_1 = \begin{pmatrix}x_1\\y_1\end{pmatrix}$ and $V_2 = \begin{pmatrix}x_2\\y_2\end{pmatrix}$ have the *same direction* if their corresponding θ's are equal.

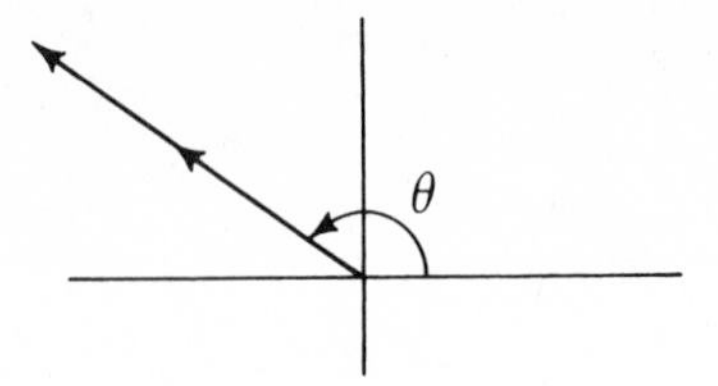

FIGURE 6.15 *Two Vectors with the Same Direction*

It can be seen from Figure 6.15 that if V_1 and V_2 have the same direction, then $V_1 = kV_2$ for some scalar $k > 0$.

Example: If $V = \begin{pmatrix} x \\ y \end{pmatrix}$, the vector

$$V_1 = \begin{pmatrix} x/\sqrt{x^2 + y^2} \\ y/\sqrt{x^2 + y^2} \end{pmatrix}$$

has the same direction as V, but has unit length. Prove this.

Two vectors V_1 and V_2 are called *parallel* if they lie along the same line (that is, if their directions are equal or differ by 180°) (Figure 6.16).

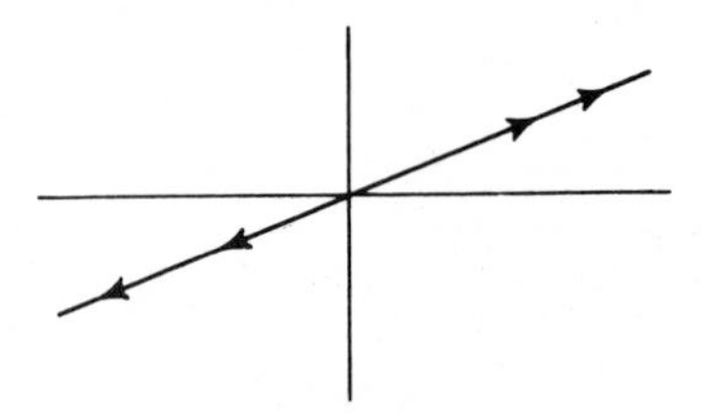

FIGURE 6.16 *Parallel Vectors*

If $V_1 = \begin{pmatrix} x_1 \\ y_1 \end{pmatrix}$ and $V_2 = \begin{pmatrix} x_2 \\ y_2 \end{pmatrix}$ are parallel then we can find a constant k (which need not be positive) such that $V_1 = kV_2$.

This means that $x_1 = kx_2$ and $y_1 = ky_2$. Hence $x_1y_2 = kx_2y_2$ and $x_2y_1 = ky_2x_2$. Therefore if V_1 and V_2 are parallel, $x_1y_2 = x_2y_1$.

The zero vector is considered to be parallel to every vector.

Two vectors V_1 and V_2 are *perpendicular* if their directions are θ and $\theta + 90°$ or θ and $\theta + 270°$ (Figure 6.17).

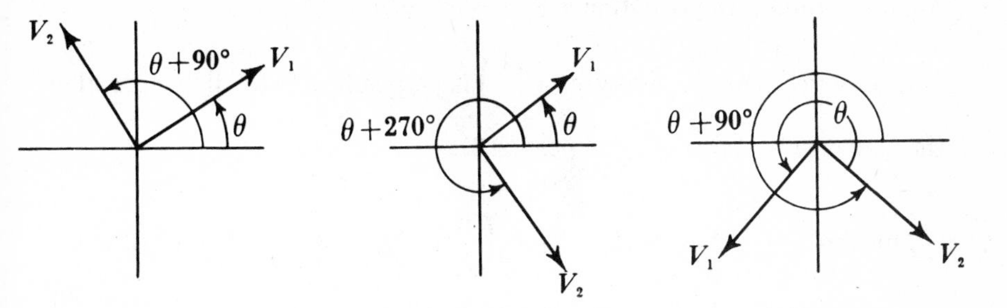

FIGURE 6.17 *Perpendicular Vectors*

Suppose that $V_1 = \begin{pmatrix} x_1 \\ y_1 \end{pmatrix}$ and $V_2 = \begin{pmatrix} x_2 \\ y_2 \end{pmatrix}$ are perpendicular. Let V_1 have direction θ. Then V_2 has direction $\theta + 90°$ or $\theta + 270°$. Now,

$$\begin{aligned} x_1 &= \| V_1 \| \cos \theta \\ y_1 &= \| V_1 \| \sin \theta. \end{aligned}$$

Moreover,

$$\begin{aligned} x_2 &= \| V_2 \| \cos (\theta + 90°) & & & x_2 &= \| V_2 \| \cos (\theta + 270°) \\ & & \text{or,} & & & \\ y_2 &= \| V_2 \| \sin (\theta + 90°) & & & y_2 &= \| V_2 \| \sin (\theta + 270°). \end{aligned}$$

Now,

$$\begin{aligned} \cos (\theta + 90°) &= \cos \theta \cos 90° - \sin \theta \sin 90° = -\sin \theta \\ \sin (\theta + 90°) &= \sin \theta \cos 90° + \cos \theta \sin 90° = \cos \theta \end{aligned}$$

Hence,

$$\begin{aligned} x_2 &= - \| V_2 \| \sin \theta \\ y_2 &= \| V_2 \| \cos \theta. \end{aligned}$$

Therefore, in the first case,

$$\begin{aligned} x_1 x_2 + y_1 y_2 = &- \| V_1 \| \, \| V_2 \| \cos \theta \sin \theta \\ &+ \| V_1 \| \, \| V_2 \| \cos \theta \sin \theta = 0. \end{aligned}$$

Also,

$$\begin{aligned} \cos (\theta + 270°) &= \sin \theta \\ \sin (\theta + 270°) &= -\cos \theta \end{aligned}$$

so that in the second case,

$$\begin{aligned} x_2 &= \| V_2 \| \sin \theta \\ y_2 &= - \| V_2 \| \cos \theta. \end{aligned}$$

Again we obtain the equation $x_1x_2 + y_1y_2 = 0$.

If we agree that the zero vector $\begin{pmatrix}0\\0\end{pmatrix}$ is perpendicular to all vectors, then the converse is also true. (See page 223).

Theorem: *Given two vectors* $V_1 = \begin{pmatrix}x_1\\y_1\end{pmatrix}$, $V_2 = \begin{pmatrix}x_2\\y_2\end{pmatrix}$. *If* V_1 *is perpendicular to* V_2 *then* $x_1x_2 + y_1y_2 = 0$. *Conversely, if* $x_1x_2 + y_1y_2 = 0$, *the vectors are perpendicular.*

Perpendicular vectors are often called *orthogonal vectors.*

PROBLEMS

1. Find the length of $\begin{pmatrix}1\\3\end{pmatrix}, \begin{pmatrix}2\\-4\end{pmatrix}, \begin{pmatrix}0\\-1\end{pmatrix}, \begin{pmatrix}1\\1\end{pmatrix}, \begin{pmatrix}-2\\-3\end{pmatrix}$.

2. Find the direction of the vectors in Problem 1.

3. Find the length of $\begin{pmatrix}1\\3\end{pmatrix} + \begin{pmatrix}2\\-4\end{pmatrix}, \begin{pmatrix}0\\-1\end{pmatrix} + \begin{pmatrix}1\\1\end{pmatrix}, \begin{pmatrix}2\\-4\end{pmatrix} + \begin{pmatrix}-2\\-3\end{pmatrix}$.

4. Find the length of $2\begin{pmatrix}1\\3\end{pmatrix}, -1\begin{pmatrix}-1\\-2\end{pmatrix}, \begin{pmatrix}1\\6\end{pmatrix} + 2\begin{pmatrix}-1\\-1\end{pmatrix}, k\begin{pmatrix}2\\1\end{pmatrix}$.

5. Find the length of $t\begin{pmatrix}1\\1\end{pmatrix} + (1 - t)\begin{pmatrix}1\\-1\end{pmatrix}$.

6. Show that the pairs of vectors $\begin{pmatrix}1\\6\end{pmatrix}, \begin{pmatrix}2\\12\end{pmatrix}; \begin{pmatrix}-1\\-1\end{pmatrix}, \begin{pmatrix}-\frac{1}{2}\\-\frac{1}{2}\end{pmatrix}; \begin{pmatrix}0\\1\end{pmatrix}, \begin{pmatrix}0\\10\end{pmatrix}$ have the same direction.

7. Show that the pairs of vectors $\begin{pmatrix}1\\6\end{pmatrix}, \begin{pmatrix}-2\\-12\end{pmatrix}; \begin{pmatrix}1\\5\end{pmatrix}, \begin{pmatrix}k\\5k\end{pmatrix}$ are parallel.

8. Show that the pairs of vectors $\begin{pmatrix}2\\1\end{pmatrix}, \begin{pmatrix}-1\\2\end{pmatrix}; \begin{pmatrix}6\\3\end{pmatrix}, \begin{pmatrix}-1\\2\end{pmatrix}; \begin{pmatrix}x\\y\end{pmatrix}, \begin{pmatrix}-y\\x\end{pmatrix}$ are perpendicular.

9. Find the direction of $\begin{pmatrix}1\\1\end{pmatrix}, \begin{pmatrix}2\\1\end{pmatrix}$ and of $\begin{pmatrix}1\\1\end{pmatrix} + \begin{pmatrix}2\\1\end{pmatrix}$.

10. Find the direction of $\begin{pmatrix}-1\\-1\end{pmatrix}$ and of $\begin{pmatrix}-1\\-2\end{pmatrix}$.

11. Suppose that $\| V_1 + V_2 \| = \| V_1 \| + \| V_2 \|$. What can you say about V_1 and V_2?

12. What happens to the example on page 214 when V_1 and V_2 are parallel?

13. Show that the vectors $V_1 = \begin{pmatrix} x_1 \\ y_1 \end{pmatrix}$ and $V_2 = \begin{pmatrix} x_2 \\ y_2 \end{pmatrix}$ are parallel if and only if $\begin{vmatrix} x_1 & x_2 \\ y_1 & y_2 \end{vmatrix} = 0$. Show that they are perpendicular if and only if $\begin{vmatrix} x_1 & -y_1 \\ y_2 & x_2 \end{vmatrix} = 0$.

14. For any V_1 and V_2 show that $\| V_1 - V_2 \| = \| V_2 - V_1 \|$.

6.3 The Inner Product and Angle Geometry

We have discussed vector addition, vector subtraction, and scalar multiplication. But we have yet to consider the matrix product $V_1' V_2$. If $V_1 = \begin{pmatrix} x_1 \\ y_1 \end{pmatrix}$ and $V_2 = \begin{pmatrix} x_2 \\ y_1 \end{pmatrix}$, then $V_1' V_2$ is the 1×1 matrix given by $V_1' V_2 = (x_1 y_1) \begin{pmatrix} x_2 \\ y_2 \end{pmatrix} = (x_1 x_2 + y_1 y_2)$. We shall concentrate on the quantity $x_1 x_2 + y_1 y_2$—considering it as a number and not as an element in a matrix —and shall derive algebraic rules and a geometric interpretation for it.

Definition: *If* $\mathrm{V}_1 = \begin{pmatrix} \mathrm{x}_1 \\ \mathrm{y}_1 \end{pmatrix}$ *and* $\mathrm{V}_2 = \begin{pmatrix} \mathrm{x}_2 \\ \mathrm{y}_2 \end{pmatrix}$ *the quantity* $\mathrm{x}_1\mathrm{x}_2 + \mathrm{y}_1\mathrm{y}_2$ *is called the inner product of the vectors* V_1 *and* V_2 *and is designated by* $\mathrm{V}_1 \bullet \mathrm{V}_2$.

Vector analysis makes use of *three* kinds of products: the scalar product (a vector), the inner product (a number), and the outer product (again a vector). We shall not use the outer product in this book.

The inner product appears with considerable frequency in mathematics. For column vectors V_1, V_2 of higher order, the inner product is defined similarly as the element in the matrix $V_1' V_2$. At this point, the reader should recall that the inner product was originally introduced in this book in order to help formulate the definition of matrix multiplication.

Examples: If $V_1 = \begin{pmatrix} 1 \\ 3 \end{pmatrix}$, $V_2 = \begin{pmatrix} -2 \\ 1 \end{pmatrix}$, then $V_1 \bullet V_2 = (1)(-2) + (3)(1) = 1$.

If $V_1 = \begin{pmatrix} 2 \\ 1 \end{pmatrix}$, $V_2 = \begin{pmatrix} p \\ q \end{pmatrix}$, then $V_1 \bullet V_2 = 2p + q$.

The inner product has the following properties.

Theorem:

(a) $V_1 \cdot V_2 = V_2 \cdot V_1$
(b) $(kV_1) \cdot V_2 = k(V_1 \cdot V_2) = V_1 \cdot (kV_2)$
(c) $V_1 \cdot (V_2 + V_3) = (V_1 \cdot V_2) + (V_1 \cdot V_3)$
(d) $V \cdot V = \| V \|^2$
(e) $V \cdot V \geq 0$
(f) $V \cdot V = 0$ if and only if $V = 0$ (that is, if and only if V is the zero vector $\begin{pmatrix} 0 \\ 0 \end{pmatrix}$.)

PROOF: Let $V_1 = \begin{pmatrix} x_1 \\ y_1 \end{pmatrix}$, $V_2 = \begin{pmatrix} x_2 \\ y_2 \end{pmatrix}$, $V_3 = \begin{pmatrix} x_3 \\ y_3 \end{pmatrix}$, and $V = \begin{pmatrix} x \\ y \end{pmatrix}$.

Then:

(a) $V_1 \cdot V_2 = x_1x_2 + y_1y_2 = V_2 \cdot V_1$.

(b) $(kV_1) \cdot V_2 = \begin{pmatrix} kx_1 \\ ky_1 \end{pmatrix} \cdot \begin{pmatrix} x_2 \\ y_2 \end{pmatrix} = kx_1x_2 + ky_1y_2 =$
$k(x_1x_2 + y_1y_2) = k(V_1 \cdot V_2) = x_1kx_2 + y_1ky_2 = V_1 \cdot (kV_2)$.

(c) $V_1 \cdot (V_2 + V_3) = \begin{pmatrix} x_1 \\ y_1 \end{pmatrix} \cdot \begin{pmatrix} x_2 + x_3 \\ y_2 + y_3 \end{pmatrix} = x_1x_2 + x_1x_3 + y_1y_2 +$
$y_1y_3 = (x_1x_2 + y_1y_2) + (x_1x_3 + y_1y_3) = (V_1 \cdot V_2) + (V_1 \cdot V_3)$.

(d) $\| V \|^2 = x^2 + y^2 = \begin{pmatrix} x \\ y \end{pmatrix} \cdot \begin{pmatrix} x \\ y \end{pmatrix} = V \cdot V$.

(e) Since x^2 and y^2 are both squares, they are ≥ 0. Hence $\| V \|^2 \geq 0$.

(f) If $V = \begin{pmatrix} 0 \\ 0 \end{pmatrix}$ then $V \cdot V = 0$. Conversely, if $V \cdot V = 0$, then $x^2 + y^2 = 0$. But since $x^2 \geq 0$ and $y^2 \geq 0$, this can only happen if $x = 0$ and $y = 0$. Hence $V = 0$.

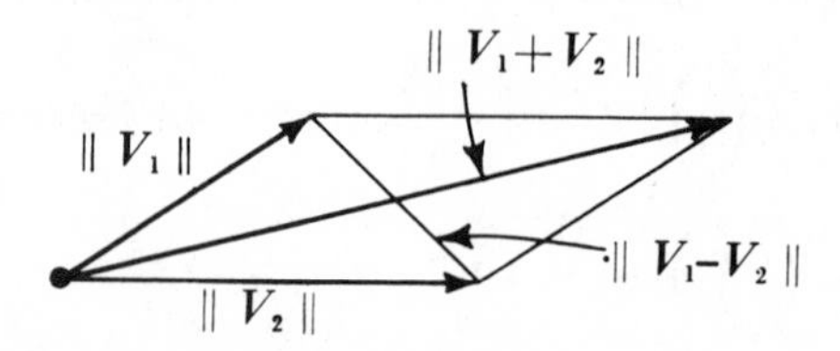

FIGURE 6.18

Theorem: $\| V_1 + V_2 \|^2 + \|V_1 - V_2\|^2 = 2\, \|V_1\|^2 + 2\, \|V_2\|^2.$

This is often called the "Parallelogram Theorem."

PROOF: From part (d) of the previous theorem, $\| V_1 + V_2 \|^2 = (V_1 + V_2) \bullet (V_1 + V_2)$. Now $(V_1 + V_2) \bullet (V_1 + V_2) = V_1 \bullet V_1 + V_1 \bullet V_2 + V_2 \bullet V_1 + V_2 \bullet V_2$. Similarly, $\| V_1 - V_2 \|^2 = (V_1 - V_2) \bullet (V_1 - V_2) = V_1 \bullet V_1 - V_1 \bullet V_2 - V_2 \bullet V_1 + V_2 \bullet V_2$. Hence, adding these equations, we obtain

$$\begin{aligned} \| V_1 + V_2 \|^2 + \| V_1 - V_2 \|^2 &= 2V_1 \bullet V_1 + 2V_2 \bullet V_2 \\ &= 2\, \| V_1 \|^2 + 2\, \| V_2 \|^2. \end{aligned}$$

Refer to Figure 6.18 and show that the parallelogram theorem can be reformulated as the following proposition of plane geometry: *in a parallelogram, the sum of the squares of the sides equals the sum of the squares of the diagonals.*

PROBLEMS

1. If $V_1 = 0$ (that is, the vector $\begin{pmatrix} 0 \\ 0 \end{pmatrix}$) prove that $V_1 \bullet V_2 = 0$.

2. Prove that $V_1 \bullet (aV_2 + bV_3) = aV_1 \bullet V_2 + bV_1 \bullet V_3$.
3. Prove that $(aV_1) \bullet (bV_2) = ab(V_1 \bullet V_2)$.
4. Prove that $V \bullet (V_1 + V_2 + \ldots + V_n) = (V \bullet V_1) + (V \bullet V_2) + \ldots + (V \bullet V_n)$.
5. Does the expression $V_1 \bullet V_2 \bullet V_3$ have meaning? What about the expression $(V_1 \bullet V_2)\, V_3$?
6. Prove that $(V_1 + V_2) \bullet V_3 = V_1 \bullet V_3 + V_2 \bullet V_3$.
7. Prove that $(V_1 + V_2) \bullet (V_3 + V_4) = V_1 \bullet (V_3 + V_4) + V_2 \bullet (V_3 + V_4) = V_1 \bullet V_3 + V_1 \bullet V_4 + V_2 \bullet V_3 + V_2 \bullet V_4$.

8. If $V = \begin{pmatrix} x \\ y \end{pmatrix}$ and $V_1 = \begin{pmatrix} 3 \\ 2 \end{pmatrix}$, what is the set of points (x,y) for which $V \bullet V_1 = 1$? For which $V \bullet V_1 = 0$?

9. Verify the Parallelogram Theorem if $V_1 = \begin{pmatrix} 3 \\ 2 \end{pmatrix}$, $V_2 = \begin{pmatrix} -2 \\ 5 \end{pmatrix}$.

10. Let $V_1 = \begin{pmatrix} x_1 \\ y_1 \end{pmatrix}$, $V_2 = \begin{pmatrix} x_2 \\ y_2 \end{pmatrix}$ and prove the Parallelogram Theorem without using inner products.

What does the inner product of two vectors mean geometrically? We can show that it is closely related to the angle between the vectors (Figure 6.19).

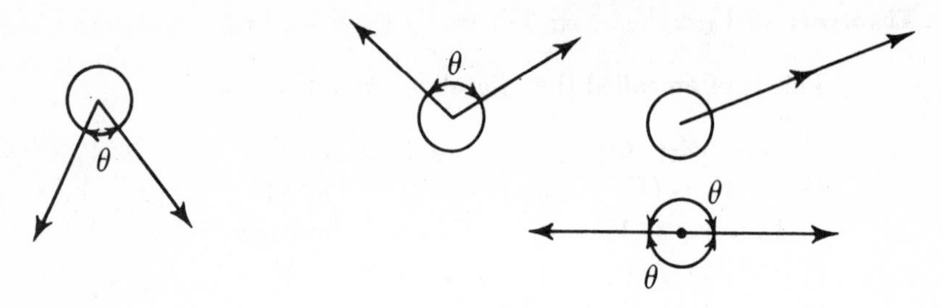

FIGURE 6.19

Between two vectors there is always one angle θ that is less than or equal to $180°$: $0 \leq \theta \leq 180°$. The other angle is between $180°$ and $360°$. We select the smaller of the two angles (that is, the first) and call it *the* angle between the two vectors.

Theorem: *If θ is the angle between two vectors V_1 and V_2, then*

$$V_1 \bullet V_2 = \| V_1 \| \| V_2 \| \cos \theta.$$

Or, if neither V_1 nor V_2 is 0, $\cos \theta = \dfrac{V_1 \bullet V_2}{\| V_1 \| \| V_2 \|}$.

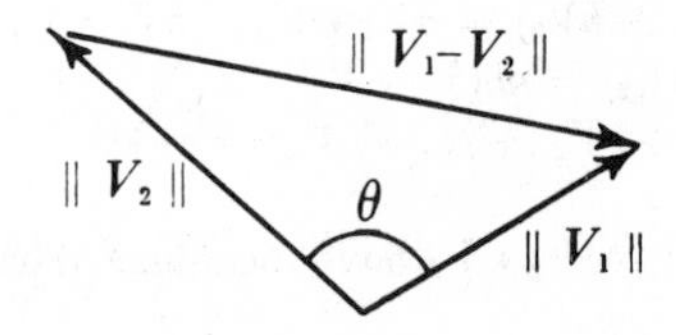

FIGURE 6.20

PROOF: Construct the triangle whose sides are V_1 and V_2. As we have already seen, the sides of this triangle have length $\| V_1 \|$, $\| V_2 \|$, and $\| V_1 - V_2 \|$. Now, by the Law of Cosines, $\| V_1 - V_2 \|^2 = \| V_1 \|^2 + \| V_2 \|^2 - 2 \| V_1 \| \| V_2 \| \cos \theta$. But $\| V_1 \|^2 = V_1 \bullet V_1$, $\| V_2 \|^2 = V_2 \bullet V_2$, and $\| V_1 - V_2 \|^2 = (V_1 - V_2) \bullet (V_1 - V_2) = V_1 \bullet V_1 - V_2 \bullet V_1 - V_1 \bullet V_2 + V_2 \bullet V_2$. Hence, $V_1 \bullet V_1 - 2V_1 \bullet V_2 + V_2 \bullet V_2 = V_1 \bullet V_1 + V_2 \bullet V_2 - 2 \| V_1 \| \| V_2 \| \cos \theta$. This implies that $-2V_1 \bullet V_2 = -2 \| V_1 \| \| V_2 \| \cos \theta$ or $V_1 \bullet V_2 = \| V_1 \| \| V_2 \| \cos \theta$.

The Law of Cosines is still valid when the triangle degenerates to a straight line, that is, when $\theta = 0°$ or $180°$, and so the proof just given holds in these cases also.

The equation $V_1 \bullet V_2 = \| V_1 \| \, \| V_2 \| \cos \theta$ means that apart from the "scale factors" $\| V_1 \|$ and $\| V_2 \|$, the inner product of two vectors is the cosine of the angle between them. If the vectors V_1 and V_2 have unit length (that is, $\| V_1 \| = 1$ and $\| V_2 \| = 1$), we have $V_1 \bullet V_2 = \cos \theta$. In this case, the inner product is exactly equal to the cosine of the angle between the vectors.

This geometric interpretation of the inner product holds in spaces of dimension 3 and higher.

Example: Find the angle between the vectors $V_1 = \begin{pmatrix} 3 \\ 1 \end{pmatrix}$ and $V_2 = \begin{pmatrix} 2 \\ -2 \end{pmatrix}$.

$$\| V_1 \| = \sqrt{3^2 + 1^2} = \sqrt{10}, \; \| V_2 \| = \sqrt{2^2 + (-2)^2} = \sqrt{8}$$
$$V_1 \bullet V_2 = (3)(2) + (1)(-2) = 4.$$

Hence, $\cos \theta = \dfrac{4}{\sqrt{10}\,\sqrt{8}} = \dfrac{4}{\sqrt{80}} = .4472.$ Therefore, $\theta = 63° \, 26'$.

Theorem: *The vectors* V_1 *and* V_2 *are perpendicular if and only if*

$$V_1 \bullet V_2 = 0.$$

PROOF: The vectors are perpendicular if and only if $\theta = 90°$. But $\cos 90° = 0$. Hence, $\dfrac{V_1 \bullet V_2}{\| V_1 \| \, \| V_2 \|} = 0$ and this leads to $V_1 \bullet V_2 = 0$.

If $V_1 = \begin{pmatrix} x_1 \\ y_1 \end{pmatrix}$ and $V_2 = \begin{pmatrix} x_2 \\ y_2 \end{pmatrix}$, then the condition for perpendicularity is that $V_1 \bullet V_2 = x_1 x_2 + y_1 y_2 = 0$. This condition was already noted in a previous paragraph.

Example: If V_1 and V_2 are perpendicular, so are aV_1 and bV_2. We know that $V_1 \bullet V_2 = 0$. Hence, $aV_1 \bullet bV_2 = ab(V_1 \bullet V_2) = ab \cdot 0 = 0$. What is the geometrical interpretation of this?

The laws (a)–(c) on page 220 show that the inner product has many algebraic properties in common with the ordinary product. But one word of caution is necessary. We have just seen the interpretation of the equation $V_1 \bullet V_2 = 0$. This means the vectors V_1 and V_2 are orthogonal. Thus, an inner product can be equal to zero without either factor equalling zero. Inner products and matrix products have this peculiarity in common. In ordinary arithmetic, if a product of two numbers is zero, at least one of the factors must be zero.

PROBLEMS

1. Determine the angle between $\begin{pmatrix}1\\1\end{pmatrix}$ and $\begin{pmatrix}-1\\-3\end{pmatrix}$.

2. Determine the angle between $\begin{pmatrix}0\\4\end{pmatrix}$ and $\begin{pmatrix}4\\-3\end{pmatrix}$.

3. If $V_1 = \begin{pmatrix}1\\3\end{pmatrix}$ and $V_2 = \begin{pmatrix}-1\\2\end{pmatrix}$ find the angle between $V_1 + V_2$ and $V_1 - V_2$.

4. Show that $\begin{pmatrix}2\\4\end{pmatrix}$ and $\begin{pmatrix}8\\-4\end{pmatrix}$ are orthogonal.

5. When is the inner product between two vectors positive? When is it negative?
6. What is the relation between the angle between V_1 and V_2 and the angle between V_1 and kV_2?
7. Find the condition that the angle between V_1 and V_2 be 60°.
8. If V_1 and V_2 are orthogonal prove that $\| V_1 + V_2 \|^2 = \| V_1 \|^2 + \| V_2 \|^2$.
9. Prove that $(V_1 + V_2)\bullet(V_1 - V_2) = \| V_1 \|^2 - \| V_2 \|^2$.
10. What is wrong with this argument? Let $V_1 = \begin{pmatrix}3\\4\end{pmatrix}$, $V_2 = \begin{pmatrix}1\\2\end{pmatrix}$, $V_3 = \begin{pmatrix}5\\-1\end{pmatrix}$. Then, $V_1 \bullet V_2 = 11$, $V_1 \bullet V_3 = 11$. Hence, $V_1 \bullet V_2 = V_1 \bullet V_3$, and hence $V_2 = V_3$.
11. If $\| V_1 \| = \| V_2 \|$, prove that $(V_1 + V_2)\bullet(V_1 - V_2) = 0$. Give a geometrical interpretation of this.
12. $V_1 = \begin{pmatrix}2\\2+t\end{pmatrix}$ and $V_2 = \begin{pmatrix}t+1\\t\end{pmatrix}$ are two vectors that move with time. The time is t. Are there any times at which V_1 and V_2 are orthogonal?
13. Give a geometric interpretation of the identity $V_1\bullet V_2 = V_2\bullet V_1$.

We know that

$$\frac{V_1 \bullet V_2}{\| V_1 \| \, \| V_2 \|} = \cos\theta.$$

Now $\cos\theta$ is a number that is always between -1 and $+1$ inclusive. Hence, we conclude that the quantity on the left side of the above equation is between -1 and $+1$ inclusive: $-1 \le \dfrac{V_1 \bullet V_2}{\| V_1 \| \, \| V_2 \|} \le 1$. By multiplying this inequality by $\| V_1 \| \| V_2 \|$ (which is a positive quantity) we obtain

$$- \| V_1 \| \| V_2 \| \leq V_1 \bullet V_2 \leq \| V_1 \| \| V_2 \|.$$

This is known as the *Schwarz Inequality* and is a mathematical theorem of great importance.

Theorem: *For any two vectors* V_1 *and* V_2 *the following inequality holds*

$$- \| V_1 \| \| V_2 \| \leq V_1 \bullet V_2 \leq \| V_1 \| \| V_2 \|.$$

PROOF: If either V_1 or $V_2 = 0$ (that is, the zero vector) then $V_1 \bullet V_2 = 0$ and $\| V_1 \| \| V_2 \| = 0$. Since $-0 \leq 0 \leq 0$, the inequality is true. If neither V_1 nor V_2 is zero then the argument given above is valid.

Example: $V_1 = \begin{pmatrix} 2 \\ 1 \end{pmatrix}$ and $V_2 = \begin{pmatrix} -1 \\ 3 \end{pmatrix}$

$$V_1 \bullet V_2 = (2)(-1) + (1)(3) = 1$$

$$\| V_1 \| = \sqrt{2^2 + 1^2} = \sqrt{5}$$

$$\| V_2 \| = \sqrt{(-1)^2 + 3^2} = \sqrt{10}.$$

The Schwarz inequality says that $-\sqrt{5}\sqrt{10} \leq 1 \leq \sqrt{5}\sqrt{10}$ which is certainly true.

PROBLEMS

1. Verify the Schwarz inequality directly for the following cases:

$$V_1 = \begin{pmatrix} 2 \\ 3 \end{pmatrix}, \quad V_2 = \begin{pmatrix} 3 \\ -2 \end{pmatrix};$$

$$V_1 = \begin{pmatrix} 1 \\ 1 \end{pmatrix}, \quad V_2 = \begin{pmatrix} 2 \\ 2 \end{pmatrix};$$

$$V_1 = \begin{pmatrix} 1 \\ 6 \end{pmatrix}, \quad V_2 = \begin{pmatrix} 2 \\ 5 \end{pmatrix}.$$

2. Prove that the Schwarz inequality can be phrased in the following way: if a, b, c, d are any four numbers, then

$$-\sqrt{a^2 + b^2}\sqrt{c^2 + d^2} \leq ac + bd \leq \sqrt{a^2 + b^2}\sqrt{c^2 + d^2}.$$

3. What happens in the Schwarz inequality when $V_1 = V_2$? What happens when $V_1 = 2V_2$?

6.4 Inner Products, Lines, and Half-Planes

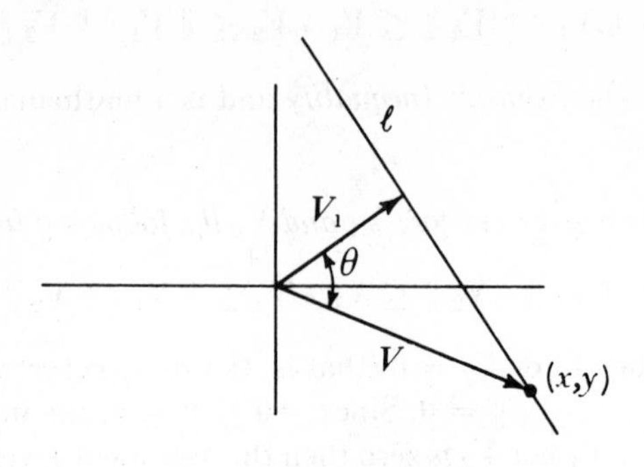

FIGURE 6.21

Let V_1 be a fixed vector, and at its tip draw the straight line ℓ perpendicular to it. We are interested in obtaining a vector form of the equation of ℓ. Draw an arbitrary vector V whose tip lies on ℓ. Then, we know that

$$V \bullet V_1 = \| V \| \| V_1 \| \cos \theta.$$

But, from Figure 6.21, $\cos \theta = \| V_1 \| / \| V \|$. Hence,

$$V \bullet V_1 = \| V \| \| V_1 \| \| V_1 \| / \| V \| = \| V_1 \|^2.$$

Thus, the equation of the straight line is

$$V \bullet V_1 = \| V_1 \|^2.$$

Example: Find the equation of the line in Figure 6.22, using vectors and inner products.

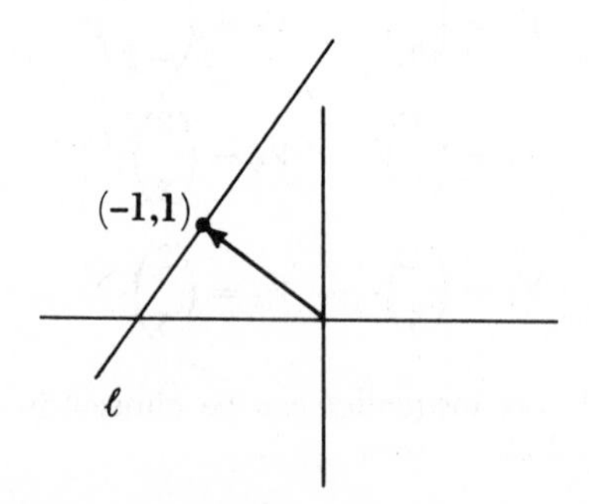

FIGURE 6.22

$$V_1 = \begin{pmatrix} -1 \\ 1 \end{pmatrix}, \| V_1 \|^2 = (-1)^2 + (1)^2 = 2.$$

The vector equation is $V \bullet \begin{pmatrix} -1 \\ 1 \end{pmatrix} = 2$. If we write $V = \begin{pmatrix} x \\ y \end{pmatrix}$, we have

$$\begin{pmatrix} x \\ y \end{pmatrix} \bullet \begin{pmatrix} -1 \\ 1 \end{pmatrix} = 2, \text{ or } -x + y = 2.$$

This is the usual coordinate form of the equation.

The vector equation of the straight line can be rewritten in the form

$$\frac{V \bullet V_1}{\| V_1 \|} = \| V_1 \| .$$

(This assumes that $\| V_1 \| \neq 0$). Now $V_1/\| V_1 \|$ is a vector that has length 1. Moreover, it points in the direction of V_1. $\| V_1 \|$ is the distance of the line ℓ to the origin. If the straight line ℓ passes through the origin, we argue differently.

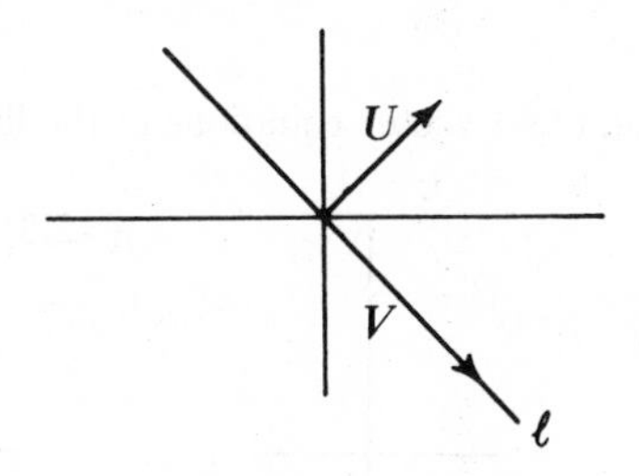

FIGURE 6.23

Let U be a vector of unit length perpendicular to ℓ (Figure 6.23). If the tip of V is on ℓ, $V \perp U$, and we have $V \bullet U = 0$. The result of this discussion is the following theorem.

Theorem: *Any straight line ℓ in the plane has the equation*

$$\mathrm{V} \bullet \mathrm{U} = \mathrm{d}.$$

U *is a vector of unit length perpendicular to ℓ and* d *is the distance from ℓ to the origin.*

This equation is known as the *normal form* of the equation of the straight line.

Example: Let the line ℓ have the equation $2x + 3y = 6$ (Figure 6.24). Form $\sqrt{2^2 + 3^2} = \sqrt{13}$, and write this equation as

$$\frac{2}{\sqrt{13}} x + \frac{3}{\sqrt{13}} y = \frac{6}{\sqrt{13}}.$$

If $V = \begin{pmatrix} x \\ y \end{pmatrix}$, this is equivalent to $V \bullet \begin{pmatrix} 2/\sqrt{13} \\ 3/\sqrt{13} \end{pmatrix} = 6/\sqrt{13}$. The vector

$$U = \begin{pmatrix} 2/\sqrt{13} \\ 3/\sqrt{13} \end{pmatrix}$$

has unit length. Hence, U is perpendicular to ℓ and the distance d from ℓ to the origin is $6/\sqrt{13}$.

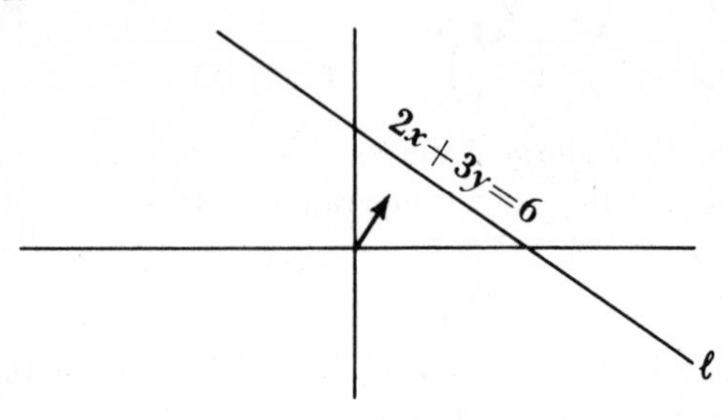

FIGURE 6.24

PROBLEMS

1. Use inner products and find vector equations of the lines in Figure 6.25.

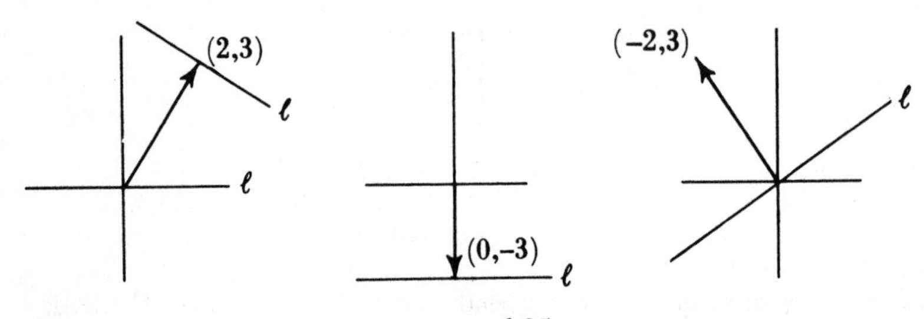

FIGURE 6.25

2. Write the following equations in normal form and interpret: $4x + 5y = 6$; $x - 7y = -1$; $2x = 3$; $x + 3y = 0$; $y = -1$.

3. Find all vectors V that satisfy the simultaneous equations

$$V \bullet \begin{pmatrix} 1 \\ 1 \end{pmatrix} = 2 \quad \text{and} \quad V \bullet \begin{pmatrix} 1 \\ -1 \end{pmatrix} = 3. \text{ Interpret geometrically.}$$

4. Let U_1 and U_2 be two vectors whose length is 1. If a vector V satisfies $V \bullet U_1 = 1$ and $V \bullet U_2 = 1$ simultaneously, prove that $V \bullet (U_1 - U_2) = 0$. Interpret this as a theorem in geometry.

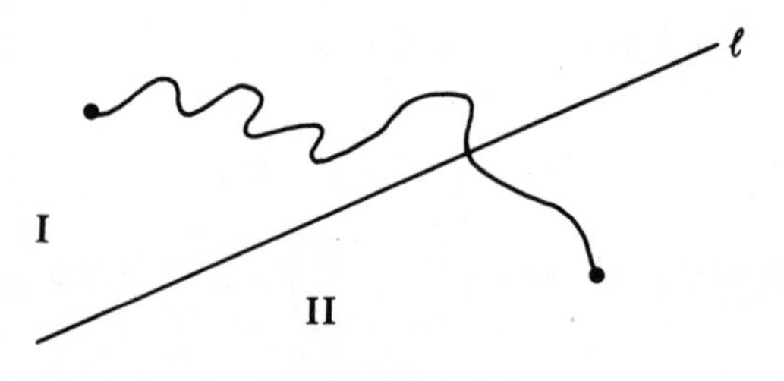

FIGURE 6.26

A straight line ℓ (of infinite extent in both directions) lying in a plane separates the plane into two parts (Figure 6.26). It is not possible to pass continuously from Part I to Part II without crossing the straight line.

Either part is known as a *half plane.*

The vectors whose heads all lie in a half plane satisfy a simple inequality. Let the separating line ℓ be as in Figure 6.27. All the vectors V whose heads lie on ℓ satisfy the equation $V \bullet V_1 = \| V_1 \|^2$. Suppose, now, that V is any vector whose head lies on the "far" side of ℓ from the origin.

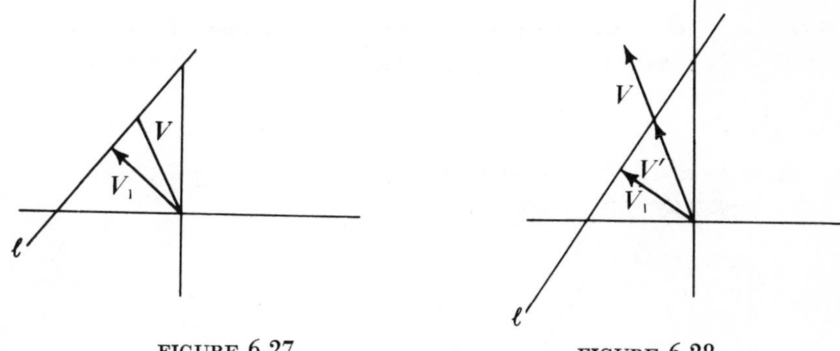

FIGURE 6.27

FIGURE 6.28

Then, it is clear from Figure 6.28 that there is a vector V' lying along V whose head lies on ℓ. We must have $V' = kV$ where $0 < k < 1$. Now $V' \bullet V_1 = \| V_1 \|^2$, so that $kV \bullet V_1 = \| V_1 \|^2$. Hence $V \bullet V_1 = \| V_1 \|^2/k$. But $1/k > 1$, so that $\| V_1 \|^2/k > \| V_1 \|^2$. Therefore $V \bullet V_1 > \| V_1 \|^2$.

If the head of V lies on the near side of ℓ from 0, then a similar argument will show that $V \bullet V_1 < \| V_1 \|^2$. Conversely, if V is a vector satisfying the inequality $V \bullet V_1 > \| V_1 \|^2$, its head must lie on the far side of ℓ from the origin. (For if it lay on ℓ, $V \bullet V_1 = \| V_1 \|^2$, and if it were on the near side, then $V \bullet V_1 < \| V_1 \|^2$).

If the line ℓ passes through the origin, we must argue somewhat differently.

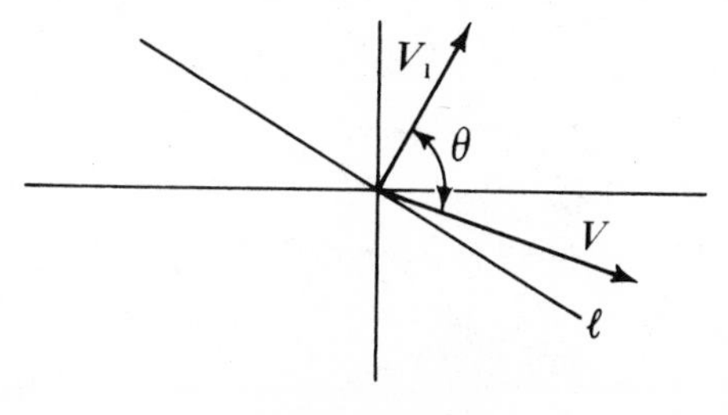

FIGURE 6.29

Let V_1 be a vector perpendicular to ℓ (Figure 6.29). (There are two directions for such vectors, and it makes no difference which is selected.) If, now, V is a vector whose head lies on the same side of ℓ as does V_1, the angle θ between V and V_1 must satisfy $0 \leq \theta < 90°$. Hence $\cos\theta > 0$. Now $V \cdot V_1 = \| V \| \| V_1 \| \cos\theta$. Since $\| V \|$ and $\| V_1 \|$ are positive, $V \cdot V_1 > 0$. If the head of V lay on the opposite side of ℓ from V_1 then θ must satisfy $90° < \theta \leq 180°$ and therefore $\cos\theta < 0$. This would mean that $V \cdot V_1 < 0$.

This discussion can be summarized by the following theorem.

Theorem: *Let* V_1 *be a fixed vector and* c *a fixed constant. Then the heads of the vectors* V *that satisfy the inequality*

$$V \cdot V_1 > c$$

lie in a half plane. Conversely, all half planes can be described by an inequality of this type.

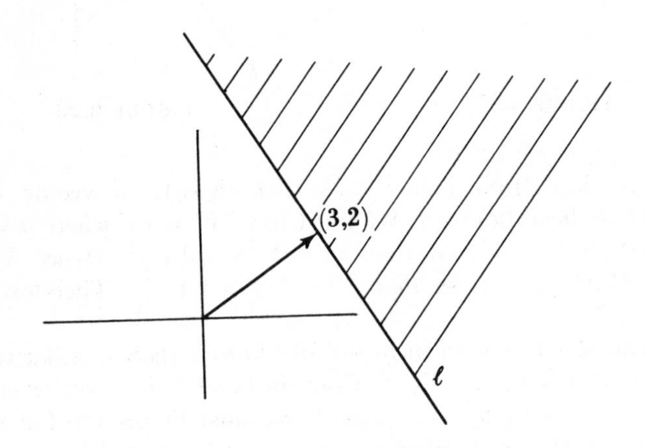

FIGURE 6.30

Example: Find the inequality satisfied by points lying in the half plane shown in Figure 6.30.

$$V_1 = \begin{pmatrix} 3 \\ 2 \end{pmatrix}, \qquad \| V_1 \|^2 = 3^2 + 2^2 = 13$$

$V \cdot V_1 > 13$, or in terms of x and y, $3x + 2y > 13$.

PROBLEMS

1. Find the inequalities satisfied by the half planes drawn in Figure 6.31.

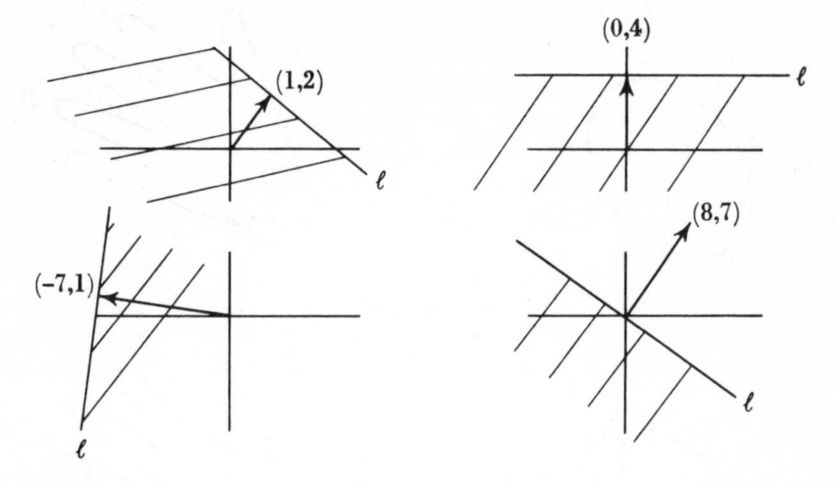

FIGURE 6.31

2. Interpret the following inequalities as half planes:

$$4x - 3y > 2; \qquad 2x + y > 0; \qquad 3x + 4y > 1.$$

3. $V \cdot V_1 > 0$ is a certain half plane H. If U and W both lie in H show algebraically that $U + W$ also lies in H. Give a geometric proof of this fact.

4. Referring to Problem 3, if a and b are positive quantities, prove that $aU + bW$ also lies in H.

5. Describe the set of vectors V that simultaneously satisfy both inequalities

$$V \cdot \begin{pmatrix} 1 \\ 1 \end{pmatrix} > 0 \text{ and } V \cdot \begin{pmatrix} -1 \\ 2 \end{pmatrix} > 0.$$

6. Do the points (1, 7) and (−1, 6) lie on the same side or on different sides of the line $2x - 3y = 1$?

7. Show how generally to resolve the type of question raised in Problem 6.

6.5 Convex Sets of Points

A set of points in the plane such as the eggshape labelled A is called convex (Figure 6.32). A set of points with bumps such as B is nonconvex. What is the difference between them? If you take any two points of A and join these points by a straight line segment, the points of the segment belong to A (Figure 6.33). This is not true of B: we can find pairs of points such that the line segment connecting them does not entirely lie in B. This observation becomes the basis of a definition.

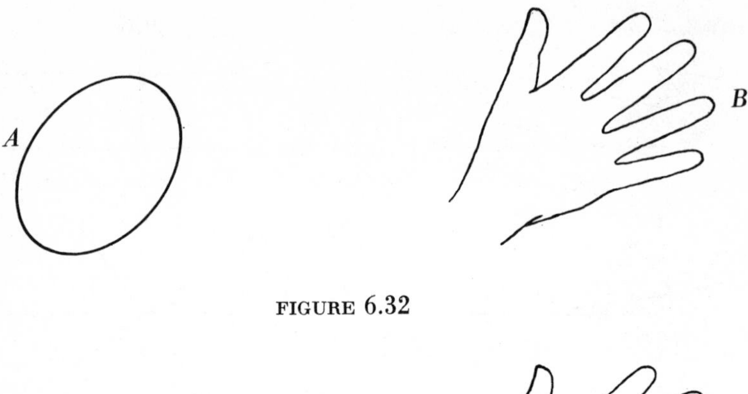

FIGURE 6.32

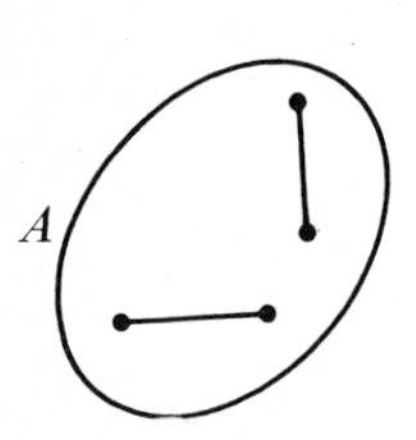

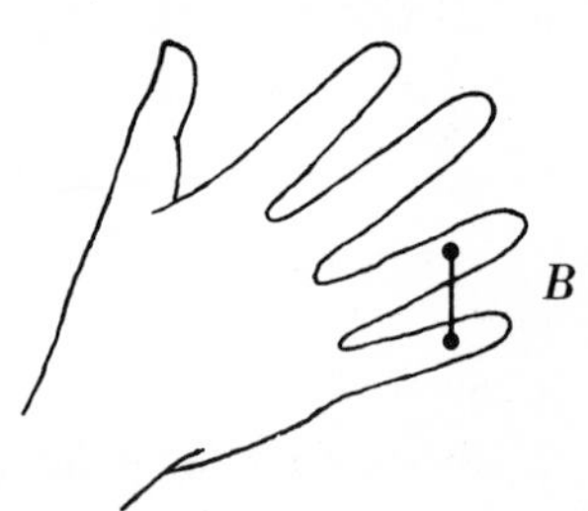

FIGURE 6.33

Definition: *A set of points in the plane is called convex if, given any two points in the set, all the points of the straight line segment joining them also lie in the set.*

PROBLEMS

1. Which of the sets in Figure 6.34 is convex and which is not?

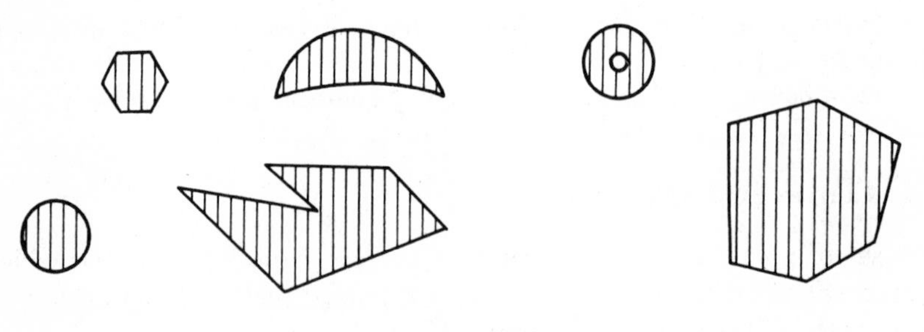

FIGURE 6.34

2. If a set is convex, does it remain convex after it has been rotated? After it has been translated? After it has been reflected in a line?
3. Prove that a straight line segment is a convex set.

Theorem: *Let* V_1 *and* V_2 *be two distinct vectors. Set*

$$V = (1 - t)V_1 + tV_2.$$

As t *varies from* 0 *to* 1 *inclusive, the tip of the vector* V *traces out the line segment that extends from the tip of* V_1 *to the tip of* V_2. (Figure 6.35.)

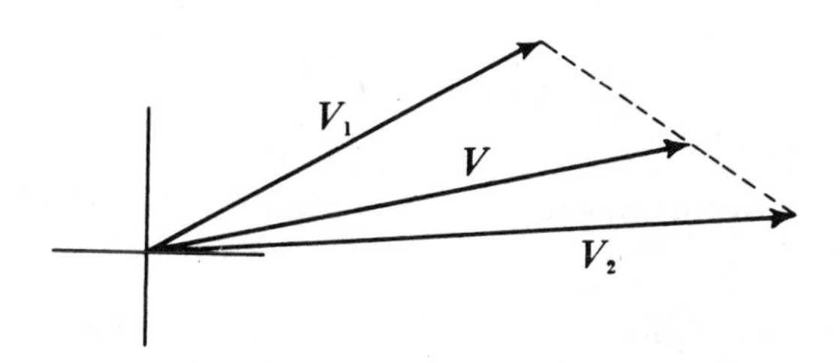

FIGURE 6.35

PROOF: Let

$$V_1 = \begin{pmatrix} x_1 \\ y_1 \end{pmatrix}, \qquad V_2 = \begin{pmatrix} x_2 \\ y_2 \end{pmatrix}, \qquad \text{and} \qquad V = \begin{pmatrix} x \\ y \end{pmatrix}.$$

Then,

$$V = \begin{pmatrix} x \\ y \end{pmatrix} = \begin{pmatrix} (1 - t)x_1 + tx_2 \\ (1 - t)y_1 + ty_2 \end{pmatrix}.$$

Hence, it follows that $(x - x_1) = t(x_2 - x_1)$ and $(y - y_1) = t(y_2 - y_1)$. Hence, $(x - x_1)(y_2 - y_1) = (y - y_1)(x_2 - x_1) = t(x_2 - x_1)(y_2 - y_1)$ and the first equality, considered as an equation in x and y, is that of the straight line connecting (x_1, y_1) and (x_2, y_2). Note, in particular, that when $t = 0$, $V = V_1$ and when $t = 1$, $V = V_2$.

We must prove, finally, that if $0 \leq t \leq 1$, the tip of V lies on the line segment that joins (x_1, y_1) and (x_2, y_2).

Suppose, for the sake of the argument, that $x_1 < x_2$. Since $0 \leq t \leq 1$, $(1 - t)$ and t are both ≥ 0 and $(1 - t) + t = 1$. Moreover, $tx_1 \leq tx_2$ and $(1 - t)x_1 \leq (1 - t)x_2$. Now $x_1 = (1 - t)x_1 + tx_1 \leq (1 - t)x_1 + tx_2 \leq (1 - t)x_2 + tx_2 = x_2$. Hence, $x_1 \leq (1 - t)x_1 + tx_2 \leq x_2$. Since $x = (1 - t)x_1 + tx_2$, this means that $x_1 \leq x \leq x_2$. Therefore, the x coordinate of the tip of V lies *between* those of V_1 and V_2 (Figure 6.36). We can argue similarly for the y coordinate.

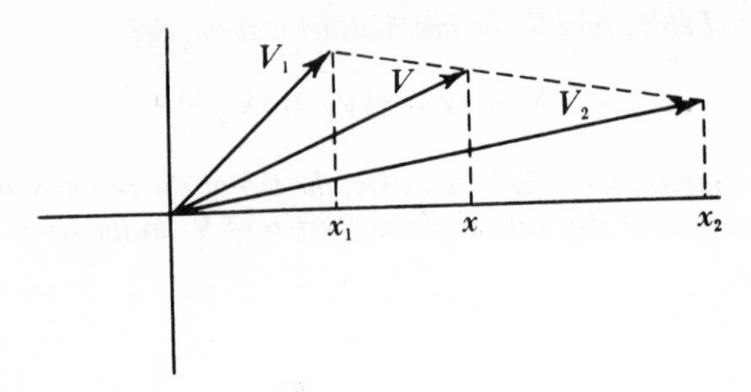

FIGURE 6.36

By making use of this theorem, we may rephrase the definition on page 232 as follows:

A set, S, *is convex if given any two vectors* $\begin{pmatrix} x_1 \\ y_1 \end{pmatrix}, \begin{pmatrix} x_2 \\ y_2 \end{pmatrix}$ *whose tips lie in* S, *then the tips of all the vectors* $(1 - t)\begin{pmatrix} x_1 \\ y_1 \end{pmatrix} + t\begin{pmatrix} x_2 \\ y_2 \end{pmatrix}$ *for* $0 \le t \le 1$ *also lie in* S.

A half plane is very obviously a convex set. But here is an algebraic proof of this fact that makes use of the ideas just developed.

Write the equation of the half plane in the form $V \cdot V_1 > h$. Let U and W be two vectors whose tips both lie in this half plane. Then $U \cdot V_1 > h$ and $W \cdot V_1 > h$. Now $(1 - t)(U \cdot V_1) > (1 - t)h$ and $t(W \cdot V_1) > th$. This is so because $(1 - t) > 0$ and $t > 0$. Hence $(1 - t)(U \cdot V_1) + t(W \cdot V_1) > (1 - t)h + th = h$. Therefore, $[(1 - t)U + tW] \cdot V_1 > h$. It follows that all the tips of the vectors $(1 - t)U + tW$ lie in the half plane.

Theorem: *The common portion of two convex sets is itself convex.*

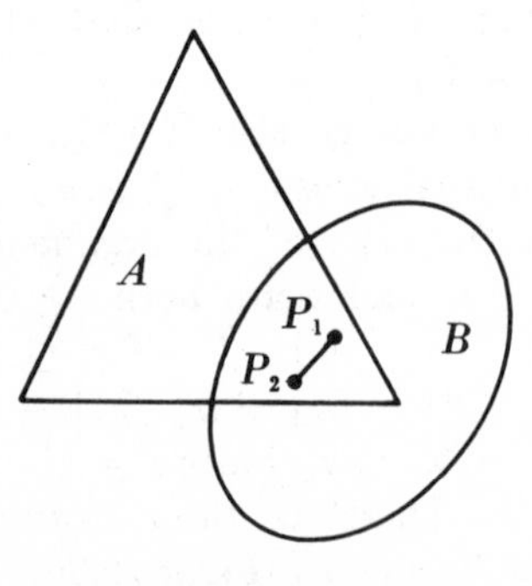

FIGURE 6.37

PROOF: Let A and B be two convex sets (Figure 6.37). Select two points P_1 and P_2 in their common part. Since P_1 and P_2 belong to A and A is convex, the whole segment P_1P_2 belongs to A. Since P_1 and P_2 belong to B and B is convex, the whole segment P_1P_2 belongs to B. Therefore the whole segment P_1P_2 belongs to the common part of A and B. The common part is therefore convex.

Question: What if the common part of A and B does not contain two points?

PROBLEMS

1. Let $V_1 = \begin{pmatrix}1\\1\end{pmatrix}$ and $V_2 = \begin{pmatrix}2\\3\end{pmatrix}$. Draw the vectors $V = (1 - t)V_1 + tV_2$ for the values $t = 0, \frac{1}{4}, \frac{1}{2}, \frac{3}{4}, 1$.

2. Draw the vectors V in Problem 1 for $t = 2, 3, -1, -2$. What conclusion do you draw about the relative positions of V for different values of t?

3. Let $V_1 = \begin{pmatrix}0\\1\end{pmatrix}$, $V_2 = \begin{pmatrix}2\\1\end{pmatrix}$, $V_3 = \begin{pmatrix}1\\3\end{pmatrix}$. Make numerous selections of numbers t, u, w that simultaneously satisfy (1) $t \geq 0, u \geq 0, w \geq 0$ and (2) $t + u + w = 1$, and plot the vector $V = tV_1 + uV_2 + wV_3$. Where do the tips of the vectors V fall? See if you can formulate a conjecture and prove a theorem about this. The numbers t, u, and w are called the *barycentric coordinates* of the vector V.

4. Show that the interior of every triangle is the common part of three half-planes and hence is convex.

5. Show that the interior of a circle (that is, the disc) is the common part of an infinite number of half-planes and hence is convex.

6. Give another proof that a circle is a convex set.

7. Prove that the only convex set that contains a finite number of points is a set consisting of one point.

8. Is the common part of two nonconvex sets nonconvex?

9. Prove that the infinite strip lying between two straight lines is a convex point set.

6.6 Vectors and Transformations

In the previous chapter, transformations of the plane were considered as movements of the points of the plane or as mappings of one plane onto another plane. In this section, we shall consider the points of the plane to be represented by the vector extending from the origin to the point, and shall develop a vector interpretation of linear transformations.

The symbol V will stand for the general vector in the plane. The coordinates of its tip are (x, y); or, we can write $V = \begin{pmatrix}x\\y\end{pmatrix}$.

(a) $V \to V$ V goes into V. This is the identity transformation.
(b) $V \to 2V$ Each vector goes into twice itself. This is equivalent to $\begin{pmatrix} x \\ y \end{pmatrix} \to \begin{pmatrix} 2x \\ 2y \end{pmatrix}$. This is a similarity transformation with a factor 2.
(c) $V \to -V$. This is a reflection in the origin.
(d) Let V_1 be a fixed vector. Then $V = V_1 + V$ is a translation of the plane.

The reader should illustrate (b), (c), and (d) with vector diagrams.

The general homogeneous line or transformation of the plane has been written as

$$\begin{cases} x' = ax + by \\ y' = cx + dy, \end{cases}$$

or in matrix form

$$\begin{pmatrix} x' \\ y' \end{pmatrix} = \begin{pmatrix} a & b \\ c & d \end{pmatrix} \begin{pmatrix} x \\ y \end{pmatrix}.$$

If we let $V' = \begin{pmatrix} x' \\ y' \end{pmatrix}$ then $V' = \begin{pmatrix} a & b \\ c & d \end{pmatrix} V$. By this means, the vector V is converted into the vector V'. We shall write this as $V \to V'$ or $V' = f(V)$. Now what does this transformation do to the vectors of the plane? It preserves vector sums and scalar products. That is to say, *the image of the sum of any two vectors is the sum of the images of vectors, and the image of a scalar product is the scalar product of the image.* We shall formulate this as a theorem.

Theorem: *A linear (homogeneous) transformation of the plane induces a mapping of the vectors,* $V' = f(V)$, *such that*
(a) *For any two vectors* V_1 *and* V_2, $f(V_1 + V_2) = f(V_1) + f(V_2)$
(b) *For any scalar* k, *and any vector* V, $f(kV) = kf(V)$.

PROOF: Let $A = \begin{pmatrix} a & b \\ c & d \end{pmatrix}$. Then $f(V) = V' = AV$. In particular, $f(V_1) = AV_1$ and $f(V_2) = AV_2$. Hence, $f(V_1 + V_2) = A(V_1 + V_2) = AV_1 + AV_2 = f(V_1) + f(V_2)$. Moreover, $f(kV) = AkV = kAV = kf(V)$.

This theorem is illustrated in Figures 6.38 and 6.39.

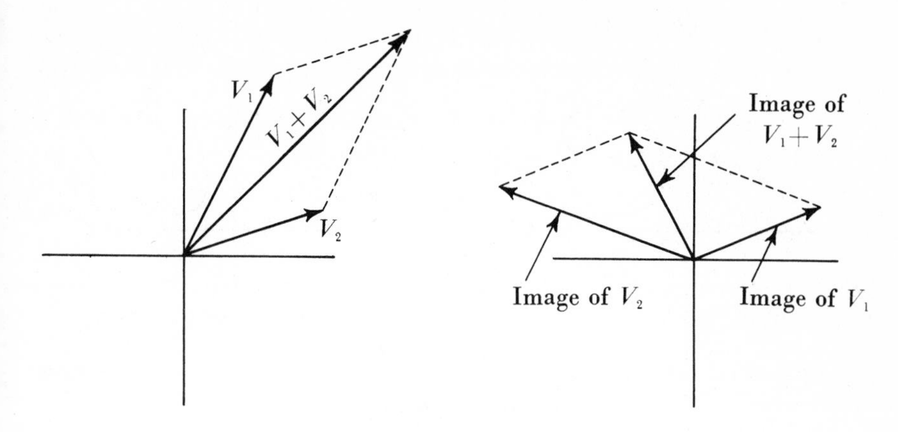

FIGURE 6.38

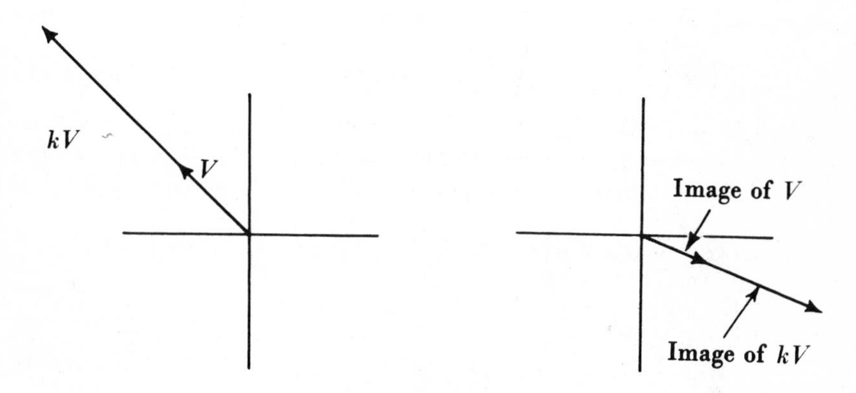

FIGURE 6.39

A transformation of vectors that possesses the two properties (a) and (b) is known as a *linear transformation* of the vectors. A further consequence of (a) and (b) is that for any two scalars k_1 and k_2 and any two vectors V_1 and V_2, $f(k_1V_1 + k_2V_2) = k_1f(V_1) + k_2f(V_2)$. This is true because $f(k_1V_1 + k_2V_2) = f(k_1V_1) + f(k_2V_2) = k_1f(V_1) + k_2f(V_2)$.

As an illustration of how these ideas may be used, we shall prove the following remarkable characteristic of linear transformations of the plane.

Theorem: *A linear transformation of the plane transforms any convex set into a convex set.*

PROOF: Let S be a convex set and S' its image. (Figure 6.40.) Take any two points in S': (x_1', y_1') and (x_2', y_2'). If we can show that any

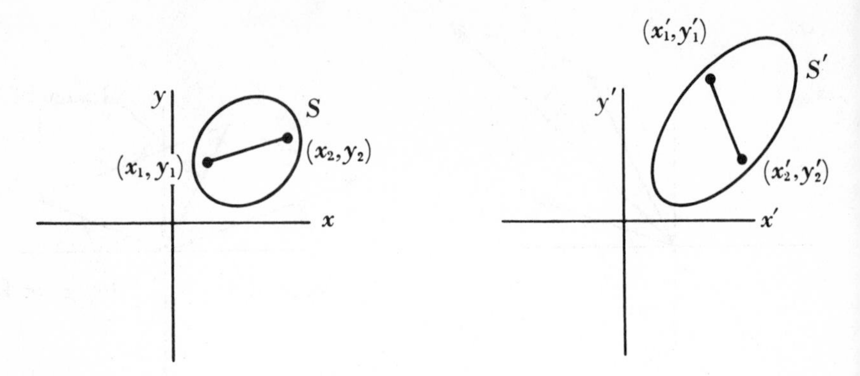

FIGURE 6.40

point on the line segment joining them is in S', then this will establish that S' is convex. Think of these points as tips of vectors $V_1' = \begin{pmatrix} x_1' \\ y_1' \end{pmatrix}$, $V_2' = \begin{pmatrix} x_2' \\ y_2' \end{pmatrix}$. If we can show that $(1 - t)V_1' + tV_2'$ is in S', where t is any number between 0 and 1, then it follows from the theorem of page 234 that S' is convex. Since (x_1', y_1') and (x_2', y_2') are in S', they are images of points in S. Call these points (x_1, y_1), (x_2, y_2) or $V_1 = \begin{pmatrix} x_1' \\ y_1' \end{pmatrix}$, $V_2 = \begin{pmatrix} x_2' \\ y_2' \end{pmatrix}$. Now if $0 \leq t \leq 1$, the point $(1 - t)V_1 + tV_2$ is in S (because S is convex). The image of this point is in S' (S' is the set of all images). But the image of $(1 - t)V_1 + tV_2$ is $(1 - t)V_1' + tV_2'$ (by the property of linearity). Hence $(1 - t)V_1' + tV_2'$ is in S'.

PROBLEMS

1. If f is a linear transformation, prove that $f(k_1V_1 + k_2V_2 + \ldots + k_nV_n) = k_1f(V_1) + k_2f(V_2) + \ldots + k_nf(V_n)$.

2. Draw the image of the region R (Figure 6.41) under the transformation

$$\begin{cases} x' = 2x + y \\ y' = 2x + (3/2)y \end{cases}$$

and see whether it is convex.

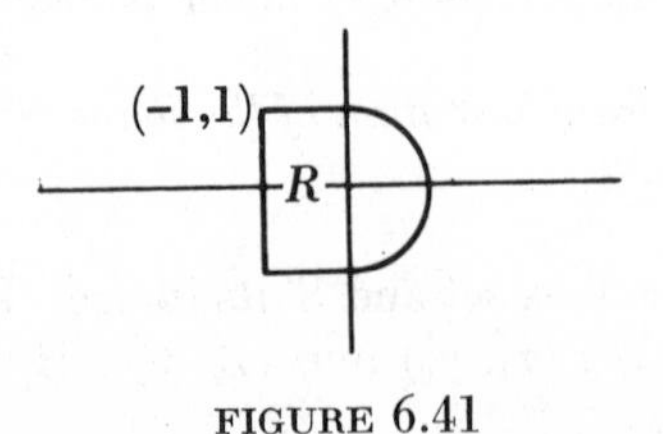

FIGURE 6.41

3. Draw the image of the region B (Figure 6.42) under the transformation

$$\begin{cases} x' = 2x - 3y \\ y' = -x - y. \end{cases}$$

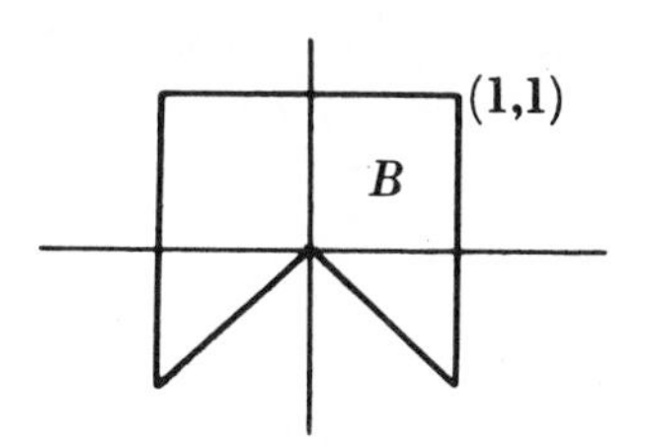

FIGURE 6.42

4. Prove that the image of a nonconvex set under a one-to-one linear transformation is nonconvex.

5. In Problem 4, is it necessary that the transformation be one-to-one for the statement to be true?

6. The center of gravity of a set of vectors $V_1, V_2, \ldots, V_n$ is defined as the vector $V = \frac{1}{n}(V_1 + V_2 + \ldots + V_n)$. Compute the center of gravity of the four vectors

$$\begin{pmatrix} 2 \\ 1 \end{pmatrix}, \begin{pmatrix} 3 \\ 7 \end{pmatrix}, \begin{pmatrix} -1 \\ -1 \end{pmatrix}, \begin{pmatrix} 4 \\ 0 \end{pmatrix}.$$

7. Compute the center of gravity of the vectors

$$\begin{pmatrix} 1 \\ 1 \\ -1 \end{pmatrix}, \begin{pmatrix} 1 \\ -1 \\ 1 \end{pmatrix}, \begin{pmatrix} -1 \\ 1 \\ 1 \end{pmatrix}.$$

Compute the center of gravity of the four vectors

$$\begin{pmatrix} 0 \\ 0 \\ 0 \end{pmatrix}, \begin{pmatrix} 1 \\ 0 \\ 0 \end{pmatrix}, \begin{pmatrix} 0 \\ 1 \\ 0 \end{pmatrix}, \begin{pmatrix} 0 \\ 0 \\ 1 \end{pmatrix}.$$

8. Let $V_1, \ldots, V_n$ have a center of gravity V. Let these vectors be subjected to a linear transformation and suppose that the images are respectively $V_1', V_2', \ldots, V_n'$ and V'. Show that V' is the center of gravity of $V_1', \ldots, V_n'$.

6.7 A Glimpse at n-Dimensional Space and its Geometry

All the materials are now at hand to construct a theory of n-dimensional geometry. We only have sufficient space to give an inkling of how this theory works. It will be an algebraic theory; the possibility of concrete physical representation in the real world belongs to a different sort of inquiry.

POINTS: A point in n-space is an n-tuple of numbers or a row vector, $(x_1, x_2, \ldots, x_n)$. When the point is regarded as a vector drawn from the origin $(0, 0, \ldots, 0)$, we can write

$$V = \begin{pmatrix} x_1 \\ x_2 \\ \cdot \\ \cdot \\ \cdot \\ x_n \end{pmatrix}.$$

The n-dimensional space is the set of all row or column vectors.

DISTANCE: The length or magnitude of V is $V = (V'V)^{1/2} = (x_1^2 + x_2^2 + \ldots + x_n^2)^{1/2}$. This is the distance from the point $(x_1, x_2, \ldots, x_n)$ to the origin. The distance between two points $(a_1, a_2, \ldots, a_n)$ and $(b_1, b_2, \ldots, b_n)$ is $((a_1 - b_1)^2 + (a_2 - b_2)^2 + \ldots + (a_n - b_n)^2)^{1/2}$. If

$$V_1 = \begin{pmatrix} a_1 \\ \cdot \\ \cdot \\ \cdot \\ a_n \end{pmatrix},$$

and

$$V_2 = \begin{pmatrix} b_1 \\ \cdot \\ \cdot \\ \cdot \\ b_n \end{pmatrix},$$

then this distance may be written as $\| V_1 - V_2 \|$. This number is known as a *Euclidean distance*.

ANGLES: The inner product $V_1 \bullet V_2$ is $a_1b_1 + a_2b_2 + \ldots + a_nb_n$. The angle θ between the vectors V_1 and V_2 is defined by the equation

$$\cos \theta = \frac{V_1 \bullet V_2}{\| V_1 \| \| V_2 \|}.$$

The quantity $\dfrac{V_1 \bullet V_2}{\| V_1 \| \| V_2 \|}$ can be shown to lie between -1 and 1 inclusive; and for a number in this range, there is precisely one angle θ between 0 and

180° whose cosine equals it. It makes sense, then, to use this formula to define the angle between two vectors.

Two vectors V_1 and V_2 are *parallel* if the angle between them is 0° or 180°. The two vectors V_1 and V_2 are *perpendicular* or *orthogonal* if the angle between them is 90°. This is equivalent to the condition $V_1 \bullet V_2 = 0$.

PLANES: A *hyperplane* of dimension $n - 1$ is given by the formula

$$V \bullet U = d$$

In this formula, U is a vector of length 1 and d is the distance from the origin to the hyperplane. If

$$V = \begin{pmatrix} x_1 \\ x_2 \\ \cdot \\ \cdot \\ \cdot \\ x_n \end{pmatrix}, \qquad U = \begin{pmatrix} a_1 \\ a_2 \\ \cdot \\ \cdot \\ \cdot \\ a_n \end{pmatrix}$$

then the equation of the hyperplane is $a_1x_1 + a_2x_2 + \cdots + a_nx_n = d$.

HALF-SPACES: A half-space is the set of points

$$V = \begin{pmatrix} x_1 \\ x_2 \\ \cdot \\ \cdot \\ \cdot \\ x_n \end{pmatrix}$$

satisfying an inequality of the form $V \bullet U > d$.

DIMENSION: What is it that characterizes the dimensionality of space? From one point of view it is this: in two dimensions two vectors can be perpendicular, but three or more vectors cannot be mutually perpendicular. (Of course the vectors under consideration must not be zero.) In three

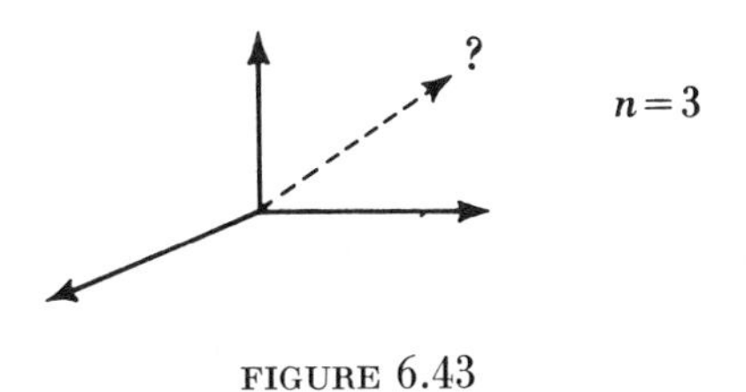

FIGURE 6.43

dimensions, three vectors can be mutually perpendicular but four or more vectors cannot be mutually perpendicular (Figure 6.43). Let us show this for two dimensions. Suppose, for simplicity, that $V_1 = \begin{pmatrix} 1 \\ 0 \end{pmatrix}$ and $V_2 = \begin{pmatrix} 0 \\ 1 \end{pmatrix}$. These vectors are perpendicular. Suppose that there is a vector $V = \begin{pmatrix} a \\ b \end{pmatrix}$ which is perpendicular to V_1 and V_2. Then, $V \bullet V_1 = 0$ and $V \bullet V_2 = 0$. Now $V \bullet V_1 = a$ and $V \bullet V_2 = b$. Hence $a = 0, b = 0$, so that V must be 0.

By the same token, we would expect that in a space of n dimensions, we can find n mutually perpendicular nonzero vectors, and indeed, in n dimensions, the n vectors $(1, 0, \ldots, 0), (0, 1, \ldots, 0), \ldots, (0, 0, \ldots, 1)$ are mutually perpendicular. Moreover it can be shown that it is impossible to find an $n + 1$st vector that is not zero and is perpendicular to these n.

VOLUME: The n vectors

$$\begin{pmatrix} x_{11} \\ x_{21} \\ \vdots \\ x_{n1} \end{pmatrix}, \begin{pmatrix} x_{12} \\ x_{22} \\ \vdots \\ x_{n2} \end{pmatrix}, \ldots, \begin{pmatrix} x_{1n} \\ x_{2n} \\ \vdots \\ x_{nn} \end{pmatrix}$$

can be thought of as forming the edges of an n-dimensional *parallelotope*. This is the generalization of a parallelogram in two dimensions or of a parallelepiped in three dimensions (Figure 6.44). The volume of this parallelotope is the absolute value of the number

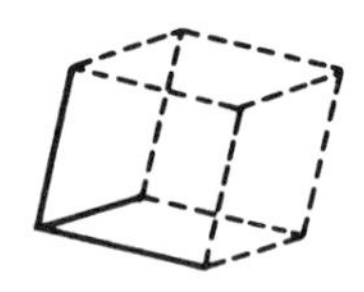

FIGURE 6.44

$$\begin{vmatrix} x_{11} & x_{12} & \cdots & x_{1n} \\ x_{21} & x_{22} & & \cdot \\ \vdots & \vdots & & \vdots \\ x_{n1} & x_{n2} & \cdots & x_{nn} \end{vmatrix}.$$

TRANSFORMATIONS: A linear transformation of the n-dimensional space is given by the matrix equation

$$\begin{pmatrix} x_1' \\ \vdots \\ x_n' \end{pmatrix} = \begin{pmatrix} a_{11} & \cdots & a_{1n} \\ \vdots & & \vdots \\ a_{n1} & \cdots & a_{nn} \end{pmatrix} \begin{pmatrix} x_1 \\ \vdots \\ x_n \end{pmatrix}.$$

One can speak of reflections, shears, rotations, et cetera. For example, an n-dimensional rotation is given by a matrix equation of the form:

$$\begin{pmatrix} x_1' \\ \vdots \\ x_n \end{pmatrix} = A \begin{pmatrix} x_1 \\ \vdots \\ x_n \end{pmatrix} \tag{1}$$

where A is an orthogonal matrix, that is, a matrix that satisfies the equation $A'A = I$.

The use of the term "rotation" can be justified by an argument of this sort: In two dimensions a rotation carries a point x, y into a point (x', y'). The distance from the origin to (x', y') is the same as from the origin to (x, y). Hence $x^2 + y^2 = x'^2 + y'^2$.

We can show similarly, that if $(x_1, \ldots, x_n)$ and $(x_1', \ldots, x_n')$ are related by equation (1), then $x_1^2 + x_2^2 + \cdots + x_n^2 = x_1'^2 + \cdots + x_n'^2$. This would mean, that all points in the n-dimensional space preserve the distance from the origin upon rotation.

We have,

$$(x_1'^2 + x_2'^2 + \cdots + x_n'^2) = (x_1', \ldots, x_n') \begin{pmatrix} x_1' \\ \vdots \\ x_n' \end{pmatrix}$$

Now, taking transposes in Equation (1), we get $(x_1', \ldots, x_n') = (x_1, \ldots, x_n)A'$, so that

$$x_1'^2 + x_2'^2 + \cdots + x_n'^2 = (x_1, \ldots, x_n)A'A \begin{pmatrix} x_1 \\ x_2 \\ \vdots \\ x_n \end{pmatrix}.$$

But $A'A = I$, hence,

$$x_1'^2 + x_2'^2 + \cdots + x_n'^2 = (x_1, \ldots, x_n)\begin{pmatrix} x_1 \\ \cdot \\ \vdots \\ \cdot \\ x_n \end{pmatrix} = x_1^2 + x_2^2 + \cdots + x_n^2.$$

The reader should now go over these elements of the geometry of n-dimensional space, and write out the formulas explicitly in the case of $n = 3$.

PROBLEMS

1. Find the distance between the points (1,1,2) and (2,1,1). Between (3,0,−1) and (1,1,4).
2. Find the angle between the vectors

$$\begin{pmatrix} 1 \\ 1 \\ 2 \end{pmatrix} \quad \text{and} \quad \begin{pmatrix} 1 \\ 2 \\ 1 \end{pmatrix}.$$

Between the vectors

$$\begin{pmatrix} -1 \\ -1 \\ 0 \end{pmatrix} \quad \text{and} \quad \begin{pmatrix} 4 \\ 1 \\ -1 \end{pmatrix}.$$

3. If the n vectors $V_1, V_2, \ldots, V_n$ are mutually perpendicular, prove that $\| V_1 + V_2 + \cdots + V_n \|^2 = \| V_1 \|^2 + \| V_2 \|^2 + \cdots + \| V_n \|^2$. This is the Pythagorean Theorem in n-dimensions.

Hint: Use the fact that $\| V \|^2 = V \bullet V$.

4. Find the volume of the parallelepiped that has three continguous edges given by the vectors

$$\begin{pmatrix} 1 \\ 1 \\ 0 \end{pmatrix}, \quad \begin{pmatrix} -1 \\ 2 \\ 1 \end{pmatrix}, \quad \begin{pmatrix} 1 \\ 2 \\ 1 \end{pmatrix}.$$

Work the same problem with

$$\begin{pmatrix} 1 \\ 0 \\ 0 \end{pmatrix}, \quad \begin{pmatrix} 0 \\ 1 \\ 0 \end{pmatrix}, \quad \begin{pmatrix} 0 \\ 0 \\ 1 \end{pmatrix}.$$

5. The plane $x - 3y + 2z = 7$ can be written in the form $\frac{x}{\sqrt{14}} - \frac{3y}{\sqrt{14}} + \frac{2z}{\sqrt{14}} = \frac{7}{\sqrt{14}}$. Note that

$$\left(\frac{1}{\sqrt{14}}\right)^2 + \left(\frac{-3}{\sqrt{14}}\right)^2 + \left(\frac{2}{\sqrt{14}}\right)^2 = 1.$$

Interpret the new equation geometrically.

CHAPTER 7

Matrices as Operators

The object of this chapter is to introduce a number of concepts that are currently employed in applied mathematics and to show how these concepts relate to the theory of matrices and how they provide further examples of matrix multiplication.

7.1 The Concept of the Black Box

The term "black box" has achieved currency in several parts of science: in electrical engineering, in the theory of control mechanisms, in computer sciences, in automation, in mathematical logic. The term is a striking one, and has even begun to appear in common speech.

A black box is a mechanism or a device that accepts an input, and in response, produces an output. The inputs and outputs may vary widely. Put a coin in a machine and a cup of soda emerges. If a pilot deflects the elevators of his plane, he will note a change on his altimeter. When you use a telephone, the sound waves you make will be transmitted over the wires and will be received at the other end in a modified form. These are all examples of black boxes. There is an input to the box and an output

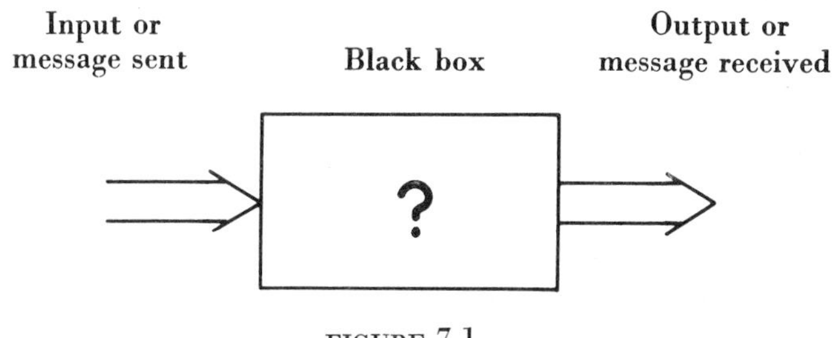

FIGURE 7.1

emerges: a message is sent and a message is received. Figure 7.1 presents a conceptual diagram of a black box.

Historically, the word "black box" comes from the fact that many electronic devices are actually housed in black boxes. The word "black," suggestive of mystery, and the question mark placed inside the box in Figure 7.1 call attention to the fact that we may not know, or may not care to know, just what is inside the box; how the internal mechanism converts the input into an output. When a typist depresses the "T" key, she does not as a rule inquire how it comes about that the letter "T" appears on the paper. As far as she is concerned, the typewriter is a black box. Nor does a person in California dialing his friend in Philadelphia dwell on the millions of dollars of equipment that intervene and convert his message sent into a message received.

FIGURE 7.2 *Black Box: Popular Conception*

A certain input-output system may be so complicated that an analysis of its behavior is difficult. In certain other instances, it may not be possible to break into the box to see what is there and to analyze its behavior. The behavior of the device may vary with time: put a coin into a depleted candy machine and the output is the coin and not the candy. "Noise" or malfunction may intervene to corrupt the output. In such cases, the word "black" is an admission that we have only an incomplete knowledge of how the box responds.*

The black box associates an output with an input; this concept, therefore, has some features in common with the function concept of mathematics. Put a number into a mathematical prescription, say a formula, and it yields another number as an output (Figure 7.3).

---

*The mystery of the black box and its limitations as a way of life have even been satirized by a black box toy. When a switch is turned on, a hand emerges from a black box and turns off the switch. The hand then recedes into the box and all is quiet once again.

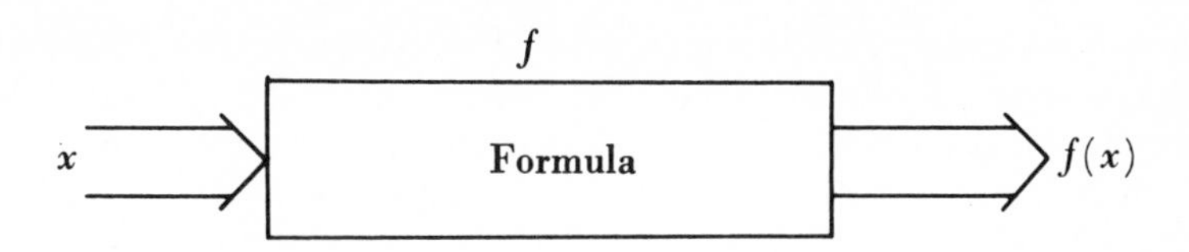

FIGURE 7.3 *Mathematical Formula as a Black Box*

Other more elaborate types of mathematical box may accept more than single numbers as an input. A whole curve may be an input and another curve, or a single number, might be the output.

Boxes can be hooked up to one another, the output of the first box becoming the input to the second box (Figure 7.4). This corresponds to the process of forming functions of functions.

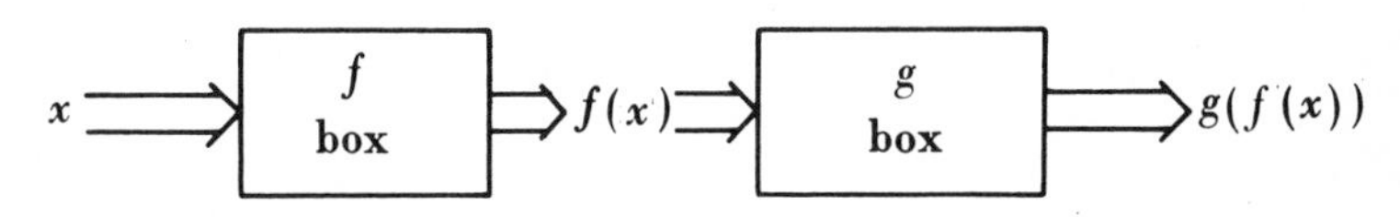

FIGURE 7.4 *Boxes in Series: Functions of Functions*

The concept of functional boxes is a useful one in the coding of problems for electronic computers. The functional box corresponds to a certain block of instructions which forms a conceptual unit and which actually may be available in a package.

One of the major problems associated with black boxes is that of studying their behavior so as to predict the output corresponding to any particular input. If a device accepts only a small number of inputs, we can test all the inputs separately and see what they lead to. But if a device can accept an abnormally larger number of inputs (such as a digital computing machine) or even an infinite number of inputs (such as a telephone), then we have no hope of testing the inputs separately; we must find other means of prediction.

The second major problem is just the reverse of this. Given the output, what can be said about the input? We received a message, and we would like to come to some conclusion about the message sent.

PROBLEMS

1. A typewriter-like device has been rigged up so as to print a letter when a key is depressed. The response to A, B, C, D, E, F is B, C, D, E, F, G. What would you guess the response to P would be. How much confidence do you have in your

answer?* What would the response to Z be? What input gave rise to the output EPH?

2. Suppose the response to A, B, C, D, E, F, G is X, X, X, X, X, X, X. Predict the response to X.

3. A device accepts integers as inputs and puts out integers in response. The response to 1, 2, 3, 4, 5, 6, 7, is 1, 2, 3, 4, 5, 6, 7. Predict the response to 15. Suppose the response to 1, 2, 3, 4, 5, 6, 7, 8, 9, 10 was 1, 2, 3, 4, 4, 6, 7, 8, 9, 10. Predict the response to 15. How much confidence do you have in your answer?*

4. Suppose the response to 1, 2, 3, 4, 5, 6, 7 was 3, 5, 7, 9, 11, 13, 15. Predict the response to 15.

5. A common device accepts pairs of integers as an input and puts out a single number as an output. The input 1, 7 yielded 8 as a response. The input 2, 4 yielded 6 as a response. The input 10, 20 yielded 30. Predict the response to 4, 13. What is this device called?

6. A device that has become rather common has four possible inputs; 10, 25, 50, 100. The input 10 yields 5, 5. The input 25 yields 10, 10, 5. The input 50 yields 25, 10, 10, 5. Predict the response to 100. What device is this?

7. A Las Vegas device, known as a "one arm bandit," accepts half dollars as an input. Discuss the output.

7.2 Linear Boxes: Matrices as Linear Boxes

The concept of a black box is so general that a theory is possible only when drastic assumptions are made that limit the scope of the discussion. There is a class of physical device whose behavior is *linear*. Though the inputs and outputs are certain physical quantities such as displacements, voltages, loads, et cetera, we will think of the input as represented by a row vector $A = (a_1, a_2, \ldots, a_m)$ and the output by a row vector $B = (b_1, b_2, \ldots, b_n)$. The number of elements in the input and output vectors need not be the same, and the elements can be thought of as representing certain measurements at different places or times.

Definition: *A linear box is one that has the following properties*

1. *A zero input yields a zero output.*
2. *If the input* A *yields output* B, *then the input* kA *will yield the output* kB; k *is a scalar.*
3. *If the input* A_1 *yields output* B_1 *and if the input* A_2 *yields the output* B_2, *then* $A_1 + A_2$ *yields* $B_1 + B_2$.

The first two requirements express the *homogeneity* of the behavior of the device; double the input, and you double the output, et cetera. Actually,

*This is by no means easy to answer. It lies at the heart of a dilemma that plagues the philosophy of science: the proper role of deductive reasoning and inductive reasoning, and the relation between the two.

the first requirement can be deduced from the second by placing $k = 0$. The third requirement is known as the *law of superposition.* It states that each input contributes its share to the output independently and without interference; if two inputs are added the outputs are added.

By combination, if inputs $A_1 \ldots A_p$ have outputs $B_1 \ldots B_p$ then the input $c_1A_1 + c_2A_2 + \cdots + c_pA_p$ has output $c_1B_1 + c_2B_2 + \cdots + c_pB_p$.

To obtain a concrete picture of a linear box the reader might recall the example of the loaded beam given on page 68. The inputs are the loads at certain places. The outputs are deflections at these stations. The matrix equation relating the two states that the device is linear.

Example: In a linear box, the response to (2, 0, 3) is (1, 1, 1). The response to (4, 0, 6) will be (2, 2, 2). If the response to (1, 1, 5) is (1, 1, − 3), then the response to (3, 1, 8) = (2, 0, 3) + (1, 1, 5) will be (1, 1, 1) + (1, 1, −3) = (2, 2, −2).

Multiplication by a fixed matrix has all the properties required of linear boxes. Suppose that A is a $1 \times m$ row vector, and M is an $m \times n$ matrix (considered fixed). Then, the product AM is a $1 \times n$ row vector. If A is considered as an input and AM an output, then from matrix algebra,

1. $0M = 0$
2. $(kA)M = k(AM)$
3. $(A_1 + A_2)M = A_1M + A_2M,$

and these express the linearity of the system.

But the converse is also true: linear boxes may be represented by matrices. In order to see this, suppose that we record the outputs corresponding to the following inputs, $(1, 0, 0, \ldots, 0)$, $(0, 1, 0, 0, \ldots, 0)$, $\ldots$, $(0, 0, \ldots, 0, 1)$.

The input	yields	The output
$(1, 0, 0, \ldots, 0, 0)$	⇨	$(b_{11}, b_{12}, \ldots, b_{1n})$
$(0, 1, 0, \ldots, 0, 0)$	⇨	$(b_{21}, b_{22}, \ldots, b_{2n})$
	.	
	.	
	.	
$(0, 0, 0, \ldots, 0, 1)$	⇨	$(b_{m1}, b_{m2}, \ldots, b_{mn})$.

Then, with this information, the response to any input can be determined immediately. For, suppose we would like to find the output corresponding to the input $(a_1, a_2, \ldots, a_m)$. We have,

$$(a_1, a_2, \ldots, a_m) = a_1(1, 0, \ldots, 0) + a_2(0, 1, 0, \ldots, 0) + \cdots + a_m(0, 0, \ldots, 1).$$

It follows by the requirements of linearity, that the response to input $(a_1, a_2, \ldots, a_m)$ must be

$a_1(b_{11}, b_{12}, \ldots, b_{1n}) + a_2(b_{21}, b_{22}, \ldots, b_{2n}) + \cdots + a_m(b_{m1}, b_{m2}, \ldots, b_{mn})$.
If we denote this response by $(r_1, r_2, \ldots, r_n)$, then we have

$$(a_1, a_2, \ldots, a_m) \begin{pmatrix} b_{11} & b_{12} & \cdots & b_{1n} \\ b_{21} & b_{22} & & b_{2n} \\ \vdots & \vdots & & \vdots \\ b_{m1} & b_{m2} & \cdots & b_{mn} \end{pmatrix} = (r_1, r_2, \ldots, r_n).$$

This is the matrix representation of the box. One should note that the behavior of a linear box is completely determined by its responses to the unit vectors $(1, 0, \ldots, 0), (0, 1, 0, \ldots, 0), \ldots$.

PROBLEMS

1. In a linear box, the response to $(0, 1)$ is $(6, 2)$, and to $(1, 0)$ is $(1, 1)$. Find the responses to $(-3, -3)$, $(1, 2)$, and $(0, 1)$.

2. In a linear box, the response to $(1, 1)$ is $(0, 5)$ and the response to $(1, 2)$ is $(-6, 3)$. Find the response to $(0, 1)$ and to $(1, 0)$ and hence write the matrix representation.

3. A box responds with $(1, 7)$ to $(1, 1)$; with $(2, 2)$ to $(2, 1)$; with $(4, 5)$ to $(3, 6)$ and with $(3, 7)$ to $(0, 4)$. Is it a linear box?

4. A device accepts as input 2×2 matrices A that are nonsingular. For each A, it puts out A^{-1}. Is it linear?

5. Some desk calculators have a "square root feature." You enter a number on the keyboard, press the square root button and the square root of the number appears on the dials. Is this a linear device?

6. A black box (Figure 7.5) has as input two calibrated rods. Its output is indicated by a calibrated needle.

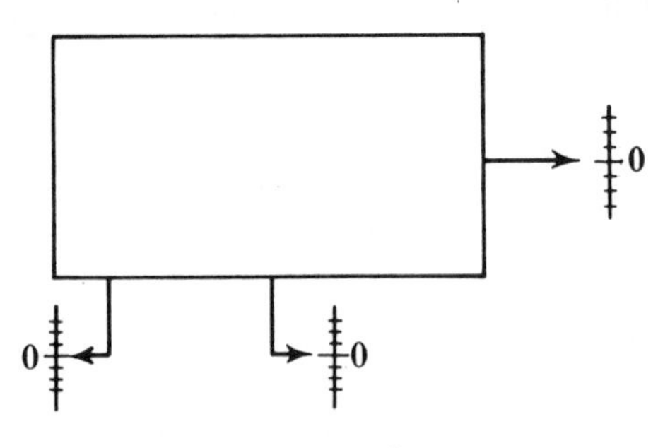

FIGURE 7.5

Further analysis reveals that the box is really a mechanical device consisting of pulleys and ropes (Figure 7.6).

Is this a linear device?

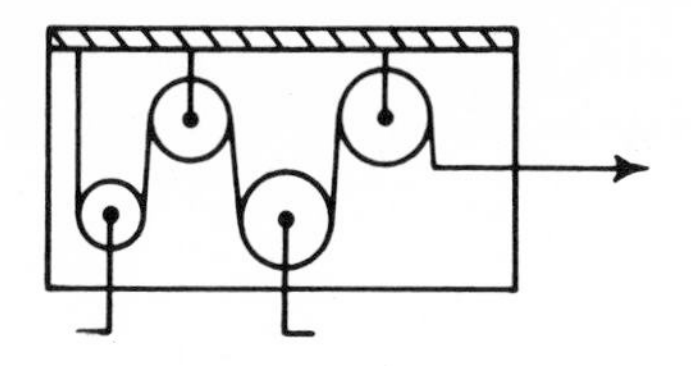

FIGURE 7.6

7. Examine the linkage in Figure 7.7 for linearity. The quantities x and y are inputs and w is the output.

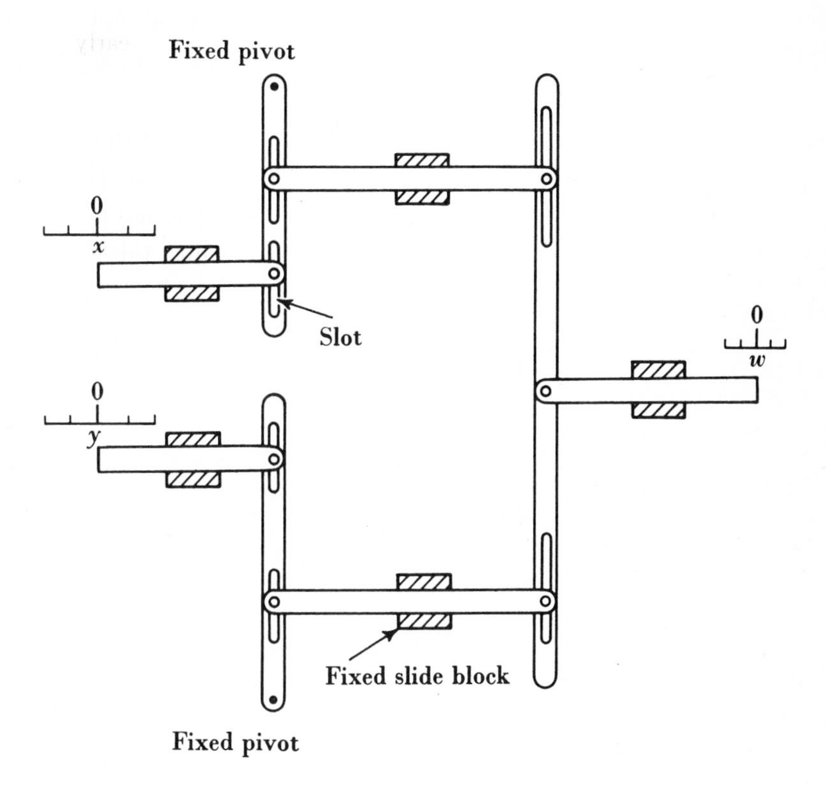

FIGURE 7.7

7.3 Linear Analysis in Applied Mathematics

The response of a matrix to an input is, under the conventions we have observed, a linear response; and the analysis of the response of a system by means of matrix multiplication is the prototype of what is called *linear analysis*. This is a very extensive subject, but cannot be carried to any great depth without introducing differential and integral equations.

Linear analysis in applied mathematics is first met at a very early stage. If one apple costs 5¢ how much will two apples cost? The reasoning that leads to the answer 10¢ is an example of linear analysis. If one apple costs 5¢ and one pear costs 8¢, how much will three apples and four pears cost? Linear analysis says 47¢.

This type of reasoning is common throughout applied mathematics. It is an expression of the idea that effect is proportional to cause, that output is proportional to input. If a graph is drawn in which output is plotted against input (Figure 7.8), the graph will be a straight line; this accounts for the term "linear."

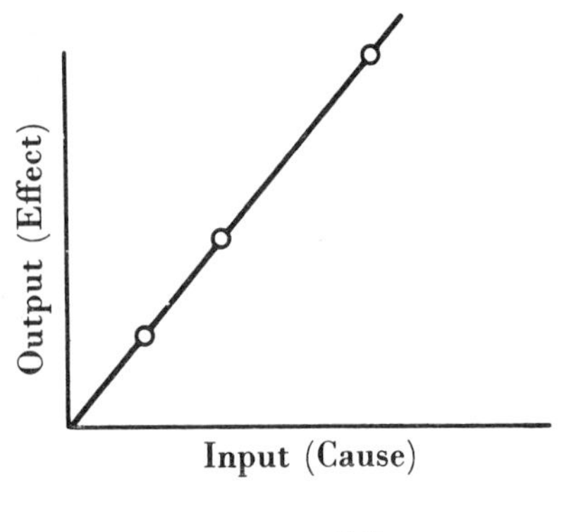

FIGURE 7.8

Linear analysis is common because: (a) It very often provides an accurate description of what is observed. (b) If it is not completely accurate, it is often a good approximation. For if an input-output graph is not exactly linear, it can be approximated by a linear relationship over small intervals with good accuracy (Figure 7.9). (c) Linear analysis is simple and relatively easy to carry out. The fully developed theory of linear algebra and matrices comes to our assistance.

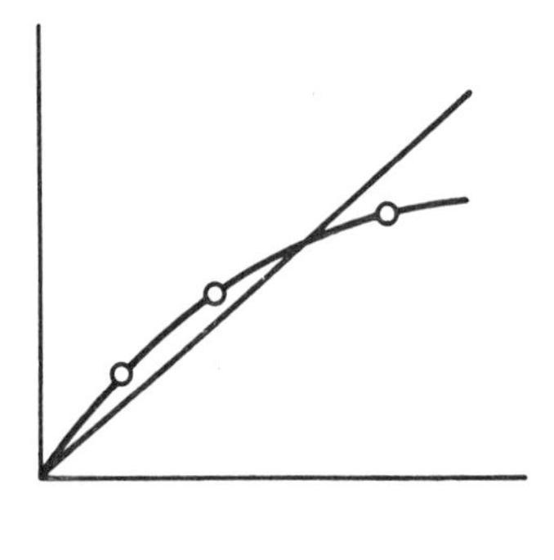

FIGURE 7.9

However, linear analysis has its limitations and these must also be appreciated at an early stage. The real world may not be very linear. One apple costs 5¢ and Mr. Arigo, my fruit man, tells me that two apples cost 9¢. Or consider this one, if the Mona Lisa is valued at \$10,000,000, what is the valuation of two Mona Lisas? Linear analysis would lead in mathematics to all sorts of simple and tempting, but false, identities such as $(a + b)^2 = a^2 + b^2$ or $\sqrt{a + b} = \sqrt{a} + \sqrt{b}$. An example of linearity in mathematical physics is Hooke's Law: in an elastic material stretch is proportional to load (Figure 7.10).

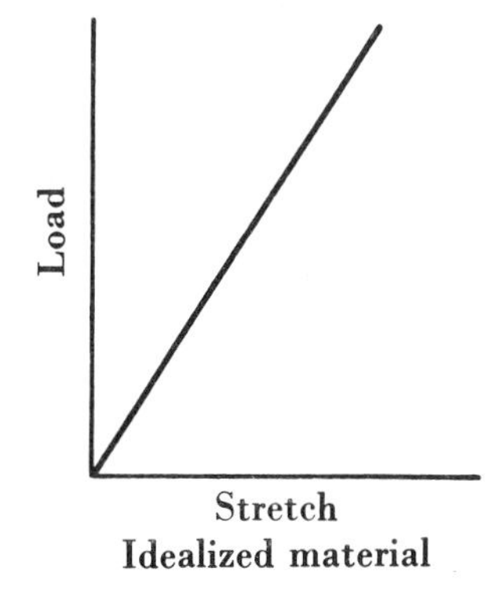

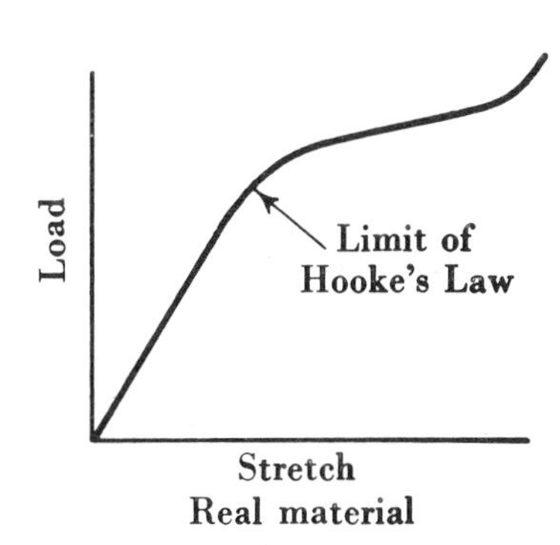

FIGURE 7.10

This law is valid only for loads under a certain amount. Figure 7.10 shows what happens when a real material is loaded beyond this limit. Linear analysis applied blindly may lead to demonstrably false conclusions.

7.4 Some Simple Operations and Their Matrices

In Section 2, we restricted the length of our input and output vectors. Accordingly, the size of the matrices representing the box was restricted. But in numerous instances, it is convenient to think of the input as being potentially unbounded in length (perhaps it is a signal whose value every second has been given) and the output as being also unbounded. We shall therefore deal with matrices whose size is left unspecified.

Here are some simple linear boxes and their matrices.

AMPLIFICATION:

$$(a, b, c, \ldots)\begin{pmatrix} k & 0 & 0 & 0 & \cdots \\ 0 & k & 0 & 0 & \cdots \\ 0 & 0 & k & 0 & \cdots \\ \vdots & & & & \end{pmatrix} = (ak, bk, ck, \ldots).$$

The message $(a, b, c, \ldots)$ has been multiplied by the factor k.

DELAY:

$$(a, b, c, \ldots)\begin{pmatrix} 0 & 0 & 0 & 1 & 0 & 0 & \cdots \\ 0 & 0 & 0 & 0 & 1 & 0 & \cdots \\ 0 & 0 & 0 & 0 & 0 & 1 & \cdots \\ \vdots & & & & & & \end{pmatrix} = (0, 0, 0, a, b, c, \ldots).$$

The message $(a, b, c, d, \ldots)$ is delayed by three units and becomes

$$(0, 0, 0, a, b, c, d, \ldots).$$

It should be clear how to produce delays of any number of units.

DIFFERENCING:

$$(a, b, c, d, \ldots)\begin{pmatrix} 1 & -1 & 0 & 0 & \cdots \\ 0 & 1 & -1 & 0 & \cdots \\ 0 & 0 & 1 & -1 & \cdots \\ 0 & 0 & 0 & 1 & \cdots \\ 0 & 0 & 0 & 0 & \cdots \end{pmatrix} = (a, b - a, c - b, d - c, \ldots).$$

Here the message is replaced by the difference of consecutive values. Differencing measures change, and is particularly important since many of the laws of physics involve rates of change. These laws are expressed in terms of *differentiation*, an operation of calculus which is analogous to differencing. When numerical work is performed, differencing becomes of prime importance.

RUNNING SUMMATION: Here the input is transformed into its "running sum"; that is, the sum of the first term, the sum of the first two terms, et cetera.

$$(a, b, c, d, \ldots)\begin{pmatrix} 1 & 1 & 1 & 1 & \cdots \\ 0 & 1 & 1 & 1 & \cdots \\ 0 & 0 & 1 & 1 & \cdots \\ 0 & 0 & 0 & 1 & \cdots \\ 0 & & & & \\ 0 & & & & \end{pmatrix}$$
$$= (a, a + b, a + b + c, a + b + c + d, \ldots).$$

Running summation is the inverse operation to differencing. Its analog in the calculus is *integration*.

SMOOTHING: Records of the time variation of quantities such as temperature, voltage, prices, production, often exhibit slight tremors or other disturbances. These tremors may be unwanted, and the records are frequently smoothed before being further processed and interpreted. For example, a recently constructed meteorological computer that automatically records and processes wind velocities, has a smoother built into it so that gusts of wind of short duration will not unduly affect the interpretation. One method of smoothing a sequence of numbers is to replace them by the average of two consecutive numbers. Thus, the sequence of numbers 1, 1, 2, 3, 4, 4, 5, 4, 5, 3, 3, 2, 2, 1 would be smoothed into * $\frac{1}{2}$, 1, $1\frac{1}{2}$, $2\frac{1}{2}$, $3\frac{1}{2}$, 4, $4\frac{1}{2}$, $4\frac{1}{2}$, $4\frac{1}{2}$, 4, 3, $2\frac{1}{2}$, 2, $1\frac{1}{2}$ (Figure 7.11).

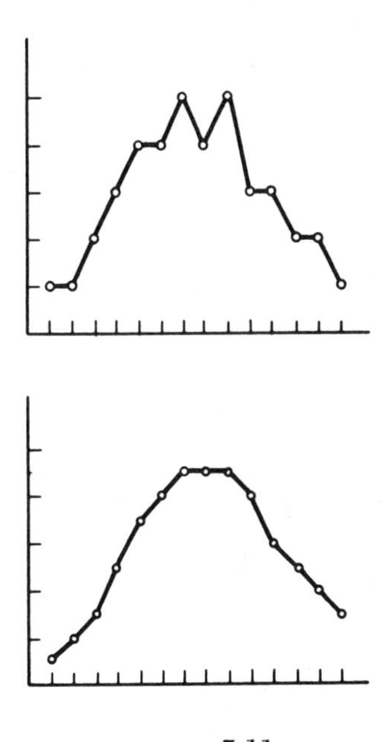

FIGURE 7.11

Here is the matrix formulation of this type of smoothing operation:

$$(a, b, c, d, \ldots) \begin{pmatrix} \frac{1}{2} & \frac{1}{2} & 0 & 0 & 0 & \cdot \\ 0 & \frac{1}{2} & \frac{1}{2} & 0 & 0 & \cdot \\ 0 & 0 & \frac{1}{2} & \frac{1}{2} & 0 & \cdot \\ 0 & 0 & 0 & \frac{1}{2} & \frac{1}{2} & \cdot \\ \cdot & & & & & \\ \cdot & & & & & \\ \cdot & & & & & \end{pmatrix} = \left(\frac{a}{2}, \frac{a+b}{2}, \frac{b+c}{2}, \frac{c+d}{2}, \ldots\right).$$

* For convenience, the first smoothed value is reckoned as one-half the original value.

The matrix representation of these processes shows clearly how each process can be split into two parts: the fixed matrix representing the operation, and the vector input which may vary from case to case. If I_1 denotes the input and I_2 the output, and if M is the operation, we have

$$I_1M = I_2.$$

It may be desired to place several elementary boxes in a series so that the action of one box is followed immediately by that of the next box. This is accomplished by matrix multiplication. Input I_1 is operated upon by M_1 and produces I_2. Output I_2 is input to operation M_2 and produces I_3. Hence

$$\begin{aligned} I_1M_1 &= I_2 \\ I_2M_2 &= I_3. \end{aligned}$$

Hence $(I_1M_1)M_2 = I_3$ or $I_1(M_1M_2) = I_3$.

The matrix M_1M_2 takes us directly from I_1 to I_3. The multiplication here occurs in an opposite order to what it did when we considered transformations of the plane. This is because we have chosen to write

$$I_1M = I_2$$

in conformity with the input-output flow diagram in Figure 7.1.

Example 1: A message is delayed by one unit, doubled in intensity, and then smoothed. Find the single matrix that does this job.

$$\begin{pmatrix} 0 & 1 & 0 & 0 & \cdots \\ 0 & 0 & 1 & 0 & \cdots \\ 0 & 0 & 0 & 1 & \cdots \\ \vdots \end{pmatrix} \begin{pmatrix} 2 & 0 & 0 & \cdots \\ 0 & 2 & 0 & \cdots \\ 0 & 0 & 2 & \cdots \\ \vdots \end{pmatrix} \begin{pmatrix} \frac{1}{2} & \frac{1}{2} & 0 & 0 & \cdots \\ 0 & \frac{1}{2} & \frac{1}{2} & 0 & \cdots \\ 0 & 0 & \frac{1}{2} & \frac{1}{2} & \cdots \\ \vdots \end{pmatrix}$$

$$= \begin{pmatrix} 0 & 1 & 1 & 0 & 0 & 0 & \cdots \\ 0 & 0 & 1 & 1 & 0 & 0 & \cdots \\ 0 & 0 & 0 & 1 & 1 & 0 & \cdots \\ \vdots \end{pmatrix}.$$

Example 2: Occasionally it is thought desirable to smooth data that has already been smoothed once before. For example,

Original data: 1, 1, 2, 3, 4, 4, 5, 4, 5, 3, 3, 2, 2, 1

Data, smoothed: $\frac{1}{2}$, 1, $1\frac{1}{2}$, $2\frac{1}{2}$, $3\frac{1}{2}$, 4, $4\frac{1}{2}$, $4\frac{1}{2}$, $4\frac{1}{2}$, 4, 3, $2\frac{1}{2}$, 2, $1\frac{1}{2}$

Data, smoothed once again: $\frac{1}{4}, \frac{3}{4}, 1\frac{1}{4}, 2, 3, 3\frac{3}{4}, 4\frac{1}{4}, 4\frac{1}{2}, 4\frac{1}{2}, 4\frac{1}{4}, 3\frac{1}{2}, 2\frac{3}{4}, 2\frac{1}{4}, 1\frac{3}{4}$.

Let
$$S = \begin{pmatrix} \frac{1}{2} & \frac{1}{2} & 0 & 0 & 0 & \cdots \\ 0 & \frac{1}{2} & \frac{1}{2} & 0 & 0 & \cdots \\ 0 & 0 & \frac{1}{2} & \frac{1}{2} & 0 & \cdots \\ \vdots & & & & & \end{pmatrix}.$$

If A is the data input, then AS is the smoothed output. Hence, $(AS)S$ is the smoothed output smoothed once again. Now $(AS)S = AS^2$. The double process is therefore equivalent to operating on the data by the matrix S^2. A computation yields
$$S^2 = \begin{pmatrix} \frac{1}{4} & \frac{1}{2} & \frac{1}{4} & 0 & 0 & 0 & \cdots \\ 0 & \frac{1}{4} & \frac{1}{2} & \frac{1}{4} & 0 & 0 & \cdots \\ 0 & 0 & \frac{1}{4} & \frac{1}{2} & \frac{1}{4} & 0 & \cdots \\ \vdots & & & & & & \end{pmatrix}.$$

S^2 is another example of a smoothing matrix.

Example 3: A recording aneroid barometer inside an airplane is connected to an orifice on the wing by a long tube. If $A_1, A_2, \ldots$ are the outside air pressure every $1/2$ second and if $B_1, B_2, \ldots$ are the corresponding barometer readings, then it is found that the relation between the two can be expressed fairly accurately by
$$\frac{3}{2} B_n - \frac{1}{2} B_{n-1} = A_n.$$

This can be set up in matrix form by means of the product
$$(B_1, B_2, B_3, \ldots) \begin{pmatrix} \frac{3}{2} & -\frac{1}{2} & 0 & 0 & 0 & \cdots \\ 0 & \frac{3}{2} & -\frac{1}{2} & 0 & 0 & \\ 0 & 0 & \frac{3}{2} & -\frac{1}{2} & 0 & \\ 0 & 0 & 0 & \frac{3}{2} & -\frac{1}{2} & \\ \vdots & & & & & \end{pmatrix} = (A_1, A_2, A_3, A_4, \ldots).$$

In certain tests, the engineer would like to determine the outside air pressure in terms of his barometer reading. This can be done by inverting the matrix.

PROBLEMS

1. Form the matrix S^3 and interpret it as a smoothing operator.
2. Let T designate the delay matrix. Form T^2 and T^3 and interpret them.
3. Let D designate the differencing matrix. Form D^2 and D^3 and interpret them in terms of their action on an input record. Do you recognize the entries in these matrices?

4. Let K designate the matrix of running summation. Form K^2 and K^3 and interpret their action.

5. The matrix

$$M = \begin{pmatrix} 0 & 0 & 0 & \cdots \\ 1 & 0 & 0 & \cdots \\ 0 & 1 & 0 & \cdots \\ 0 & 0 & 1 & \cdots \\ \vdots & & & \end{pmatrix}$$

has been called a *destruction matrix*. Justify this term by describing its action on an input. Form M^2 and interpret.

6. Let D designate the differencing matrix and U the running summation matrix. Show that $DU = UD = I$ and hence differencing and running summation are inverse operations.

7. In Example 3 page 257 let $(B_1, B_2, \ldots) = (1, 1, 1, 1, \ldots)$. Compute $(A_1, A_2, \ldots)$. Do the same if $(B_1, B_2, \ldots) = (1, 2, 3, 4, \ldots)$. Do the same if $(B_1, B_2, \ldots) = (1, 2, 3, 2, 1, 2, 3, 2, 1, 2, 3, 2, \ldots)$.

7.5 Time Independent Boxes

Take a matrix whose elements have the following pattern

$$A = \begin{pmatrix} a_1 & a_2 & a_3 & a_4 & \cdots \\ 0 & a_1 & a_2 & a_3 & \cdots \\ 0 & 0 & a_1 & a_2 & \cdots \\ 0 & 0 & 0 & a_1 & \cdots \\ \vdots & & & & \end{pmatrix}.$$

Such a matrix

(1) is upper triangular
(2) has constant entries running down the diagonals from the upper left to the lower right. Here are some examples of matrices of this kind.

$$\begin{pmatrix} 2 & 1 & 3 & \cdots \\ 0 & 2 & 1 & \cdots \\ 0 & 0 & 2 & \cdots \\ \vdots & & & \end{pmatrix}, \quad \begin{pmatrix} 6 & -1 & 7 & 3 & \cdots \\ 0 & 6 & -1 & 7 & \cdots \\ 0 & 0 & 6 & -1 & \cdots \\ 0 & 0 & 0 & 6 & \cdots \\ \vdots & & & & \end{pmatrix}.$$

What is the action of A on an input?

The response to $(1, 0, 0, 0, \ldots)$ is $(a_1, a_2, a_3, a_4, \ldots)$
The response to $(0, 1, 0, 0, \ldots)$ is $(0, a_1, a_2, a_3, \ldots)$
The response to $(0, 0, 1, 0, \ldots)$ is $(0, 0, a_1, a_2, \ldots)$ et cetera.

We can see that

(1) If the input begins with a number of zeros, the output begins with the same number of zeros. In other words, as long as a zero message is sent, a zero message will be received.

(2) The effect of delaying the input message by a number of zeros is merely to delay the output. The subsequent values are not altered in any way.

We have observed these facts with particularly simple inputs, but the same is true for any input $(m_1, m_2, m_3, \ldots)$. A device that has these properties is called *time independent.* Such devices are important in theory and in practice. A telephone is (ideally) an example of such a device. The message received depends only on what was sent and does not depend upon the time the message was initiated. We shall call a matrix A that has the two properties enumerated above a *time independent matrix.*

PROBLEMS

1. Show that the matrices that correspond to amplification, delay, differencing, running summation, and smoothing are time independent matrices.
2. Prove by a direct computation that if a message M is the input to a time independent device A, so that the output is MA, the output corresponding to a delayed version of M is simply a delayed version of MA.

Time independent matrices have a number of simple algebraic properties.

Theorem: (1) *If* A *is a time independent matrix and* k *is a scalar, then* kA *is also a time independent matrix.*

(2) *The sum of two time independent matrices is also time independent.*

(3) *The product of two time independent matrices is also time independent.*

PROOF: This is proved by writing out the matrices explicitly and observing that the stated combination also satisfies the conditions for time independence. For example, to prove (3) we note that the product

$$\begin{pmatrix} a_1 & a_2 & a_3 & a_4 & \cdots \\ 0 & a_1 & a_2 & a_3 & \cdots \\ 0 & 0 & a_1 & a_2 & \cdots \\ 0 & 0 & 0 & a_1 & \cdots \end{pmatrix} \begin{pmatrix} b_1 & b_2 & b_3 & b_4 & \cdots \\ 0 & b_1 & b_2 & b_3 & \cdots \\ 0 & 0 & b_1 & b_2 & \cdots \\ 0 & 0 & 0 & b_1 & \cdots \end{pmatrix}$$

$$= \begin{pmatrix} a_1b_1, & a_1b_2 + a_2b_1, & a_1b_3 + a_2b_2 + a_3b_1, & \cdots \\ 0 & a_1b_1, & a_1b_2 + a_2b_1, & \cdots \\ 0 & 0 & a_1b_1 & \\ \vdots & \vdots & \vdots & \end{pmatrix}$$

also has the form of a time independent matrix.

PROBLEMS

1. Prove that if S is a smoothing matrix then S^2 is time independent.
2. Prove that if A is a time independent matrix, then any polynomial in A is also time independent.
3. Is A' a time independent matrix if A is?
4. Prove that if A and B are two time independent matrices, then $AB = BA$.
5. If A is a time independent matrix and B is an arbitrary matrix, is AB time independent?
6. A special case of a time independent matrix is one of the form

$$\begin{pmatrix} a_1 & a_2 & a_3 & 0 & 0 & 0 & \cdots \\ 0 & a_1 & a_2 & a_3 & 0 & 0 & \cdots \\ 0 & 0 & a_1 & a_2 & a_3 & 0 & \cdots \\ 0 & 0 & 0 & a_1 & a_2 & a_3 & \cdots \\ \vdots & & & & & & \end{pmatrix}.$$

This is called a *second order device.* Is it true that the sum and the product of two second order devices are also second order devices?

Time independent matrices have inverses that are relatively simple to compute. As a preliminary step, we must do a bit of algebra.

Take a polynomial whose constant term is not zero and form its reciprocal. For example, $1/(1 + 2x)$ or $1/(2 + 3x - x^3)$. An expression of this sort can be expressed as an infinite series in x, and this infinite series can be found by a simple division. For instance, divide 1 by $1 + 2x$:

$$\begin{array}{r|l} & 1 - 2x + 4x^2 - 8x^3 + \cdots \\ 1 + 2x & 1 \\ & \underline{1 + 2x} \\ & -2x \\ & \underline{-2x - 4x^2} \\ & 4x^2 \\ & \underline{4x^2 + 8x^3} \\ & -8x^3 \\ & \vdots \end{array}$$

Thus, (1) $\quad 1/(1 + 2x) = 1 - 2x + 4x^2 - 8x^3 + \cdots$

Divide 1 by $2 + 3x - 4x^3$:

$$
\begin{array}{r l}
 & \tfrac{1}{2} - \tfrac{3}{4}x + \tfrac{9}{8}x^2 + \cdots \\
2 + 3x - 4x^3 \,\big)\!\!\!\! & 1 \\
 & 1 + \tfrac{3}{2}x - 2x^3 \\
\hline
 & \quad -\tfrac{3}{2}x + 2x^3 \\
 & \quad -\tfrac{3}{2}x - \tfrac{9}{4}x^2 + 3x^4 \\
\hline
 & \qquad \tfrac{9}{4}x^2 + 2x^3 - 3x^4 \\
 & \qquad \tfrac{9}{4}x^2 + \tfrac{27}{8}x^3 - \tfrac{9}{2}x^5 \\
\hline
 & \qquad\qquad -\tfrac{11}{8}x^2 - 3x^4 + \tfrac{9}{2}x^5.
\end{array}
$$

$- \tfrac{3}{4}x + \tfrac{9}{8}x^2 + \cdots$

requires a discussion of the conver-
ufficient here if we simply agree that

$c^2 - 8x^3 + \cdots) = 1$

$- 8x^3 + \cdots$

$- 8x^3 + \cdots$
$+ 8x^3 + \cdots$
$+ 0 + \cdots$

$+ 3x - 4x^3)(\tfrac{1}{2} - \tfrac{3}{4}x + \tfrac{9}{8}x^2 \ldots)$

e time independent matrix

$$
A = \begin{pmatrix}
 & & & a_4 & \cdots \\
 & & & a_3 & \cdots \\
0 & 0 & a_1 & a_2 & \cdots \\
0 & 0 & 0 & a_1 & \cdots \\
\vdots & & & &
\end{pmatrix}
$$

is the time independent matrix

$$B = \begin{pmatrix} b_1 & b_2 & b_3 & b_4 & \cdots \\ 0 & b_1 & b_2 & b_3 & \cdots \\ 0 & 0 & b_1 & b_2 & \cdots \\ 0 & 0 & 0 & b_1 & \cdots \\ \vdots & & & & \end{pmatrix}$$

where the sequence of numbers $b_1, b_2, \ldots$ *have been determined from the numbers* $a_1, a_2, \ldots$ *by means of the equation*

$$b_1 + b_2x + b_3x^2 + \cdots = \frac{1}{a_1 + a_2x + a_3x^2 + \cdots} \tag{3}$$

PROOF: If equation (3) holds, then

$$(a_1 + a_2x + a_3x^2 + \cdots)(b_1 + b_2x + b_3x^2 + \cdots) = 1.$$

Hence, $a_1b_2 + (a_1b_2 + a_2b_1)x + (a_1b_3 + a_2b_2 + a_3b_1)x^2 + \cdots = 1$

Therefore,
$$\begin{aligned} a_1b_1 &= 1 \\ a_1b_2 + a_2b_1 &= 0 \\ a_1b_3 + a_2b_2 + a_3b_1 &= 0 \\ &\vdots \end{aligned}$$

Now refer to the product AB (as given in the proof on page 260) and we find that

$$AB = BA = \begin{pmatrix} 1 & 0 & 0 & 0 & \cdots \\ 0 & 1 & 0 & 0 & \cdots \\ 0 & 0 & 1 & 0 & \cdots \\ \vdots & & & & \end{pmatrix} = I.$$

Example 1: Find the inverse of $\begin{pmatrix} 1 & -1 & 0 & 0 & 0 & \cdots \\ 0 & 1 & -1 & 0 & 0 & \cdots \\ 0 & 0 & 1 & -1 & 0 & \cdots \\ \vdots & & & & & \end{pmatrix}$.

We have $a_1 = 1$ and $a_2 = -1$. By a division, we find that $1/(1 - x) = 1 + x + x^2 + x^3 + \cdots$ so that $b_1 = 1$, $b_2 = 1$, $b_3 = 1$, ... The inverse is therefore

$$\begin{pmatrix} 1 & 1 & 1 & 1 & \cdots \\ 0 & 1 & 1 & 1 & \cdots \\ 0 & 0 & 1 & 1 & \cdots \\ 0 & 0 & 0 & 1 & \cdots \end{pmatrix}.$$

Example 2: Find the inverse of $\begin{pmatrix} 1 & -2 & 1 & 0 & 0 & \cdots \\ 0 & 1 & -2 & 1 & 0 & \cdots \\ 0 & 0 & 1 & -2 & 1 & \cdots \\ \vdots \end{pmatrix}$.

By a division, we find that $1/(1 - 2x + x^2) = 1 + 2x + 3x^2 + 4x^3 + \cdots$.

Hence the inverse is $\begin{pmatrix} 1 & 2 & 3 & 4 & \cdots \\ 0 & 1 & 2 & 3 & \cdots \\ 0 & 0 & 1 & 2 & \cdots \\ 0 & 0 & 0 & 1 & \cdots \\ \vdots \end{pmatrix}$.

PROBLEMS

1. Find the power series for $1/(1 - 2x)$.
2. Expand in a series: $1/(\frac{1}{2} - \frac{1}{2}x)$.
3. Expand in a series: $1/(1 + x + x^2)$.
4. Expand $1/(1 + 2x + 3x^2)$.
5. Expand $1/(1 - x^2)$.
6. Find the inverse of $\begin{pmatrix} 1 & -2 & 0 & 0 & \cdots \\ 0 & 1 & -2 & 0 & \cdots \\ 0 & 0 & 1 & -2 & \cdots \\ \vdots \end{pmatrix}$.
7. Find the inverse of $\begin{pmatrix} \frac{3}{2} & -\frac{1}{2} & \cdots & & \\ & \frac{3}{2} & -\frac{1}{2} & & \\ & & \frac{3}{2} & -\frac{1}{2} & \\ \vdots \end{pmatrix}$.

The elements of the matrix that are not indicated explicitly are all zero.

8. Find the inverse of
$$\begin{pmatrix} 1 & 1 & 1 & & & \cdots \\ & 1 & 1 & 1 & & \\ & & 1 & 1 & 1 & \\ & & & 1 & 1 & 1 \\ \vdots & & & & & \end{pmatrix}.$$

9. Let
$$A = \begin{pmatrix} \frac{1}{2} & \frac{1}{4} & \frac{1}{8} & \frac{1}{16} & \cdots \\ 0 & \frac{1}{2} & \frac{1}{4} & \frac{1}{8} & \cdots \\ 0 & 0 & \frac{1}{2} & \frac{1}{4} & \cdots \\ 0 & 0 & 0 & \frac{1}{2} & \cdots \\ \vdots & & & & \end{pmatrix}$$

Find the inverse of A.
Find the action of A on the input

(1): (1, 1, 1, 1, 1, 1, . . .)
(2): (1, 2, 3, 4, . . .)
(3): (0, 1, 0, 1, 0, 1, 0, 1, . . .)
(4): (1, 2, 3, 2, 1, 2, 3, 2, 1, . . .)

10. Find the inverse of
$$\begin{pmatrix} 1 & k & 0 & 0 & \cdots \\ 0 & 1 & k & 0 & \cdots \\ 0 & 0 & 1 & k & \cdots \\ 0 & 0 & 0 & 1 & \cdots \\ \vdots & & & & \end{pmatrix}.$$

CHAPTER 8

Characteristic Values and their Application

8.1 Characteristic Values of Matrices

This chapter develops a portion of matrix theory that is exceedingly rich in applications. The theory of characteristic values appears, for example, in atomic physics, in astronomy, in the mechanics of vibrating systems of particles. In mathematics itself, the theory of characteristic values is of great importance in numerical analysis, which is the study of how solutions of equations can be effectively computed. The subject has also been developed for its own sake.

Characteristic values made their appearance on the mathematical horizon as early as 1772 when Pierre Simon Laplace (1749–1827), a French astronomer and mathematician, employed them to discuss perturbations of planetary motion.

Some time ago, I was talking to a garage mechanic about a new car I bought. The mechanic assured me that although it was a fine car, the particular model had a tendency to develop vibrations around 45 m.p.h. which would disappear around 48 m.p.h. This phenomenon of "resonance" is common in engineering, and its mathematical description involves characteristic values of matrices. In this way, matrix theory can be brought down from the heavens to the man in the street, the phenomenon referred to in the preface.

Definition: *If* $A = (a_{ij})$ *is an* $n \times n$ *matrix, its characteristic equation is the equation*

$$\det (A - \lambda I) = 0,$$

where λ *is a scalar variable.*

Let us expand this definition a bit. Since λI is the diagonal matrix

$$\begin{pmatrix} \lambda & 0 & \cdots & 0 \\ 0 & \lambda & & \\ \vdots & & \ddots & \\ 0 & & & \lambda \end{pmatrix},$$

this equation is the same as the equation

$$\begin{vmatrix} a_{11} - \lambda & a_{12} & \cdots & a_{1n} \\ a_{21} & a_{22} - \lambda & & a_{2n} \\ \cdot & \cdot & & \cdot \\ a_{n1} & a_{n2} & \cdots & a_{nn} - \lambda \end{vmatrix} = 0.$$

To obtain the characteristic equation of a matrix, subtract λ from each element on the principal diagonal, and equate the resulting determinant to zero.

Example 1: If $A = \begin{pmatrix} 1 & 2 \\ 3 & 4 \end{pmatrix}$, the characteristic equation of A is

$$\begin{vmatrix} 1 - \lambda & 2 \\ 3 & 4 - \lambda \end{vmatrix} = 0.$$

By expanding the determinant, there is obtained $(1 - \lambda)(4 - \lambda) - 6 = 0$, or, $\lambda^2 - 5\lambda - 2 = 0$.

Example 2: If $A = \begin{pmatrix} 1 & 3 & 2 \\ 0 & 1 & 1 \\ 1 & 0 & 1 \end{pmatrix}$, its characteristic equation is

$$\begin{vmatrix} 1 - \lambda & 3 & 2 \\ 0 & 1 - \lambda & 1 \\ 1 & 0 & 1 - \lambda \end{vmatrix} = 0.$$

By expanding this determinant according to the minors of the first column we have

$$(1 - \lambda)\begin{vmatrix} 1 - \lambda & 1 \\ 0 & 1 - \lambda \end{vmatrix} - 0\begin{vmatrix} 3 & 2 \\ 0 & 1 - \lambda \end{vmatrix} + 1\begin{vmatrix} 3 & 2 \\ 1 - \lambda & 1 \end{vmatrix} = 0,$$

or, $(1 - \lambda)^3 + 3 - 2(1 - \lambda) = 0$. This simplifies further to $\lambda^3 - 3\lambda^2 + \lambda - 2 = 0$.

The determinant on the left-hand side of the characteristic equation, when expanded, becomes a polynomial of degree n in λ. This polynomial is frequently called the *characteristic polynomial* of the matrix.

PROBLEMS

1. Find the characteristic equations of the following matrices:

$$\begin{pmatrix} 1 & 2 \\ 1 & 4 \end{pmatrix}, \begin{pmatrix} 2 & 0 \\ -7 & 3 \end{pmatrix}, \begin{pmatrix} 1 & 0 \\ 1 & 1 \end{pmatrix}, \begin{pmatrix} 1 & 0 \\ 0 & 2 \end{pmatrix}, (3), \begin{pmatrix} 0 & 0 \\ 0 & 1 \end{pmatrix}, \begin{pmatrix} 1 & 6 & 2 \\ 1 & 0 & 1 \\ 1 & 1 & 1 \end{pmatrix}.$$

2. If I is the $n \times n$ unit matrix, find its characteristic polynomial.
3. If 0 is the $n \times n$ zero matrix, find its characteristic equation.
4. Find the characteristic equations of the 2×2 and 3×3 matrices designated by J.
5. Find the characteristic equations of

$$\begin{pmatrix} 1 & 0 & 0 \\ 0 & 0 & 1 \\ 0 & 1 & 0 \end{pmatrix} \quad \text{and} \quad \begin{pmatrix} 0 & 1 & 0 \\ 1 & 0 & 0 \\ 0 & 0 & 1 \end{pmatrix}.$$

6. Prove that the value at $\lambda = 0$ of the characteristic polynomial of a matrix A equals $\det A$.

The Cayley-Hamilton Theorem which is presented next is one of the most famous in matrix theory. It says that if you have a square matrix A, form its characteristic polynomial, and in this polynomial substitute the matrix A for the variable λ, then the resulting matrix polynomial will reduce to the zero matrix. Another way of phrasing this is that *a matrix satisfies its own characteristic equation.*

Let us see how this works out. We have just computed the characteristic polynomial of the matrix $A = \begin{pmatrix} 1 & 2 \\ 3 & 4 \end{pmatrix}$. It turned out to be $\lambda^2 - 5\lambda - 2$. Write this as $\lambda^2 - 5\lambda - 2\lambda^0$. Now substitute the matrix A for λ, remembering that $A^\circ = I$. This yields $A^2 - 5A - 2I$. According to the Cayley-Hamilton Theorem, this polynomial in A should reduce to 0.

We can check this.

$$A^2 = \begin{pmatrix} 1 & 2 \\ 3 & 4 \end{pmatrix}\begin{pmatrix} 1 & 2 \\ 3 & 4 \end{pmatrix} = \begin{pmatrix} 7 & 10 \\ 15 & 22 \end{pmatrix}.$$

Hence,

$$A^2 - 5A - 2I = \begin{pmatrix} 7 & 10 \\ 15 & 22 \end{pmatrix} - 5\begin{pmatrix} 1 & 2 \\ 3 & 4 \end{pmatrix} - 2\begin{pmatrix} 1 & 0 \\ 0 & 1 \end{pmatrix} = \begin{pmatrix} 0 & 0 \\ 0 & 0 \end{pmatrix}.$$

Check.

We shall prove the theorem only in the 2×2 case. The proof of the general case is rather more advanced.

Theorem: *Any square matrix satisfies its own characteristic equation.*

PROOF: If $A = \begin{pmatrix} a & b \\ c & d \end{pmatrix}$, then the characteristic equation of A is

$$\begin{vmatrix} a - \lambda & b \\ c & d - \lambda \end{vmatrix} = 0, \text{ or, } (a - \lambda)(d - \lambda) - bc = 0.$$

The equation expands out to

$$\lambda^2 - (a + d)\lambda + (ad - bc) = 0, \quad \text{or to}$$
$$\lambda^2 - (a + d)\lambda + (ad - bc)\lambda^0 = 0.$$

By substituting A for λ in this equation, we would like to prove that

$$A^2 - (a + d)A + (ad - bc)I = 0.$$

Now,

$$A^2 = \begin{pmatrix} a & b \\ c & d \end{pmatrix}\begin{pmatrix} a & b \\ c & d \end{pmatrix} = \begin{pmatrix} a^2 + bc & ab + bd \\ ac + dc & bc + d^2 \end{pmatrix},$$

$$-(a + d)A = -(a + d)\begin{pmatrix} a & b \\ c & d \end{pmatrix} = \begin{pmatrix} -a^2 - ad & -ab - bd \\ -ac - cd & -ad - d^2 \end{pmatrix}$$

$$(ad - bc)I = \begin{pmatrix} ad - bc & 0 \\ 0 & ad - bc \end{pmatrix}.$$

With these preliminary computations performed, it is easy to read down the columns, element by element, and see that

$$A^2 - (a + d)A + (ad - bc)I = \begin{pmatrix} 0 & 0 \\ 0 & 0 \end{pmatrix}.$$

PROBLEMS

1. Show by direct computations that the matrices $\begin{pmatrix} 1 & 1 \\ 2 & 3 \end{pmatrix}$, $\begin{pmatrix} 1 & 4 \\ 5 & 7 \end{pmatrix}$, and $\begin{pmatrix} 2 & 0 \\ 1 & 3 \end{pmatrix}$ satisfy their own characteristic equations.

2. Show by a direct computation that the matrices $\begin{pmatrix} 1 & 0 & 0 \\ 0 & 0 & 1 \\ 0 & 1 & 0 \end{pmatrix}$, $\begin{pmatrix} 1 & 0 & 1 \\ 0 & 1 & 0 \\ 0 & 1 & 1 \end{pmatrix}$, and $\begin{pmatrix} 1 & 1 & 1 \\ 0 & 1 & 1 \\ 0 & 0 & 1 \end{pmatrix}$ satisfy their own characteristic equations.

3. Try to prove the Cayley-Hamilton Theorem in the 3×3 case by a direct computation as was done here in the 2×2 case. It should work out, but there will be considerable algebraic computation.

4. Prove that the $n \times n$ identity matrix satisfies its own characteristic equation.

5. A purported "proof" of the Cayley-Hamilton Theorem is as follows: The characteristic equation of A is $\det(A - \lambda I) = 0$. Now, substitute $\lambda = A$ in this equation. We obtain $\det(A - AI) = 0$. But $A - AI = 0$, and $\det 0 = 0$. Hence the matrix A satisfies its own characteristic equation. Criticise this "proof."

As we have seen, the characteristic equation of a matrix is a polynomial equation in λ. This equation can be solved for λ to determine its roots. These roots have a special name.

Definition: *The roots of the characteristic equation of a matrix are called the characteristic values or the characteristic roots of the matrix.*

Example: Determine the characteristic values of the matrix $\begin{pmatrix} 1 & 4 \\ 2 & 3 \end{pmatrix}$. This matrix has the characteristic equation $\begin{vmatrix} 1-\lambda & 4 \\ 2 & 3-\lambda \end{vmatrix} = 0$. This is the same as $(1 - \lambda)(3 - \lambda) - 8 = 0$, and this equation simplifies to $\lambda^2 - 4\lambda - 5 = 0$. This implies $(\lambda - 5)(\lambda + 1) = 0$ so that

$$\begin{cases} \lambda = 5 \\ \lambda = -1. \end{cases}$$

The numbers -1 and 5 are the characteristic values of the matrix.

Since the characteristic equation of a 2×2 matrix is a quadratic equation, it has two roots. These roots, or characteristic values, share all the possibilities that go with quadratic equations whose coefficients are real numbers.

1. The roots may be real and distinct.
2. The roots may be real and equal.
3. The roots may be complex conjugate.

The quadratic formula tells us that the two roots of the equation

$$A\lambda^2 + B\lambda + C = 0$$

are given by

$$\lambda_1 = \frac{-B + \sqrt{B^2 - 4AC}}{2A} \quad \text{and} \quad \lambda_2 = \frac{-B - \sqrt{B^2 - 4AC}}{2A}.$$

From this formula, it is not too difficult to conclude that

1. The roots are real and distinct if $B^2 - 4AC > 0$.

2. The roots are real and equal if $B^2 - 4AC = 0$.
3. The roots are complex imaginary if $B^2 - 4AC < 0$.

These three conditions can now be transferred to characteristic equations. The matrix $\begin{pmatrix} a & b \\ c & d \end{pmatrix}$ has the characteristic equation

$$\begin{vmatrix} a - \lambda & b \\ c & d - \lambda \end{vmatrix} = 0 \qquad \text{or,} \qquad \lambda^2 - (a + d)\lambda + (ad - bc) = 0.$$

Set $A = 1$, $B = -(a + d)$, $C = ad - bc$ in the quadratic formula. Then,

$$\begin{aligned} B^2 - 4AC &= (a + d)^2 - 4(ad - bc) \\ &= a^2 + 2ad + d^2 - 4ad + 4bc \\ &= (a - d)^2 + 4bc. \end{aligned}$$

This work proves the following theorem. (We assume that the numbers a, b, c, and d are real.)

Theorem: *The characteristic values of the matrix* $\begin{pmatrix} \mathrm{a} & \mathrm{b} \\ \mathrm{c} & \mathrm{d} \end{pmatrix}$ *are*

$$\begin{cases} \lambda_1 = \frac{1}{2}((\mathrm{a} + \mathrm{d}) + \sqrt{(\mathrm{a} - \mathrm{d})^2 + 4\mathrm{bc}}\,) \\ \lambda_2 = \frac{1}{2}((\mathrm{a} + \mathrm{d}) - \sqrt{(\mathrm{a} - \mathrm{d})^2 + 4\mathrm{bc}}\,). \end{cases}$$

1. *The characteristic values are real and distinct if*

$$(\mathrm{a} - \mathrm{d})^2 + 4\mathrm{bc} > 0.$$

2. *The characteristic values are real and equal if*

$$(\mathrm{a} - \mathrm{d})^2 + 4\mathrm{bc} = 0.$$

3. *The characteristic values are complex conjugate if*

$$(\mathrm{a} - \mathrm{d})^2 + 4\mathrm{bc} < 0.$$

Examples: (a) In the matrix $\begin{pmatrix} 2 & 1 \\ 1 & 2 \end{pmatrix}$, $a = 2$, $b = 1$, $c = 1$, $d = 2$, so that $(a - d)^2 + 4bc = 4 > 0$. The characteristic values of the matrix are real and distinct. They are

$$\tfrac{1}{2}((2 + 2) + \sqrt{4}\,) = 3 \qquad \text{and} \qquad \tfrac{1}{2}((2 + 2) - \sqrt{4}\,) = 1.$$

(b) In the matrix $\begin{pmatrix} 1 & 2 \\ -2 & 1 \end{pmatrix}$, $(a - d)^2 + 4bc = -16 < 0$. The characteristic values are therefore complex conjugate. They are

$$\tfrac{1}{2}(2 + \sqrt{-16}) \qquad \text{and} \qquad \tfrac{1}{2}(2 - \sqrt{-16}).$$

These numbers simplify to

$$1 + 2i \qquad \text{and} \qquad 1 - 2i, \qquad \text{where} \qquad i = \sqrt{-1}.$$

(c) The characteristic values of the matrix $\begin{pmatrix} 2 & 0 \\ 0 & 2 \end{pmatrix}$ are real and equal. They are 2 and 2.

The formulas for solving cubic and quartic equations are complicated. For equations of degree greater than 4, there are no general formulas of the sort exemplified by the quadratic formula. The solution of these equations must be described by other means, and it is natural that the study of characteristic values of higher order matrices reflect this situation.

PROBLEMS

1. Find the characteristic values of the following matrices. $\begin{pmatrix} 1 & 9 \\ 7 & 2 \end{pmatrix}$, $\begin{pmatrix} 3 & 0 \\ 1 & -1 \end{pmatrix}$, $\begin{pmatrix} 5 & 2 \\ 1 & 1 \end{pmatrix}$, $\begin{pmatrix} 2 & -4 \\ 5 & 6 \end{pmatrix}$, $\begin{pmatrix} 2 & 1 \\ 2 & 1 \end{pmatrix}$.

2. Find the characteristic values of the 2×2 matrix I. The 2×2 matrix J. The 3×3 matrix I.

3. For what values of c are the characteristic values of the matrix $\begin{pmatrix} 1 & 2 \\ c & 4 \end{pmatrix}$ real and unequal, real and equal, complex conjugate?

4. Answer the same question for the matrix $\begin{pmatrix} c & 1 \\ 2 & 4 \end{pmatrix}$.

5. Prove that the sum of the characteristic values of the matrix $\begin{pmatrix} a & b \\ c & d \end{pmatrix}$ is $a + d$, and that the product of these values is $\begin{vmatrix} a & b \\ c & d \end{vmatrix}$.

6. Use the result of Problem 5 to prove that $\begin{pmatrix} a & b \\ c & d \end{pmatrix}$ is singular if and only if one of its characteristic roots is zero.

7. If $A = \begin{pmatrix} 1 & 4 \\ 2 & 3 \end{pmatrix}$, show that its characteristic roots are -1 and 5. Verify that $(A - 5I)(A + I) = 0$. Explain.

8. Determine the characteristic roots of the matrix $\begin{pmatrix} \cos\theta & \sin\theta \\ -\sin\theta & \cos\theta \end{pmatrix}$.

9. Determine the characteristic roots of $\begin{pmatrix} 1 & 0 \\ h & 1 \end{pmatrix}$.

10. Determine the characteristic roots of the matrix $\begin{pmatrix} a & b \\ -b & a \end{pmatrix}$.

11. Determine the characteristic roots of $\begin{pmatrix} 1+h & a \\ 0 & 1 \end{pmatrix}$.

12. In Problems 12 and 13, a, b, and c are real numbers. Prove that the characteristic roots of the symmetric matrix $\begin{pmatrix} a & b \\ b & c \end{pmatrix}$ are real.

13. Prove that if $a > 0$ and $\begin{vmatrix} a & b \\ b & c \end{vmatrix} > 0$, then the characteristic roots of $\begin{pmatrix} a & b \\ b & c \end{pmatrix}$ are positive.

14. Prove that if λ is a characteristic root of $\begin{pmatrix} a & b \\ c & d \end{pmatrix}$, then $\begin{pmatrix} a-\lambda & b \\ c & d-\lambda \end{pmatrix}$ is singular.

15. Work with 2×2 matrices and determine the relationship between the characteristic roots of A and those of A'; between those of A and those of kA, where k is a scalar; between those of A and those of A^{-1}.

16. Determine the set of points in the x, y plane for which the matrix $\begin{pmatrix} x & y \\ 1 & -1 \end{pmatrix}$ has (1) real and distinct roots; (2) real and equal roots; and (3) complex conjugate roots.

17. A matrix of the form $\begin{pmatrix} a & b \\ c & a \end{pmatrix}$ has real and equal characteristic roots. Prove that either b or c equals zero.

8.2 High Powers of a Matrix

In this section we shall show how the Cayley-Hamilton Theorem can be used to find a formula for the nth power of a matrix, where n is a positive integer. Though we shall work with 2×2 matrices, the ideas can be extended to the general case.

We begin by recalling some facts about the division of one algebraic polynomial by another. An integer may be divided by another integer and this process yields a quotient and a remainder.

Example 1: $7 \div 3 = 2$, remainder: 1
or $7 = (3 \cdot 2) + 1$

Example 2: $9 \div 16 = 0$, remainder: 9
or $9 = (16 \cdot 0) + 9$.

The remainder is always *less* than the divisor. In a similar way, one polynomial may be divided by a second polynomial and will yield a quotient and a remainder.

Example 3:

$$
\begin{array}{r@{}l}
 & \lambda^2 \qquad + 1 \\
\lambda + 1 \big) & \overline{\lambda^3 + \lambda^2 + \lambda + 2} \\
 & \underline{\lambda^3 + \lambda^2} \\
 & \qquad\qquad \lambda + 2 \\
 & \qquad\qquad \underline{\lambda + 1} \\
 & \qquad\qquad\quad 1 : \text{REMAINDER}
\end{array}
$$

Example 4:

$$
\begin{array}{r@{}l}
 & \lambda^2 - \lambda + 4 \\
\lambda^2 + \lambda - 2 \big) & \overline{\lambda^4 + \lambda^2 + 1} \\
 & \underline{\lambda^4 + \lambda^3 - 2\lambda^2} \\
 & \quad -\lambda^3 + 3\lambda^2 + 1 \\
 & \quad \underline{-\lambda^3 - \lambda^2 + 2\lambda} \\
 & \qquad\qquad 4\lambda^2 - 2\lambda + 1 \\
 & \qquad\qquad \underline{4\lambda^2 + 4\lambda - 8} \\
 & \qquad\qquad\quad -6\lambda + 9 : \text{REMAINDER}
\end{array}
$$

Note (and this is important for the argument) that the degree of the remainder must be *less* than that of the divisor, for if it were not, we could perform additional divisions and reduce the degree.

The algebraic identities that emerge from this process can be written without division in the form

(In Example 3),

$$\lambda^3 + \lambda^2 + \lambda + 2 = (\lambda + 1)(\lambda^2 + 1) + 1$$

(In Example 4),

$$\lambda^4 + \lambda^2 + 1 = (\lambda^2 + \lambda - 2)(\lambda^2 - \lambda + 4) + (-6\lambda + 9).$$

In general,

$$\text{Dividend} = (\text{Divisor})(\text{Quotient}) + \text{Remainder}.$$

This decomposition is known as the *Division Algorithm* for polynomials. Its precise statement is this: *Let* a(x) *and* b(x) *be any two polynomials. Assume that* a(x) *does not have all zero coefficients. Then we can find polynomials* q(x) *and* r(x), *where* r(x) *is either* 0 *or has a degree less than* a(x), *such that*

$$b(x) = a(x)q(x) + r(x)$$

is an identity in x.

We now begin our discussion of the powers of a matrix. Let $A = \begin{pmatrix} a & b \\ c & d \end{pmatrix}$. The characteristic equation of A is

$$\lambda^2 - (a + d)\lambda + (ad - bc) = 0.$$

Suppose we abbreviate this by writing $\begin{cases} \alpha_1 = -(a - d) \\ \alpha_2 = (ad - bc) \end{cases}$, so that the characteristic equation is

$$\lambda^2 + \alpha_1\lambda + \alpha_2 = 0.$$

By the Cayley-Hamilton Theorem, the matrix A satisfies this equation. That is,

$$A^2 + \alpha_1 A + \alpha_2 I = 0. \tag{1}$$

Now, apply the Division Algorithm to the polynomials λ^n and

$$\lambda^2 + \alpha_1\lambda + \alpha_2.$$

(We do not actually have to carry out the algorithm; we need only do it conceptually.) The algorithm will yield a quotient $q(\lambda)$ and a remainder $r(\lambda)$. Both $q(\lambda)$ and $r(\lambda)$ will be certain polynomials in λ. Since the degree of the divisor is 2, the degree of the remainder *cannot exceed 1*. Therefore write $r(\lambda) = \beta_1 + \beta_2\lambda$. The result of applying the algorithm can therefore be expressed as

$$\lambda^n = (\lambda^2 + \alpha_1\lambda + \alpha_2)q(\lambda) + r(\lambda)$$

or

$$\lambda^n = (\lambda^2 + \alpha_1\lambda + \alpha_2)q(\lambda) + \beta_1 + \beta_2\lambda. \tag{2}$$

Since this is a polynomial identity in the variable λ, we know that a true matrix equation will result if the matrix A is substituted in place of λ. (See page 52.) Therefore,

$$A^n = (A^2 + \alpha_1 A + \alpha_2 I)q(A) + \beta_1 I + \beta_2 A. \tag{3}$$

Now the Cayley-Hamilton Theorem tells us that $A^2 + \alpha_1 A + \alpha_2 I = 0$, and therefore Equation (3) reduces to

$$A^n = \beta_1 I + \beta_2 A$$

or, equivalently,

$$A^n = \beta_1 \begin{pmatrix} 1 & 0 \\ 0 & 1 \end{pmatrix} + \beta_2 \begin{pmatrix} a & b \\ c & d \end{pmatrix}. \tag{4}$$

This means that A^n can be expressed as a combination of the two matrices I and A. All that need be done is to find out what the numbers β_1 and β_2

are. These two numbers will, in general, depend upon the integer n that is the power of A.

To determine β_1 and β_2, start with the polynomial Equation (2):

$$\lambda^n = (\lambda^2 + \alpha_1\lambda + \alpha_2)q(\lambda) + \beta_1 + \beta_2\lambda. \tag{2}$$

Let λ_1 and λ_2 be the two characteristic roots of A. This means that

$$\lambda_1^2 + \alpha_1\lambda_1 + \alpha_2 = 0 \tag{5}$$

and

$$\lambda_2^2 + \alpha_1\lambda_2 + \alpha_2 = 0. \tag{6}$$

By substituting λ_1 in the polynomial equation (2), we obtain

$$\lambda_1^n = (\lambda_1^2 + \alpha_1\lambda_1 + \alpha_2)q(\lambda_1) + \beta_1 + \beta_2\lambda_1.$$

In view of Equation (5), this reduces to

$$\lambda_1^n = \beta_1 + \beta_2\lambda_1. \tag{7}$$

Similarly,

$$\lambda_2^n = \beta_1 + \beta_2\lambda_2. \tag{8}$$

By solving these two equations simultaneously we obtain,

$$\beta_1 = \frac{\begin{vmatrix} \lambda_1^n & \lambda_1 \\ \lambda_2^n & \lambda_2 \end{vmatrix}}{\begin{vmatrix} 1 & \lambda_1 \\ 1 & \lambda_2 \end{vmatrix}} = \frac{\lambda_2\lambda_1^n - \lambda_1\lambda_2^n}{\lambda_2 - \lambda_1}$$

and

$$\beta_2 = \frac{\begin{vmatrix} 1 & \lambda_1^n \\ 1 & \lambda_2^n \end{vmatrix}}{\begin{vmatrix} 1 & \lambda_1 \\ 1 & \lambda_2 \end{vmatrix}} = \frac{\lambda_2^n - \lambda_1^n}{\lambda_2 - \lambda_1}.$$

Thus, substituting these values in Equation (4), we obtain

$$A^n = \frac{\lambda_2\lambda_1^n - \lambda_1\lambda_2^n}{\lambda_2 - \lambda_1}\begin{pmatrix} 1 & 0 \\ 0 & 1 \end{pmatrix} + \frac{\lambda_2^n - \lambda_1^n}{\lambda_2 - \lambda_1}\begin{pmatrix} a & b \\ c & d \end{pmatrix}. \tag{9}$$

This gives us a formula for A^n.

There is one slight difficulty with this result, and we must overcome it by a separate argument. If the characteristic equation has equal roots,

$\lambda_1 = \lambda_2$, then we cannot solve equations simultaneously since $\begin{vmatrix} 1 & \lambda_1 \\ 1 & \lambda_2 \end{vmatrix} = 0.$

We proceed as follows. If the characteristic equation has two roots equal to λ_1, this equation must be $(\lambda - \lambda_1)^2 = 0$. In this case, we can rewrite Equation (2) as

$$\lambda^n = (\lambda - \lambda_1)^2 q(\lambda) + \beta_1 + \beta_2\lambda. \tag{10}$$

Set* $\lambda = \lambda_1 + h$ where h is a new variable. Then Equation 10 becomes

$$(\lambda_1 + h)^n = h^2 q(\lambda_1 + h) + \beta_1 + \beta_2\lambda_1 + \beta_2 h. \tag{11}$$

This is now an identity in the variable h.

Expand the left-hand side of Equation (11) by the binomial formula,

$$\lambda_1^n + nh\lambda_1^{n-1} + n\frac{(n-1)}{2}h^2\lambda_1^{n-2} + \cdots = h^2 q(\lambda_1 + h) + \beta_1 + \beta_2\lambda_1 + \beta_2 h. \tag{12}$$

The left-hand side as well as the right-hand side are polynomials in the variable h. All the other quantities are constants. Since this is so, the term involving the first power of h on the left-hand side must equal the terms involving the first power of h on the right-hand side. On the left-hand side, the powers of h are ascending and we find only $nh\lambda_1^{n-1}$. On the right-hand side, $h^2 q(\lambda_1 + h)$ (if expanded out) involves h^2 and higher powers of h. The term $\beta_1 + \beta_2\lambda$ does not involve h, so that the only term that does is $\beta_2 h$. Therefore, $nh\lambda_1^{n-1} = \beta_2 h$ or, dividing through by h,

$$n\lambda_1^{n-1} = \beta_2. \tag{13}$$

As before, we have

$$\lambda_1^n = \beta_1 + \beta_2\lambda_1. \tag{7}$$

Therefore,

$$\beta_1 = \lambda_1^n - \beta_2\lambda_1 = \lambda_1^n - n\lambda_1^n = (1 - n)\lambda_1^n. \tag{14}$$

By substituting Equations (14) and (13) into Equation (4) we obtain the final answer in this case:

$$A^n = (1 - n)\lambda_1^n \begin{pmatrix} 1 & 0 \\ 0 & 1 \end{pmatrix} + n\lambda_1^{n-1} \begin{pmatrix} a & b \\ c & d \end{pmatrix}. \tag{15}$$

---

*The reader who is acquainted with differential calculus will recognize that this process is equivalent to obtaining the derivative of both sides of Equation (10) at the point $\lambda = \lambda_1$.

We summarize this derivation as a theorem.

Theorem: *Let* $A = \begin{pmatrix} a & b \\ c & d \end{pmatrix}$, *and let* λ_1 *and* λ_2 *be the characteristic roots of* A

(1) *If* $\lambda_1 \neq \lambda_2$, *then* A^n *is given by Equation* (9).

(2) *If* $\lambda_1 = \lambda_2$, *then* A^n *is given by Equation* (15).

Example 1: $A = \begin{pmatrix} 1 & 0 \\ 0 & 1 \end{pmatrix}$. It is obvious from inspection that $A^n = I$, but let us proceed as above. The characteristic equation is $\begin{vmatrix} 1-\lambda & 0 \\ 0 & 1-\lambda \end{vmatrix} = 0$ or $(1-\lambda)^2 = 0$. The roots are $\lambda_1 = 1$, $\lambda_2 = 1$, and are identical. From Equation (15), we have $A^n = (1-n)I + nI = I$, as required.

Example 2: $A = \begin{pmatrix} 1 & 4 \\ 2 & 3 \end{pmatrix}$. As we saw on page 269, the characteristic roots are 5 and -1. These are distinct. An application of the Formula (9) yields

$$A^n = \frac{(-1)5^n - 5(-1)^n}{-6}\begin{pmatrix} 1 & 0 \\ 0 & 1 \end{pmatrix} + \frac{(-1)^n - (5)^n}{-6}\begin{pmatrix} 1 & 4 \\ 2 & 3 \end{pmatrix}.$$

This answer can be simplified. Since

$$\frac{-1}{-6}\begin{pmatrix} 1 & 0 \\ 0 & 1 \end{pmatrix} + \frac{-1}{-6}\begin{pmatrix} 1 & 4 \\ 2 & 3 \end{pmatrix} = \frac{1}{6}\begin{pmatrix} 2 & 4 \\ 2 & 4 \end{pmatrix} = \frac{1}{3}\begin{pmatrix} 1 & 2 \\ 1 & 2 \end{pmatrix}, \text{ and}$$

$$\frac{-5}{-6}\begin{pmatrix} 1 & 0 \\ 0 & 1 \end{pmatrix} + \frac{1}{-6}\begin{pmatrix} 1 & 4 \\ 2 & 3 \end{pmatrix} = \frac{1}{6}\begin{pmatrix} 4 & -4 \\ -2 & 2 \end{pmatrix} = \frac{1}{3}\begin{pmatrix} 2 & -2 \\ -1 & 1 \end{pmatrix},$$

it follows that

$$A^n = \frac{5^n}{3}\begin{pmatrix} 1 & 2 \\ 1 & 2 \end{pmatrix} + \frac{(-1)^n}{3}\begin{pmatrix} 2 & -2 \\ -1 & 1 \end{pmatrix}.$$

Let us test this for $n = 1$ and $n = 2$.

$$A^1 = A = \frac{5}{3}\begin{pmatrix} 1 & 2 \\ 1 & 2 \end{pmatrix} - \frac{1}{3}\begin{pmatrix} 2 & -2 \\ -1 & 1 \end{pmatrix} = \begin{pmatrix} 1 & 4 \\ 2 & 3 \end{pmatrix}, \text{ check.}$$

For $n = 2$ we have

$$A^2 = \frac{25}{3}\begin{pmatrix} 1 & 2 \\ 1 & 2 \end{pmatrix} + \frac{1}{3}\begin{pmatrix} 2 & -2 \\ -1 & 1 \end{pmatrix} = \begin{pmatrix} 9 & 16 \\ 8 & 17 \end{pmatrix}.$$

Direct multiplication yields $\begin{pmatrix} 1 & 4 \\ 2 & 3 \end{pmatrix}\begin{pmatrix} 1 & 4 \\ 2 & 3 \end{pmatrix} = \begin{pmatrix} 9 & 16 \\ 8 & 17 \end{pmatrix}$, check.

Example 3: $A = \begin{pmatrix} 2 & 1 \\ -2 & -1 \end{pmatrix}$. The characteristic equation is

$$\begin{vmatrix} 2-\lambda & 1 \\ -2 & -1-\lambda \end{vmatrix} = 0.$$

Expanded, this is $(2 - \lambda)(-1 - \lambda) + 2 = 0$, or $\lambda^2 - \lambda = 0$. The characteristic roots are $\lambda_1 = 0$, $\lambda_2 = 1$, and are distinct. Therefore from Equation (9),

$$A^n = 0\begin{pmatrix} 1 & 0 \\ 0 & 1 \end{pmatrix} + \frac{1-0}{1-0}\begin{pmatrix} 2 & 1 \\ -2 & -1 \end{pmatrix} = A.$$

This result was to be expected since $A^2 = A$. Hence, $A^3 = A \cdot A^2 = A \cdot A = A^2 = A$; et cetera.

PROBLEMS

1. Find $\begin{pmatrix} 2 & 0 \\ 0 & 3 \end{pmatrix}^n$ (a) by inspection, and (b) by using the method explained in this chapter.

2. Find $\begin{pmatrix} 1 & -1 \\ -1 & 1 \end{pmatrix}^n, \begin{pmatrix} 1 & 0 \\ 0 & 0 \end{pmatrix}^n, \begin{pmatrix} 1 & 1 \\ 0 & 0 \end{pmatrix}^n.$

3. Find $\begin{pmatrix} 2 & -1 \\ -2 & 1 \end{pmatrix}^n, \begin{pmatrix} 2 & 0 \\ 3 & 1 \end{pmatrix}^n, \begin{pmatrix} 3 & -3 \\ -1 & 1 \end{pmatrix}^n, \begin{pmatrix} 1 & 1 \\ 1 & 1 \end{pmatrix}^n.$

4. Find $\begin{pmatrix} 5 & 3 \\ 1 & 3 \end{pmatrix}^n, \begin{pmatrix} 7 & 3 \\ 2 & 6 \end{pmatrix}^n, \begin{pmatrix} 0 & 6 \\ 1 & -1 \end{pmatrix}^n.$

5. If the matrix A satisfies the equation $A^2 = A + I$, show that $A^n = \alpha_n A + \beta_n I$ where α_n and β_n are certain constants.

6. Show that α_n and β_n in Problem 5 satisfy the relations

$$\begin{cases} \alpha_1 = 1 \\ \beta_1 = 0 \end{cases} \qquad \begin{cases} \alpha_{n+1} = \alpha_n + \beta_n \\ \beta_{n+1} = \alpha_n \end{cases}.$$

7. If the matrix A satisfies $A^2 = A + I$, show that $I + A + A^2 + \cdots + A^n = \alpha_n A + \beta_n I$ where α_n and β_n are certain constants satisfying

$$\begin{cases} \alpha_{n+1} = \alpha_n + \beta_n \\ \beta_{n+1} = \alpha_n + 1 \end{cases} \qquad \begin{cases} \alpha_1 = 1 \\ \beta_1 = 1. \end{cases}$$

8. What is wrong here? Let $A = \begin{pmatrix} 1 & 3 \\ 2 & 6 \end{pmatrix}$. The characteristic roots of A are $\lambda_1 = 7$ and $\lambda_2 = 0$. These are distinct, hence, $A^n = \frac{-7^n}{-7}\begin{pmatrix} 1 & 3 \\ 2 & 6 \end{pmatrix} = 7^{n-1}\begin{pmatrix} 1 & 3 \\ 2 & 6 \end{pmatrix}$. In this formula, set $n = -1$. Then, $A^{-1} = \frac{1}{49}\begin{pmatrix} 1 & 3 \\ 2 & 6 \end{pmatrix}$. But A is singular, so how can it have an inverse?

This section will be concluded with a brief indication of how this method can be extended to find the nth power of a 3×3 matrix, A.

The characteristic equation of A is a cubic, $\lambda^3 + \alpha_1\lambda^2 + \alpha_2\lambda + \alpha_3 = 0$, and has three roots λ_1, λ_2, and λ_3. The remainder $r(\lambda)$ in (2) can be *at most* a quadratic $\beta_1 + \beta_2\lambda + \beta_3\lambda^2$. Hence, as in (3),

$$A^n = \beta_1 I + \beta_2 A + \beta_3 A^2.$$

We must now determine β_1, β_2, and β_3. An identical argument to that which leads to (7) and (8) now leads to

$$\begin{cases} \lambda_1^n = \beta_1 + \beta_2\lambda_1 + \beta_3\lambda_1^2 \\ \lambda_2^n = \beta_1 + \beta_2\lambda_2 + \beta_3\lambda_2^2 \\ \lambda_3^n = \beta_1 + \beta_2\lambda_3 + \beta_3\lambda_3^2. \end{cases}$$

The determinant of this system is

$$\begin{vmatrix} 1 & \lambda_1 & \lambda_1^2 \\ 1 & \lambda_2 & \lambda_2^2 \\ 1 & \lambda_3 & \lambda_3^2 \end{vmatrix} = (\lambda_1 - \lambda_2)(\lambda_2 - \lambda_3)(\lambda_3 - \lambda_1)$$

(see page 175). If the characteristic roots are distinct, none of these factors is zero. Therefore, the determinant $\neq 0$, and the system can be solved for λ_1, λ_2, and λ_3. If two or three of the roots are equal, then we must use a trick that is parallel to that presented in the 2×2 case.

Example: Find

$$\begin{pmatrix} 2 & 2 & 0 \\ 1 & 2 & 1 \\ 1 & 2 & 1 \end{pmatrix}^n.$$

The characteristic equation

$$\begin{vmatrix} 2-\lambda & 2 & 0 \\ 1 & 2-\lambda & 1 \\ 1 & 2 & 1-\lambda \end{vmatrix} = 0$$

reduces to $\lambda(1-\lambda)(\lambda-4) = 0$. The characteristic roots are therefore $\lambda_1 = 0$, $\lambda_2 = 1$, and $\lambda_3 = 4$ and are distinct.

We must now solve the system of equations

$$\begin{cases} \beta_1 + 0\beta_2 + 0\beta_3 = 0 \\ \beta_1 + \beta_2 + \beta_3 = 1 \\ \beta_1 + 4\beta_2 + 16\beta_3 = 4^n. \end{cases}$$

The solution is $\beta_1 = 0$, $\beta_2 = \frac{1}{12}(16 - 4^n)$, and $\beta_3 = \frac{1}{12}(4^n - 4)$.

Hence,

$$A^n = \tfrac{1}{12}(16 - 4^n)\begin{pmatrix} 2 & 2 & 0 \\ 1 & 2 & 1 \\ 1 & 2 & 1 \end{pmatrix} + \tfrac{1}{12}(4^n - 4)\begin{pmatrix} 6 & 8 & 2 \\ 5 & 8 & 3 \\ 5 & 8 & 3 \end{pmatrix}$$

$$= \frac{1}{3}\begin{pmatrix} 2 & 0 & -2 \\ -1 & 0 & 1 \\ -1 & 0 & 1 \end{pmatrix} + \frac{4^n}{6}\begin{pmatrix} 2 & 3 & 1 \\ 2 & 3 & 1 \\ 2 & 3 & 1 \end{pmatrix}.$$

PROBLEMS

1. Find $\begin{pmatrix} 2 & 0 & 0 \\ 0 & 1 & 0 \\ 0 & 0 & -1 \end{pmatrix}^n$.

2. Find $\begin{pmatrix} 1 & 2 & 3 \\ 0 & 4 & 5 \\ 0 & 0 & 6 \end{pmatrix}^n$.

3. Find $\begin{pmatrix} 1 & 0 & 0 \\ 2 & -1 & 0 \\ 3 & 1 & 2 \end{pmatrix}^n$.

4. Check the example of the text for $n = 1, 2$, and 3.

8.3 Progressions, and Difference Equations

An arithmetic progression is a sequence of numbers whose differences of successive terms are constant.

Thus, the sequence $-1, 3, 7, 11, 15, \ldots$, has the constant differences $4, 4, 4, 4, \ldots$, and is an arithmetic progression.

A geometric progression is a sequence of numbers whose ratios of successive terms are constant. The sequence $3, 6, 12, 24, 48, \ldots$, has the constant ratios $2, 2, 2, 2, \ldots$, and is a geometric progression. The sequence $2, -2, 2, -2, \ldots$, with constant ratios $-1, -1, -1, \ldots$, is another example of a geometric progression. Arithmetic and geometric progressions are by no means the only useful or important types of progressions in mathematics. The sequence of squares $1, 4, 9, 16, 25, 36, \ldots$, is of great importance, yet it is neither arithmetic nor geometric. What is true about this sequence is that its second differences—that is, the differences of the differences—are constant. This is illustrated by the following table:

Sequence:	1,		4,		9,		16,		25,		36,	...
First Difference:		3,		5,		7,		9,		11,	...	
Second Difference:			2,		2,		2,		2,	...		

Some of the goals of the study of progressions are to

(1) Find a formula for the nth term of the progression.

(2) Find a formula for the sum of the first n terms of the progression.

(3) Examine the behavior of the individual terms and of their sum as n becomes larger and larger.

We recall from previous work in algebra that:

(A) If we have an arithmetic progression whose first term is a_1 and whose common difference is d, the nth term a_n, is given by

$$a_n = a_1 + (n - 1)d,$$

and the sum of the first n terms, S_n, is

$$S_n = na_1 + \frac{n(n-1)}{2} d.$$

(B) If we have a geometric progression whose first term is a_1 and whose common ratio is r, then

$$a_n = a_1 r^{n-1}$$

and the sum of n terms is given by

$$S_n = a_1 \left(\frac{r^n - 1}{r - 1} \right).$$

The object of this section is to present a theory of sequences or progressions which encompasses both the arithmetic and the geometric variety and goes beyond. It is a theory which will be presented from a matrix point of view, and one which has many applications. We begin by examining progressions further. If the numbers $a_1, a_2, a_3, \ldots$ form an arithmetic progression, then

$$\left.\begin{aligned} a_2 - a_1 &= d \\ a_3 - a_2 &= d \\ a_4 - a_3 &= d \\ &\vdots \\ a_{n+1} - a_n &= d \\ &\vdots \end{aligned}\right\} \text{ where } d \text{ is the common difference.}$$

The equation

$$(1) \qquad a_{n+1} - a_n = d$$

governs the progression. Written in the form

$$a_{n+1} = a_n + d,$$

this equation tells us how to go from the nth term to the $n + 1$st term. If we know what the first term is, we can start the ball rolling. We start with the first term. Equation (1) then gives us the second. By another application of the equation, it leads to the third, et cetera. This equation is called the *recurrence equation* or the *difference equation* for the arithmetic progression.

If the numbers a_1, a_2, a_3 ... form a geometric progression, then

$$\left.\begin{aligned} a_2 &= ra_1 \\ a_3 &= ra_2 \\ &\vdots \\ a_{n+1} &= ra_n \\ &\vdots \end{aligned}\right\} \text{where } r \text{ is the common ratio.}$$

The equation

$$(2) \qquad a_{n+1} = ra_n,$$

governs the geometric progression. This equation, plus a knowledge of the first term, enables one to construct the whole progression by recurrence.

To obtain such a relationship for the sequence of squares 1, 4, 9, ..., use the observation that the differences of the differences are constant and are equal to 2.

$$\begin{aligned} &\text{Sequence:} && \ldots, a_{n-1}, a_n, a_{n+1} \ldots \\ &\text{First difference:} && \ldots, a_n - a_{n-1}, a_{n+1} - a_n, \ldots \\ &\text{Second difference:} && \ldots, (a_{n+1} - a_n) - (a_n - a_{n-1}) \\ &&& = a_{n+1} - 2a_n + a_{n-1}, \ldots . \end{aligned}$$

Therefore,

$$a_{n+1} - 2a_n + a_{n-1} = 2$$

is the desired recurrence relationship.

A formula which relates the general term of a sequence to its past terms is called a *recurrence formula* or a *difference formula*. Such an equation enables us to construct the sequence in a step by step fashion. A difference equation is *solved* if we have found a formula for the nth term of the sequence it generates.

Example 1: If $a_{n+1} = 2a_n - 1$ and if $a_1 = 2$, construct the first few terms of the sequence. We find, successively,

$$a_1 = 2;\ a_2 = 2a_1 - 1 = 2\cdot 2 - 1 = 3;\ a_3 = 2a_2 - 1 = 2\cdot 3 - 1 = 5;$$
$$a_4 = 2\cdot 5 - 1 = 9, \ldots .$$

Example 2: If $a_{n+1} = (n + 1)a_n$ and $a_1 = 1$, we find successively, $a_2 = 2\cdot 1 = 2$; $a_3 = 3\cdot 2 = 6$; $a_4 = 4\cdot 6 = 24$.

This difference equation generates the sequence of numbers called the *factorials.*

Example 3: Suppose that $a_{n+2} = 2a_{n+1} - a_n$. A moment's reflection will show us that we need *two* values at the beginning to get started. Given $a_1 = 2$, $a_2 = 1$. Then,

$$a_3 = 2\cdot 1 - 2 = 0,\ a_4 = 2\cdot 0 - 1 = -1,\ a_5 = 2(-1) - 0 = -2, \ldots .$$

PROBLEMS

1. A sequence whose general term is a_n satisfies the recurrence relationship $a_{n+1} = 3a_n - 2$. Determine the first six terms of the sequence if $a_1 = 1$. What if $a_1 = 0$?

2. Do the same if $a_{n+1} = (a_n)^2$. Start with $a_1 = 1$. Start with $a_1 = 2$.

3. Do the same if $a_{n+1} = a_n(a_n - 1)$. Start with $a_1 = 2$. Start with $a_1 = 3$. Start with $a_1 = 1$. Start with $a_1 = -1$.

4. The sequence $a_1, a_2, \ldots$ satisfies $a_{n+2} = a_{n+1} + a_n + 1$. Determine the first seven terms of the sequence if $a_1 = -1$, $a_2 = 1$. If $a_1 = 1$, $a_2 = 2$.

5. S_n designates the side of the regular polygon of 2^n sides inscribed in the circle whose radius is 1. Show that $S_{n+1} = \sqrt{2 - \sqrt{4 - S_n^2}}$. Start from $S_2 = 2$ and compute S_3 and S_4.

6. Here is a rule of thumb for car values. The average car is worth 70% of what it was worth the previous year. Express this rule as a difference equation. Find a formula for the value after n years. After how many years is the average worth of the car only 10% of its cost?

7. Determine whether the sequence 0, 1, 3, 7, 15, 31 seems to be satisfying a recurrence relation of the form $x_{n+1} = Ax_n + B$ for appropriate constants A and B. Predict the next term of the sequence.

8. Prove that the sequence of squares 1, 4, 9, ... does not satisfy a recurrence relationship of the form $x_{n+1} = Ax_n + B$.

9. If $1/(1 + 2x - x^2) = a_0 + a_1x + a_2x^2 + a_3x^3 + \cdots$, prove that the coefficients a_n satisfy the recurrence relationship $a_{n+2} + 2a_{n+1} - a_n = 0$.

10. The sequence $a_1, a_2, \ldots$ determined by the recurrence relationship $a_{n+1} =$

$\frac{1}{2}\left(a_n + \frac{x}{a_n}\right)$ has the property that a_n approaches the number $\sqrt{x}$ as n becomes large. This formula is used in high speed computation machines for computing square roots. Try it out with $x = 2$ and $a_1 = 1$.

11. Designate the sequence of fractions

$$3,\ 3 + {}^1/_3,\qquad 3 + \cfrac{1}{3 + {}^1/_3}\qquad 3 + \cfrac{1}{3 + \cfrac{1}{3 + {}^1/_3}}\qquad \text{by}\quad \frac{a_n}{b_n}.$$

Show that

$$\begin{cases} a_{n+1} = 3a_n + b_n \\ b_{n+1} = a_n \end{cases} \quad \text{and} \quad \begin{cases} a_1 = 3 \\ b_1 = 1. \end{cases}$$

Find the seventh fraction in the sequence. Sequences of this sort are called *continued fractions.*

12. Designate the sequence of fractions,

$$x,\quad x + \frac{y^2}{2x},\quad x + \cfrac{y^2}{2x + \cfrac{y^2}{2x}},\quad x + \cfrac{y^2}{2x + \cfrac{y^2}{2x + \cfrac{y^2}{2x}}},\quad \cdots$$

by a_n/b_n. Prove that $a_{n+1}/b_{n+1} = x + y^2/(x + a_n/b_n)$, and that $a_1 = x$, $b_1 = 1$. Hence, prove that the numbers a_n, b_n satisfy the simultaneous recurrence relationship

$$\begin{cases} a_{n+1} = xa_n + (x^2 + y^2)b_n \\ b_{n+1} = a_n + xb_n. \end{cases}$$

8.4 Difference Equations and Matrices

The system of equations

$$\text{(1)}\qquad \begin{cases} x_{n+1} = ax_n + by_n \\ y_{n+1} = cx_n + dy_n \end{cases}$$

is called a system of *two linear simultaneous difference equations.* The numbers x_n and y_n together constitute two sequences

$$x_1, x_2, \ldots$$

$$y_1, y_2, \ldots$$

which are linked by Equation (1) and which are to be determined. To start the process, we assume that we have been given the values of x_1 and y_1.

We then compute x_2 and y_2:

$$\begin{cases} x_2 = ax_1 + by_1 \\ y_2 = cx_1 + dy_1. \end{cases}$$

Once we know x_2 and y_2 we can compute x_3 and y_3:

$$\begin{cases} x_3 = ax_2 + by_2 \\ y_3 = cx_2 + dy_2. \end{cases}$$

All subsequent values can be computed successively in this way. This determination can be compressed by matrix algebra. From Equation (1) we have

$$\begin{pmatrix} x_{n+1} \\ y_{n+1} \end{pmatrix} = \begin{pmatrix} a & b \\ c & d \end{pmatrix} \begin{pmatrix} x_n \\ y_n \end{pmatrix}.$$

Set $A = \begin{pmatrix} a & b \\ c & d \end{pmatrix}.$

Then,
$$\begin{pmatrix} x_2 \\ y_2 \end{pmatrix} = A \begin{pmatrix} x_1 \\ y_1 \end{pmatrix}.$$

$$\begin{pmatrix} x_3 \\ y_3 \end{pmatrix} = A \begin{pmatrix} x_2 \\ y_2 \end{pmatrix} = AA \begin{pmatrix} x_1 \\ y_1 \end{pmatrix} = A^2 \begin{pmatrix} x_1 \\ y_1 \end{pmatrix}.$$

$$\begin{pmatrix} x_4 \\ y_4 \end{pmatrix} = A \begin{pmatrix} x_3 \\ y_3 \end{pmatrix} = AA^2 \begin{pmatrix} x_1 \\ y_1 \end{pmatrix} = A^3 \begin{pmatrix} x_1 \\ y_1 \end{pmatrix}.$$

$$\vdots$$

In general, we see that

$$\begin{pmatrix} x_n \\ y_n \end{pmatrix} = A^{n-1} \begin{pmatrix} x_1 \\ y_1 \end{pmatrix}. \tag{2}$$

The Formula (2) for the nth term in the sequence is completely analogous to the formula for the simple geometrical progression. But a matrix A replaces the scalar ratio r. If Equation (2) is combined with the formula for A^n developed in the second section of this chapter, we obtain a complete solution to the system of equations (1).

Example:

(1) Solve the system of difference equations.

$$\begin{cases} x_{n+1} = x_n + 2y_n \\ y_{n+1} = 2x_n + y_n \end{cases} \quad \text{where} \quad \begin{cases} x_1 = 0 \\ y_1 = 1. \end{cases}$$

Here $A = \begin{pmatrix} 1 & 2 \\ 2 & 1 \end{pmatrix}$. Its characteristic roots are $\lambda_1 = 3$ and $\lambda_2 = -1$. Since the roots are distinct,

$$A^{n-1} = \tfrac{1}{4}(3^{n-1} + 3(-1)^{n-1})\begin{pmatrix} 1 & 0 \\ 0 & 1 \end{pmatrix} + \tfrac{1}{4}(3^{n-1} - (-1)^{n-1})\begin{pmatrix} 1 & 2 \\ 2 & 1 \end{pmatrix}.$$

Hence,

$$\begin{pmatrix} x_n \\ y_n \end{pmatrix} = A^{n-1}\begin{pmatrix} 0 \\ 1 \end{pmatrix} = \tfrac{1}{4}(3^{n-1} + 3(-1)^{n-1})\begin{pmatrix} 1 & 0 \\ 0 & 1 \end{pmatrix}\begin{pmatrix} 0 \\ 1 \end{pmatrix}$$

$$+ \tfrac{1}{4}(3^{n-1} - (-1)^{n-1})\begin{pmatrix} 1 & 2 \\ 2 & 1 \end{pmatrix}\begin{pmatrix} 0 \\ 1 \end{pmatrix}$$

$$= \tfrac{1}{4}(3^{n-1} + 3(-1)^{n-1})\begin{pmatrix} 0 \\ 1 \end{pmatrix} + \tfrac{1}{4}(3^{n-1} - (-1)^{n-1})\begin{pmatrix} 2 \\ 1 \end{pmatrix}.$$

This matrix equation tells us that

$$\begin{cases} x_n = \tfrac{1}{2}(3^{n-1} + (-1)^n) \\ y_n = \tfrac{1}{2}(3^{n-1} + (-1)^{n-1}). \end{cases}$$

PROBLEMS

Solve the following systems of difference equations.

1. $\begin{cases} x_{n+1} = x_n + 2y_n \\ y_{n+1} = 2x_n + y_n \end{cases}$ where $\begin{cases} x_1 = 1 \\ y_1 = 0; \end{cases}$ Where $\begin{cases} x_1 = 0 \\ y_1 = 0. \end{cases}$

2. $\begin{cases} x_{n+1} = 6x_n + 2y_n \\ y_{n+1} = 2x_n + 3y_n \end{cases}$ where $\begin{cases} x_1 = 1 \\ y_1 = 1; \end{cases}$ Where $\begin{cases} x_1 = 0 \\ y_1 = 1. \end{cases}$

3. $\begin{cases} x_{n+1} = 2x_n + 6y_n \\ y_{n+1} = 6x_n - 3y_n \end{cases}$ where $\begin{cases} x_1 = 0 \\ y_1 = -1. \end{cases}$ Where $\begin{cases} x_1 = 1 \\ y_1 = -1. \end{cases}$

4. The plane is transformed over and over again by means of

$$\begin{cases} x' = 5x + 2y \\ y' = 2x + 2y. \end{cases}$$

Find a formula for the successive images of the point (1,1).

5. The plane is transformed over and over again by means of

$$\begin{cases} x' = \tfrac{1}{2}x + \tfrac{1}{4}y \\ y' = \tfrac{1}{4}x + \tfrac{1}{2}y. \end{cases}$$

Find and plot successive images of the point (1,1). What type of behavior do you observe?

6. Solve the system of difference equations

$$\begin{cases} x_{n+1} = tx_n + (1 - t)y_n \\ y_{n+1} = (1 - t)x_n + ty_n. \end{cases}$$

Initial values are $\begin{cases} x_1 = 0 \\ y_1 = 1. \end{cases}$

7. Solve the following difference equation:

$$\begin{cases} x_{n+1} = y_n \\ y_{n+1} = x_n \end{cases} \quad \text{where} \quad \begin{cases} x_1 = 0 \\ y_1 = 1. \end{cases}$$

8. Solve the difference equation:

$$\begin{cases} a_{n+1} = 3a_n + b_n \\ b_{n+1} = a_n \end{cases} \quad \text{where} \quad \begin{cases} a_1 = 3 \\ b_1 = 1. \end{cases}$$

Use the solution of this problem to find a formula for the nth term of the sequence of fractions in Problem 11, page 284.

The system of difference equations designated by (1) contains two important special cases. The first special case is the single difference equation

$$x_{n+1} = ax_n + b \tag{3}$$

which is known as a *first order linear difference equation.*

In order to put the single Equation (3) into the form (1), we introduce quantities $y_1 = 1$, $y_2 = 1$, ..., $y_n = 1$, ... Now observe that Equation (3) can be written as

$$\begin{cases} x_{n+1} = ax_n + by_n \\ y_{n+1} = 0x_n + y_n. \end{cases} \tag{4}$$

The first equation of this pair is precisely Equation (3), and the second equation, $y_{n+1} = y_n$, is obviously true (since $y_1 = 1$, $y_2 = 1$, et cetera) but adds no more information. It is a "dummy" equation and the quantities y_n are "dummy" quantities.

The matrix $A = \begin{pmatrix} a & b \\ 0 & 1 \end{pmatrix}$ has the characteristic roots $\lambda_1 = a$, $\lambda_2 = 1$. We must therefore distinguish two possibilities.

Case 1. $a \neq 1$. In this case the characteristic roots are distinct and we find by substituting in Equation (9) of Section 2 that

$$A^n = \frac{a^n - a}{1 - a}\begin{pmatrix} 1 & 0 \\ 0 & 1 \end{pmatrix} + \frac{1 - a^n}{1 - a}\begin{pmatrix} a & b \\ 0 & 1 \end{pmatrix}.$$

This simplifies to

$$A^n = \frac{1}{1 - a}\begin{pmatrix} a^n - a^{n+1} & b(1 - a^n) \\ 0 & 1 - a \end{pmatrix}$$

$$= \begin{pmatrix} a^n & \dfrac{b(1 - a^n)}{1 - a} \\ 0 & 1 \end{pmatrix}.$$

Since, $\begin{pmatrix} x_n \\ y_n \end{pmatrix} = A^{n-1} \begin{pmatrix} x_1 \\ y_1 \end{pmatrix}$, we have,

$$\begin{pmatrix} x_n \\ 1 \end{pmatrix} = \begin{pmatrix} a^{n-1} & \dfrac{b(1 - a^{n-1})}{1 - a} \\ 0 & 1 \end{pmatrix} \begin{pmatrix} x_1 \\ 1 \end{pmatrix}$$

and therefore, multiplying out,

$$x_n = a^{n-1}x_1 + \frac{b(1 - a^{n-1})}{1 - a}. \tag{5}$$

Case 2. $a = 1$. In this case, the characteristic roots are equal: $\lambda_1 = 1$, $\lambda_2 = 1$. We find from Equation (15) of Section 2

$$A^n = (1 - n)\begin{pmatrix} 1 & 0 \\ 0 & 1 \end{pmatrix} + n\begin{pmatrix} 1 & b \\ 0 & 1 \end{pmatrix} = \begin{pmatrix} 1 & nb \\ 0 & 1 \end{pmatrix}.$$

Since $\begin{pmatrix} x_n \\ y_n \end{pmatrix} = A^{n-1} \begin{pmatrix} x_1 \\ y_1 \end{pmatrix}$, we have,

$$\begin{pmatrix} x_n \\ 1 \end{pmatrix} = \begin{pmatrix} 1 & (n - 1)b \\ 0 & 1 \end{pmatrix} \begin{pmatrix} x_1 \\ 1 \end{pmatrix}.$$

Therefore, multiplying out,

$$x_n = x_1 + (n - 1)b. \tag{6}$$

The reader should note that Case 1 with $b = 0$ leads to a geometric progression, whereas Case 2 leads to an arithmetic progression.

PROBLEMS

1. If $x_{n+1} = 3x_n - 2$ and if $x_1 = 2$, find a formula for x_n.
2. If $x_{n+1} = \frac{1}{2}x_n + \frac{1}{2}$ and if $x_1 = 1$, find a formula for x_n. The same if $x_1 = -1$.
3. If $x_{n+1} = x_n - 1$ and if $x_1 = 10$, find a formula for x_n.
4. $X_1, X_2, \ldots, A$ and B are all $n \times n$ matrices. Moreover, $X_{n+1} = AX_n + B$. Show that $X_n = A^{n-1}X_1 + (A^{n-2} + A^{n-3} + \cdots + A^2 + A + I)B$.
5. In Problem 4 prove that if $(A - I)$ has an inverse, then

$$X_n = A^{n-1}X_1 + (A^{n-1} - I)(A - I)^{-1}B.$$

The second important special case contained in the system (1) is the difference equation

$$x_{n+1} = ax_n + bx_{n-1}. \tag{7}$$

This is known as a *second order linear homogeneous difference equation*. The expression "second order" refers to the fact that the general term x_{n+1} is related to the *two* preceding terms: x_n and x_{n-1}. In order to obtain a solution, we need two initial values. For example, if

$$x_{n+1} = x_n + x_{n-1},$$

and if we specify that $x_1 = 1$ and $x_2 = 1$, then we can compute successively $x_3 = x_2 + x_1 = 1 + 1 = 2$, $x_4 = x_3 + x_2 = 2 + 1 = 3$, $x_5 = x_4 + x_3 = 3 + 2 = 5$, et cetera.

Equation (7) may also be reduced to the system of equations (1). We introduce the quantities y_n by means of Equation

$$y_n = x_{n-1}. \tag{8}$$

This is the same as writing

$$y_{n+1} = x_n. \tag{9}$$

Equation (7) becomes

$$x_{n+1} = ax_n + by_n.$$

If we attach Equation (9) to it, we obtain the *pair* of equations

$$\begin{cases} x_{n+1} = ax_n + by_n \\ y_{n+1} = x_n \ \ + 0y_n. \end{cases} \tag{10}$$

This system is precisely of form (1). Its matrix is

$$A = \begin{pmatrix} a & b \\ 1 & 0 \end{pmatrix},$$

The characteristic equation of A is

$$\lambda^2 - a\lambda - b = 0.$$

The roots of this equation are $\lambda = \frac{1}{2}(a \pm \sqrt{a^2 + 4b}\,)$. The roots are distinct if $a^2 + 4b \neq 0$. The power A^n can now be computed with due regard for this information. Now,

$$\begin{pmatrix} x_3 \\ y_3 \end{pmatrix} = A \begin{pmatrix} x_2 \\ y_2 \end{pmatrix}, \quad \begin{pmatrix} x_4 \\ y_4 \end{pmatrix} = A \begin{pmatrix} x_3 \\ y_3 \end{pmatrix} = A^2 \begin{pmatrix} x_2 \\ y_2 \end{pmatrix}.$$

Therefore,

$$\begin{pmatrix} x_n \\ y_n \end{pmatrix} = A^{n-2} \begin{pmatrix} x_2 \\ y_2 \end{pmatrix}.$$

Since $y_n = x_{n-1}$, it follows that $y_2 = x_1$ and therefore, the matrix equation

$$\begin{pmatrix} x_n \\ x_{n-1} \end{pmatrix} = A^{n-2} \begin{pmatrix} x_2 \\ x_1 \end{pmatrix} \tag{11}$$

contains the solution of the difference Equation (7).

Example: Solve the difference equation

$$x_{n+1} = 3x_n + 4x_{n-1}$$

with $x_1 = 1$, $x_2 = 1$. The matrix $A = \begin{pmatrix} 3 & 4 \\ 1 & 0 \end{pmatrix}$ has distinct characteristic roots $\lambda_1 = 4$, $\lambda_2 = -1$. Hence, we have

$$A^{n-2} = \frac{(-1)4^{n-2} - 4(-1)^{n-2}}{-5}\begin{pmatrix} 1 & 0 \\ 0 & 1 \end{pmatrix} + \frac{(-1)^{n-2} - 4^{n-2}}{-5}\begin{pmatrix} 3 & 4 \\ 1 & 0 \end{pmatrix}.$$

Since

$$\begin{pmatrix} 1 & 0 \\ 0 & 1 \end{pmatrix}\begin{pmatrix} 1 \\ 1 \end{pmatrix} = \begin{pmatrix} 1 \\ 1 \end{pmatrix} \quad \text{and} \quad \begin{pmatrix} 3 & 4 \\ 1 & 0 \end{pmatrix}\begin{pmatrix} 1 \\ 1 \end{pmatrix} = \begin{pmatrix} 7 \\ 1 \end{pmatrix},$$

$$A^{n-2}\begin{pmatrix} x_2 \\ x_1 \end{pmatrix} = A^{n-2}\begin{pmatrix} 1 \\ 1 \end{pmatrix}$$

$$= \frac{4^{n-2} + 4(-1)^{n-2}}{5}\begin{pmatrix} 1 \\ 1 \end{pmatrix} + \frac{4^{n-2} - (-1)^{n-2}}{5}\begin{pmatrix} 7 \\ 1 \end{pmatrix}.$$

Finally, $\begin{pmatrix} x_n \\ x_{n-1} \end{pmatrix} = A^{n-2}\begin{pmatrix} x_2 \\ x_1 \end{pmatrix}$, so that

$$x_n = \tfrac{1}{5}(4)^{n-2} + \tfrac{1}{5}4(-1)^{n-2} + \tfrac{7}{5}(4)^{n-2} - \tfrac{7}{5}(-1)^{n-2}$$

$$= \tfrac{8}{5}(4)^{n-2} - \tfrac{3}{5}(-1)^{n-2}. \text{ Since } 4^{-2} = \tfrac{1}{16} \text{ and } (-1)^{-3} = -1,$$

this can be written as

$$x_n = \tfrac{1}{10}(4)^n + \tfrac{3}{5}(-1)^{n+1}.$$

Example: Consider the difference equation

$$x_{n+1} = x_n + x_{n-1}$$

where $x_1 = 0$ and $x_2 = 1$. We can compute, successively, $x_3 = 1$, $x_4 = 2$, $x_5 = 3$, $x_6 = 5$, $x_7 = 8$, $x_8 = 13$, ... This is one of the most famous difference equations in mathematics and the numbers it gives rise to: 0, 1, 1, 2, 3, 5, 8, 13, . . . are known as the *Fibonacci* numbers*. What is a formula for x_n?

The matrix $A = \begin{pmatrix} 1 & 1 \\ 1 & 0 \end{pmatrix}$. Its characteristic roots are $\lambda_1 = \frac{1}{2}(1 + \sqrt{5})$ and $\lambda_2 = \frac{1}{2}(1 - \sqrt{5})$. The roots are distinct. Therefore,

$$A^{n-2} = \frac{\lambda_2\lambda_1^{n-2} - \lambda_1\lambda_2^{n-2}}{\lambda_2 - \lambda_1}\begin{pmatrix} 1 & 0 \\ 0 & 1 \end{pmatrix} + \frac{\lambda_2^{n-2} - \lambda_1^{n-2}}{\lambda_2 - \lambda_1}\begin{pmatrix} 1 & 1 \\ 1 & 0 \end{pmatrix}.$$

---

*Leonardo Fibonacci, Italian merchant and mathematician of the thirteenth century.

Since $\begin{pmatrix}1 & 0\\0 & 1\end{pmatrix}\begin{pmatrix}1\\0\end{pmatrix} = \begin{pmatrix}1\\0\end{pmatrix}$ and $\begin{pmatrix}1 & 1\\1 & 0\end{pmatrix}\begin{pmatrix}1\\0\end{pmatrix} = \begin{pmatrix}1\\0\end{pmatrix}$, we have, from $\begin{pmatrix}x_n\\x_{n-1}\end{pmatrix} = A^{n-2}\begin{pmatrix}1\\0\end{pmatrix}$,

$$x_n = \frac{1}{\lambda_2 - \lambda_1}((\lambda_2 - 1)\lambda_1^{n-2} + (1 - \lambda_1)\lambda_2^{n-2}).$$

By inserting the numerical values of λ_1 and λ_2 and simplifying, we find that

$$x_n = \frac{5 + \sqrt{5}}{10}(\tfrac{1}{2} + \tfrac{1}{2}\sqrt{5})^{n-2} + \frac{5 - \sqrt{5}}{10}(\tfrac{1}{2} - \tfrac{1}{2}\sqrt{5})^{n-2}.$$

Since $(\frac{1}{2} - \frac{1}{2}\sqrt{5})^{-2} = \frac{3}{2} + \frac{1}{2}\sqrt{5}$ and $(\frac{1}{2} + \frac{1}{2}\sqrt{5})^{-2} = \frac{3}{2} - \frac{1}{2}\sqrt{5}$, this can be written as

$$x_n = \tfrac{1}{10}(5 - \sqrt{5})(\tfrac{1}{2} + \tfrac{1}{2}\sqrt{5})^n + \tfrac{1}{10}(5 + \sqrt{5})(\tfrac{1}{2} - \tfrac{1}{2}\sqrt{5})^n.$$

We know that all the numbers $x_1, x_2, \ldots$ are integers, and one of the surprising things about this answer is that it shows that certain complicated expressions involving square roots can always turn out to be integers.

PROBLEMS

Solve the following difference equations.

1. $x_{n+1} = 3x_n + 4x_{n-1}$ with $x_1 = 0$, $x_2 = 1$.
2. $x_{n+1} = 3x_n + 4x_{n-1}$ with $x_1 = 1$, $x_2 = -1$.
3. $x_{n+1} = x_n + 20x_{n-1}$ with $x_1 = 1$, $x_2 = 0$.
4. $x_{n+1} = x_n + 20x_{n-1}$ with $x_1 = 0$, $x_2 = 0$.
5. $x_{n+1} = x_n - x_{n-1}$ with $x_1 = 1$, $x_2 = 2$.
6. $x_{n+1} = x_n - x_{n-1}$ with $x_1 = 1$, $x_2 = 3$.
7. In the theory of structures in engineering, the following difference equation appears: $M_{n+1} - 4M_n + M_{n-1} = 0$ with $M_1 = 0$, $M_2 = 1$. Solve this equation.
8. Solve the difference equation $a_{n+2} + 2a_{n+1} - a_n = 0$ where a_n are as in Problem 9 on page 283. How shall we take a_0 and a_1?
9. A set of data $x_1, x_2, x_3, \ldots$ was smoothed according to the formula $y_n = \frac{1}{2}(x_{n+1} + x_{n-1})$. It turned out that the smoothed data was exactly the same as the original data ($y_2 = x_2$, $y_3 = x_3$, et cetera). What can you conclude about the original data?
10. Insert $n = 1$, 2, and 3 in the formula for the Fibonacci numbers and check your answers.

8.5 Some Applications of Difference Equations

This chapter will be concluded by some examples showing how difference equations make their appearance in applied mathematics.

COMPOUND INTEREST. Suppose that an initial deposit of D_1 dollars is made in a bank. Suppose, further, that the interest rate is r. Then after one interest period, the principal earns rD_1 dollars. This interest is then added to the principal. If D_2 denotes the amount on deposit at the beginning of the second interest period, then

$$D_2 = D_1 + rD_1 = D_1(1 + r).$$

During the second interest period D_2 earns rD_2 so that the amount on deposit at the beginning of the third interest period is

$$D_3 = D_2 + rD_2 = D_2(1 + r).$$

In general,

$$D_{n+1} = D_n(1 + r).$$

This is the difference equation governing compound interest. Its solution is

$$D_n = D_1(1 + r)^{n-1}.$$

Example: A savings bank offers 4% per annum compounded quarterly. Determine the balance if \$100 has been left in the bank for five years.

Take $D_1 = \$100$. The interest period is one-quarter year and the interest rate, per period, is $\frac{1}{4} \times 4\% = 1\%$, so that we take $r = 1/100$. The end of five years corresponds to the beginning of the twenty-first interest period so that we take $n = 21$. Hence

$$D_{21} = \$100(1.01)^{20} \approx \$121.90.$$

ORDINARY ANNUITIES: At the beginning of each interest period, a man makes a deposit of D dollars. At the end of the period, interest at the rate of r per period is allowed on the balance and the interest is added to the balance. If D_n designates the amount of the balance at the beginning of the nth period, find a formula for D_n.

We have

$$D_{n+1} = D_n + rD_n + D = (1 + r)D_n + D.$$

Moreover, $D_1 = 0$. This is the difference equation governing this financial situation. Referring to Formula (5), we can set $a = (1 + r)$, $b = D$, and obtain

$$D_n = (1 + r)^{n-1}0 + \frac{D(1 - (1 + r)^{n-1})}{-r}$$

or

$$D_n = D\left(\frac{(1 + r)^{n-1} - 1}{r}\right).$$

ITERATIVE METHODS IN NUMERICAL ANALYSIS: An *iterative method* of the solution of an equation is one which employs a certain computational feature over and over again. Each time the feature is applied, the answer gets better.* Iterative methods are much employed in electronic computing machines since they are relatively easy to program.

The idea of an iterative computation can be made clear by a very simple example. Suppose we have the equation

$$x = \tfrac{1}{2}x + 1$$

and would like to determine x. (This particular problem poses no difficulties by ordinary methods. We find easily: $x = 2$.) Suppose we guess a value for x, say $x = 0$. Substitute this value in the right side of the equation. We obtain $x = \frac{1}{2}\cdot 0 + 1 = 1$. Perhaps, then, $x = 1$ would be a better guess than $x = 0$. Set $x = 1$ in the equation. We learn that $x = \frac{1}{2}\cdot 1 + 1 = 1.5$. Perhaps, 1.5 is still a better answer; after all, if we arrived at the *correct* answer and substituted it in the formula, we would obtain the *same* value back again. Let us keep doing this over and over again and see what happens.

x	$\frac{1}{2}x + 1$
0	1.0
1.0	1.5
1.5	1.75
1.75	1.875
1.875	1.9375
1.9375	1.96875
1.96875	1.984375
1.984375	1.9921875

Now notice that the entries in the column labelled x and those in the column labelled $\frac{1}{2}x + 1$ are getting closer and closer. For example, the entries on the eighth line differ by less than .01. Both values seem to be approaching the correct solution of the equation, namely, $x = 2$. This process can be analyzed completely by difference equations. If we designate by x_n the nth entry in the left-hand column, we have

$$x_{n+1} = \tfrac{1}{2}x_n + 1, \quad x_1 = 0.$$

By Formula (5) with $a = \frac{1}{2}$, $b = 1$, $x_1 = 0$, we have

$$x_n = \frac{1(1 - (\frac{1}{2})^{n-1})}{\frac{1}{2}} = 2 - (\tfrac{1}{2})^{n-2}.$$

Now the term $(1/2)^{n-2}$ gets closer and closer to zero as n becomes larger

*Not strictly true, but we shall ignore this fine point here.

and larger and hence, x_n gets closer and closer to two, the solution of the problem.

If we solve the linear equation $x = ax + b$ by means of iterative methods, we can analyze the process completely by difference equations. By starting with a guess x_1 we obtain $x_2 = ax_1 + b$ for a second guess, $x_3 = ax_2 + b$ for a third guess, and so forth. The difference equation governing the process is therefore

$$x_{n+1} = ax_n + b,$$

and its solution, by Equation (5) is

$$x_n = a^{n-1}x_1 + \frac{b(1 - a^{n-1})}{1 - a}.$$

If, now, the number a lies between -1 and 1, then a^{n-1} will approach zero and consequently x_n will approach $b/(1 - a)$ (which is the solution to $x = ax + b$). If a is greater than 1 or is less than -1, the terms a^{n-1} will become larger and larger in absolute value, and the process will not work.

The behavior is exhibited when we try to solve

$$x = 2x + 1 \qquad \text{(solution: } x = -1)$$

by iteration:

x	$2x + 1$
0	1
1	3
3	7
7	15
.	.
.	.
.	.

The two columns are not approaching each other in value.

Iterative methods, therefore, have limited applicability, and it is part of the study of *numerical analysis* to decide when they will work and when they will not.

PROBLEMS

1. A savings bank offers $4\frac{1}{4}\%$ per annum compounded semi-annually. How much will \$100 amount to if left in for ten years?

2. A bank compounds interest annually with an interest rate r. As soon as the interest is declared, a man who deposited D dollars originally, withdraws half the

interest and leaves the remainder. Find a formula for the amount he has at the end of n years.

3. A bank compounds its interest at $r\%$ per annum four times a year, and a man deposits a fixed amount D at the beginning of the first, third, fifth, ... interest periods. Set up a difference equation for this situation. Solve the difference equation.

4. Solve by iteration: $x = \frac{1}{3}x + 2$. Start with $x_1 = 0$.

5. Solve by iteration: $x = \frac{1}{2}x + 3$. Start with $x_1 = 1$.

CHAPTER 9

Matrices and Abstract Algebra

9.1 Complex Numbers and How to Live Without Them*

Imaginary quantities made their appearance in mathematics during the sixteenth century. In those days they were not very well understood, nor were they very useful. But after three centuries, imaginary numbers have been explained logically and have found multifold applications in both pure and applied mathematics.

An imaginary number arises from an attempt to solve the equation $x^2 = -1$. If the solution, x, to this equation were an ordinary number, it would be either positive or negative. In either case, its square would be positive, and could not possibly equal -1. Hence x, the solution of this equation, cannot be an ordinary sort of number. Yet, the mathematicians of a few hundred years ago wrote $\sqrt{-1}$ for the solution of the equation and proceeded to operate with this number in an uninhibited fashion. In this section, we shall show how imaginary numbers can be understood as certain kinds of 2×2 matrices, and how the arithmetic of imaginary numbers coincides with the arithmetic of these matrices.

If a and b are ordinary (that is, real) numbers, then a number of the form $a + b\sqrt{-1}$ is called a *complex number*.† The quantity a is called the *real part* of the imaginary number while b is called the *imaginary part* of the number. If $b = 0$, the complex number has a zero imaginary part, and it reduces to an ordinary number. On the other hand, if $a = 0$, the complex number has a zero real part, and is called a *pure imaginary* number.

---

*Some acquaintance with complex numbers is assumed.

†The current mathematical practice is to use the symbol i for $\sqrt{-1}$ and to write $a + bi$ for $a + b\sqrt{-1}$. Electrical engineers use the symbol j for $\sqrt{-1}$. In this chapter, we retain the old-fashioned notation since it suggests that there is a bit of mystery to be cleared up.

We now formulate definitions as to when two complex numbers are equal, and how they are to be added, subtracted, multiplied, and divided.

Definition: *Two complex numbers are considered equal if and only if the two numbers have the same real part and the same imaginary part. That is,*

$$a + b\sqrt{-1} = c + d\sqrt{-1} \quad \textit{if and only if} \quad a = c \quad \textit{and} \quad b = d.$$

Definition: *The sum of two complex numbers is a complex number given by the formula*

$$(a + b\sqrt{-1}) + (c + d\sqrt{-1}) = (a + c) + (b + d)\sqrt{-1}.$$

Definition: *The difference of two complex numbers is a complex number given by the formula*

$$(a + b\sqrt{-1}) - (c + d\sqrt{-1}) = (a - c) + (b - d)\sqrt{-1}.$$

Definition: *The product of two complex numbers is a complex number given by the formula*

$$(a + b\sqrt{-1}) \cdot (c + d\sqrt{-1}) = (ac - bd) + (ad + bc)\sqrt{-1}.$$

This definition of multiplication is motivated by the "ordinary" rules of multiplication, together with the fact that the symbol $\sqrt{-1}$ is supposed to satisfy the equation $x^2 = -1$, that is, $(\sqrt{-1})(\sqrt{-1}) = -1$. "Ordinary" multiplication would give

$$\begin{array}{l} a + b\sqrt{-1} \\ c + d\sqrt{-1} \\ \hline ac + bc\sqrt{-1} + ad\sqrt{-1} + bd\sqrt{-1}\sqrt{-1}. \end{array}$$

If this product is simplified by combining the terms by the usual laws of algebra, there is obtained $(ac - bd) + (ad + bc)\sqrt{-1}$. Hence the definition.

Definition: *If a complex number* $a + b\sqrt{-1}$ *is not zero (that is, if at least one of the numbers* a *or* b *is not zero), then the reciprocal of* $a + b\sqrt{-1}$ *is the complex number given by the formula*

$$\frac{1}{a + b\sqrt{-1}} = \left(\frac{a}{a^2 + b^2}\right) - \left(\frac{b}{a^2 + b^2}\right)\sqrt{-1}.$$

Motivation for this definition comes from the following observation. By assuming that the symbols satisfy all ordinary laws of arithmetic and that $(\sqrt{-1})(\sqrt{-1}) = -1$, we have

$$\frac{1}{a+b\sqrt{-1}} \cdot \frac{a-b\sqrt{-1}}{a-b\sqrt{-1}} = \frac{a-b\sqrt{-1}}{a^2+b^2}.$$

Examples:

(a) $(1+\sqrt{-1}) + (2-3\sqrt{-1}) = 3-2\sqrt{-1}$

(b) $(1+\sqrt{-1})(2-3\sqrt{-1}) = 2+2\sqrt{-1}-3\sqrt{-1}+3$

$$= 5 - \sqrt{-1}.$$

(c) $$\frac{1+3\sqrt{-1}}{1+2\sqrt{-1}} = \frac{(1+3\sqrt{-1})(1-2\sqrt{-1})}{(1+2\sqrt{-1})(1-2\sqrt{-1})}$$

$$= \frac{1+3\sqrt{-1}-2\sqrt{-1}+6}{5} = \frac{7}{5}+\frac{1}{5}\sqrt{-1}.$$

PROBLEMS

In Problems 1–5, carry out the indicated operations and express the answer as a single complex number.

1. $2+\sqrt{-1}-4\sqrt{-1}+2-\sqrt{-1}-\frac{1}{2}$.

2. $6(3-2\sqrt{-1})$; $(2+2\sqrt{-1})3$; $(\sqrt{-1})(4-2\sqrt{-1})$.

3. $(1-2\sqrt{-1})(2-3\sqrt{-1})$; $(3-2\sqrt{-1})(3+2\sqrt{-1})$; $(\sqrt{-1})(1-\sqrt{-1})(2-\sqrt{-1})$.

4. $(a+b\sqrt{-1})(a-b\sqrt{-1})$; $(a+b\sqrt{-1})(b+a\sqrt{-1})$; $(a+a\sqrt{-1})(b-b\sqrt{-1})$.

5. $1/(2-3\sqrt{-1})$; $\sqrt{-1}/(1+\sqrt{-1})$; $(1+\sqrt{-1})/(1-\sqrt{-1})$.

6. Find the real part of $(2+7\sqrt{-1})(\sqrt{-1})$. Find the imaginary part of $2+(1-\sqrt{-1})(1-6\sqrt{-1})$. Find the real part of $1/(2-3\sqrt{-1})$.

7. If z_1 and z_2 represent two complex numbers, prove that real part of $(z_1+z_2) =$ (real part of z_1) + (real part of z_2). Prove that a similar fact is true for the imaginary part.

8. If z_1 and z_2 represent two complex numbers, is it true that real part of $z_1z_2 =$ (real part of z_1)(real part of z_2)?

9. Show that if two complex numbers degenerate to real numbers (that is, have zero imaginary parts), then complex addition, subtraction, multiplication, and division reduce to these processes for real numbers.

10. Find $(\sqrt{-1})^3$; $(\sqrt{-1})^4$; $(2\sqrt{-1})^3$; $(1 - \sqrt{-1})^3$.

11. Show that if $(1 + \sqrt{-1})^n = a_n + b_n\sqrt{-1}$, then $a_{n+1} = a_n - b_n$ and $b_{n+1} = a_n + b_n$.

12. Show that the equality of complex numbers is an equivalence relationship. (The three conditions on page 00).

13. If $(2x + y\sqrt{-1}) + (y + x\sqrt{-1}) = 1 + 2\sqrt{-1}$, determine x and y.

The set of all complex numbers, with addition, subtraction, multiplication, and division defined as they have been, constitutes a mathematical system that is known as a *field*. Briefly speaking, a field is a system, such as the rational numbers, or the real numbers, in which the operation of plus, minus, times, and divide, are possible in a unique way, and in which these operations satisfy the usual laws of arithmetic. To get down to technicalities, we make a definition.

Definition: *A field is a set of elements (denoted by the letters* u, v, w, . . . et cetera) *which satisfies the following requirements.*

1. *For any two elements,* u, v, *there is a sum* u + v *and a product* uv *in the set.*
2. *Addition is commutative. That is,* u + v = v + u.
3. *Addition is associative. That is,* u + (v + w) = (u + v) + w.
4. *There is a unique element designated by* 0 *and called zero such that* u + 0 = 0 + u = u, *for all elements* u.
5. *For any element* u, *there is a unique element, designated by* −u *such that* u + (−u) = 0.
6. *Multiplication is commutative. That is* uv = vu.
7. *Multiplication is associative. That is* u(vw) = (uv)w.
8. *Multiplication distributes into addition. That is* u(v + *w*) = uv + uw, or (u + v)w = uw + vw.
9. *There is a unique element called the unit and designated by* 1 *such that* u · 1 = 1 · u = u, *for all elements* u.
10. *There corresponds to any element* u *that is not zero, a unique element called the reciprocal of* u, *designated by* u^{-1} *such that* $uu^{-1} = u^{-1}u = 1$.

Quantities of the form uv^{-1} are frequently written as fractions: u/v or $\frac{u}{v}$.

The reader, who is assumed to have done some work with complex numbers, will recognize that all these requirements are fulfilled by the system of complex numbers. But he should also not find it very difficult to establish these properties starting from the definitions of the complex operations given on page 297.

There are many examples of mathematical systems that are fields. It can be shown that arithmetic in fields follows the usual patterns of manipulation. For example,

$$\frac{u}{v} + \frac{w}{z} = \frac{uz + vw}{vz}, \qquad \left(\frac{u}{v}\right)\left(\frac{v}{u}\right) = 1, \text{ et cetera.}$$

But though all fields resemble one another insofar as they all satisfy properties 1–10, they may differ in other respects. The rational numbers and the real numbers, for example, are fields that have an infinite number of elements in them, but there are fields that are comprised of only a finite number of elements. The field of rational numbers contains in it no element x such that $x^2 = 2$. But the field of real numbers contains such an element. The fields of rational or of real numbers contain no element x such that $x^2 = -1$. But the field of complex numbers does.

PROBLEMS

1. Does the set of all integers constitute a field? Why?
2. Does the set of all 2×2 matrices with addition and multiplication defined as usual constutute a field? Why?
3. Prove that the set of all rational functions (that is, functions such as $3 + 2x^2$, $\dfrac{1 - 6x}{2 - x - x^2}$, $\dfrac{-1 + 2x + 3x^5}{1 - x}$, constitutes a field.

We have exposed in great detail the inner workings of complex numbers. But the reader might say, and with justifiable exasperation, "This is all very well and good. You have shown how complex numbers operate. But what *are* they? What do you mean that you have created a symbol such that $(\sqrt{-1}\,)^2 = -1$? Can you go about creating symbols that do anything? What is $\sqrt{-1}$ really?" Mathematics answers these questions by the *method of models*. It exhibits a system of mathematical objects which

(a) is familiar and therefore has concrete reality;

(b) mimics exactly—or models—the desired behavior of the complex numbers.

In this way, we shall be led to say that the symbols for complex numbers are merely abbreviations for certain other more familiar objects.

There are a number of different and equally good ways in which the modelling can be carried out. We shall present one way that involves matrices.

Consider all 2×2 matrices of the form $\begin{pmatrix} a & b \\ -b & a \end{pmatrix}$. This means that we are going to deal exclusively with 2×2 matrices whose diagonal elements are the same and whose two remaining elements are negatives of one another. Some examples of such matrices are

$$\begin{pmatrix} 1 & 2 \\ -2 & 1 \end{pmatrix}, \quad \begin{pmatrix} -4 & -6 \\ 6 & -4 \end{pmatrix}, \quad \begin{pmatrix} \frac{1}{2} & 0 \\ 0 & \frac{1}{2} \end{pmatrix}, \quad \begin{pmatrix} 0 & 1 \\ -1 & 0 \end{pmatrix}.$$

We will call the set of all such matrices $\mathcal{C}$.

Notice that *if the matrices* A *and* B *are in* $\mathcal{C}$, *then so are the matrices* A + B, A − B, *and* AB. *If* c *is a scalar and the matrix* A *is in* $\mathcal{C}$, *then so is the matrix* cA.

The proof of these statements is simple. For example, if A is in $\mathcal{C}$ it must be of the form $\begin{pmatrix} a & b \\ -b & a \end{pmatrix}$. If B is in $\mathcal{C}$, it must be of the form $B = \begin{pmatrix} c & d \\ -d & c \end{pmatrix}$. Hence, $A + B = \begin{pmatrix} (a+c) & (b+d) \\ -(b+d) & (a+c) \end{pmatrix}$ and this matrix has the proper form for membership in $\mathcal{C}$. Moreover, the product

$$AB = \begin{pmatrix} (ac - bd) & (ad + bc) \\ -(ad + bc) & (ac - bd) \end{pmatrix}$$

has the proper form for membership in $\mathcal{C}$. The other statements are proved in a similar fashion. Incidentally, notice that if A and B are in $\mathcal{C}$, then multiplication is commutative: $AB = BA$. (Write out the elements of the second product).

The determinant $\begin{vmatrix} a & b \\ -b & a \end{vmatrix} = a^2 + b^2$. This quantity is zero only if both a and b are zero. Hence, if at least one of the quantities a, b is not zero, then the matrix $\begin{pmatrix} a & b \\ -b & a \end{pmatrix}$ has an inverse given by the equation

$$\begin{pmatrix} a & b \\ -b & a \end{pmatrix}^{-1} = \begin{pmatrix} \dfrac{a}{a^2+b^2} & \dfrac{-b}{a^2+b^2} \\ \dfrac{b}{a^2+b^2} & \dfrac{a}{a^2+b^2} \end{pmatrix}.$$

This inverse matrix is itself a member of the class $\mathcal{C}$, for its main diagonal elements are equal, whereas the remaining elements are negatives of one another.

It does not take much pencil work now to verify that the class $\mathcal{C}$ is a field. A good many of the field requirements are already covered by the laws of matrix arithmetic. The matrix $\begin{pmatrix} 0 & 0 \\ 0 & 0 \end{pmatrix}$, which is in $\mathcal{C}$, is the zero element of the system, whereas the matrix $\begin{pmatrix} 1 & 0 \\ 0 & 1 \end{pmatrix}$ is the unit.

There is an important subset of the elements of $\mathcal{C}$. This is comprised of all the 2×2 matrices of the form $\begin{pmatrix} a & 0 \\ 0 & a \end{pmatrix}$. Call this subset $\mathcal{R}$. Notice that

$$\begin{pmatrix} a & 0 \\ 0 & a \end{pmatrix} + \begin{pmatrix} b & 0 \\ 0 & b \end{pmatrix} = \begin{pmatrix} a+b & 0 \\ 0 & a+b \end{pmatrix}.$$

$$\begin{pmatrix} a & 0 \\ 0 & a \end{pmatrix} - \begin{pmatrix} b & 0 \\ 0 & b \end{pmatrix} = \begin{pmatrix} a-b & 0 \\ 0 & a-b \end{pmatrix}$$

$$\begin{pmatrix} a & 0 \\ 0 & a \end{pmatrix} \begin{pmatrix} b & 0 \\ 0 & b \end{pmatrix} = \begin{pmatrix} ab & 0 \\ 0 & ab \end{pmatrix}$$

$$\begin{pmatrix} a & 0 \\ 0 & a \end{pmatrix}^{-1} = \begin{pmatrix} a^{-1} & 0 \\ 0 & a^{-1} \end{pmatrix} \qquad \text{(Providing } a \neq 0\text{).}$$

It appears that arithmetic of the matrices in $\mathcal{R}$ is precisely like ordinary arithmetic. A matrix $\begin{pmatrix} a & 0 \\ 0 & a \end{pmatrix}$ can be thought of as acting precisely the same way as the number a does. $\mathcal{R}$ is itself a field contained within the larger field $\mathcal{C}$. $\mathcal{R}$ can be considered to be the same as the real numbers as far as the arithmetic operations are concerned.

But the field $\mathcal{C}$ has something that the field $\mathcal{R}$ does not have: it has an element whose square is the negative unit. Here it is: $\begin{pmatrix} 0 & 1 \\ -1 & 0 \end{pmatrix}$. We can verify directly that

$$\begin{pmatrix} 0 & 1 \\ -1 & 0 \end{pmatrix} \begin{pmatrix} 0 & 1 \\ -1 & 0 \end{pmatrix} = \begin{pmatrix} -1 & 0 \\ 0 & -1 \end{pmatrix} = -I.$$

For this accumulation of reasons, the set of matrices we have called $\mathcal{C}$ behaves in the same way arithmetically as does the set of complex numbers. We can exhibit this agreement in a striking way. To each matrix $\begin{pmatrix} a & b \\ -b & a \end{pmatrix}$ of $\mathcal{C}$ we associate the complex number $a + b\sqrt{-1}$. Conversely, to each complex number $a + b\sqrt{-1}$ we associate the matrix $\begin{pmatrix} a & b \\ -b & a \end{pmatrix}$.

This association will be indicated by the double arrow '↔'. For example,

$$\begin{pmatrix} 1 & 3 \\ -3 & 1 \end{pmatrix} \leftrightarrow 1 + 3\sqrt{-1}.$$

Here are some further examples of note:

$$\begin{pmatrix} 0 & 0 \\ 0 & 0 \end{pmatrix} \leftrightarrow 0 + 0\sqrt{-1} = 0$$

$$\begin{pmatrix} 1 & 0 \\ 0 & 1 \end{pmatrix} \leftrightarrow 1 + 0\sqrt{-1} = 1$$

$$\begin{pmatrix} 0 & 1 \\ -1 & 0 \end{pmatrix} \leftrightarrow 0 + 1\sqrt{-1} = \sqrt{-1}.$$

Now if $\begin{pmatrix} a & b \\ -b & a \end{pmatrix} \leftrightarrow a + b\sqrt{-1}$ and $\begin{pmatrix} c & d \\ -d & c \end{pmatrix} \leftrightarrow c + d\sqrt{-1}$, then,

1. $\begin{pmatrix} a & b \\ -b & a \end{pmatrix} + \begin{pmatrix} c & d \\ -d & c \end{pmatrix} \leftrightarrow (a + b\sqrt{-1}) + (c + d\sqrt{-1}).$

2. $\begin{pmatrix} a & b \\ -b & a \end{pmatrix} - \begin{pmatrix} c & d \\ -d & c \end{pmatrix} \leftrightarrow (a + b\sqrt{-1}) - (c + d\sqrt{-1}).$

3. $\begin{pmatrix} a & b \\ -b & a \end{pmatrix} \begin{pmatrix} c & d \\ -d & c \end{pmatrix} \leftrightarrow (a + b\sqrt{-1})(c + d\sqrt{-1}).$

4. $\begin{pmatrix} a & b \\ -b & a \end{pmatrix}^{-1} \leftrightarrow \dfrac{1}{a + b\sqrt{-1}}.$

These associations are readily established using matrix arithmetic on the left-hand side and complex arithmetic on the right-hand side. As far as arithmetic is concerned, the two systems, $\mathfrak{C}$ and the set of all complex numbers behave alike. In technical terms, they are *isomorphic*. This word has been coined from two Greek words that mean 'same' and 'form.' All calculations performed with complex numbers could equally well have been performed with the associated matrices, and when interpreted would yield identical answers. From this point of view, the mysterious complex numbers are merely abbreviations for certain 2×2 matrices to which very little mystery can be attached. The symbol $\sqrt{-1}$ is merely an abbreviation for $\begin{pmatrix} 0 & 1 \\ -1 & 0 \end{pmatrix}$.

Example: Find $(2 + 3\sqrt{-1})(1 + 4\sqrt{-1})$ using matrices.

$$(2 + 3\sqrt{-1}) \leftrightarrow \begin{pmatrix} 2 & 3 \\ -3 & 2 \end{pmatrix},\ (1 + 4\sqrt{-1}) \leftrightarrow \begin{pmatrix} 1 & 4 \\ -4 & 2 \end{pmatrix}.$$

Now $\begin{pmatrix} 2 & 3 \\ -3 & 2 \end{pmatrix}\begin{pmatrix} 1 & 4 \\ -4 & 1 \end{pmatrix} = \begin{pmatrix} -10 & 11 \\ -11 & -10 \end{pmatrix} \leftrightarrow -10 + 11\sqrt{-1}.$

A friend of mine who is a scientist recently said to me "In the old days, a mathematician was a person whose head was full of numbers. Today, a mathematician is a person whose head is full of isomorphisms." There is considerable truth in his observation, and in this section we have given one instance of it.

PROBLEMS

1. Work Problems 1–5 on page 298 using matrices. (It is not easier to do them in this way, but the point of this exercise is to emphasize the isomorphism between the complex numbers and the matrices of $\mathcal{C}$.)

2. Find $\begin{pmatrix} a & b \\ -b & a \end{pmatrix}\begin{pmatrix} a & -b \\ b & a \end{pmatrix}$ and interpret the result in terms of complex numbers.

3. Do the same with $\begin{pmatrix} a & b \\ -b & a \end{pmatrix}\begin{pmatrix} b & a \\ -a & b \end{pmatrix}$.

4. If $C = \begin{pmatrix} a & b \\ -b & a \end{pmatrix}$ represents the complex number $a + b\sqrt{-1}$, then the complex number represented by the matrix C' is known as the *conjugate* of $a + b\sqrt{-1}$. The conjugate is frequently denoted by $\overline{a + b\sqrt{-1}}$. Find explicitly the conjugate of $a + b\sqrt{-1}$. If $D = \begin{pmatrix} c & d \\ -d & c \end{pmatrix}$, show the relationship between the matrix equation $(CD)' = D'C' = C'D'$ and the equation

$$\overline{(a + b\sqrt{-1})(c + d\sqrt{-1})} = \overline{(a + b\sqrt{-1})}\ \overline{(c + d\sqrt{-1})}.$$

5. With matrices C and D defined as in Problem 4, interpret the matrix equation $(C + D)' = C' + D'$ in terms of complex numbers.

6. The *absolute value* of a complex number $a + b\sqrt{-1}$ is defined as the quantity $\sqrt{a^2 + b^2}$. It is frequently designated by $|a + b\sqrt{-1}|$. Show that

$$|a + b\sqrt{-1}| = \left[\det\begin{pmatrix} a & b \\ -b & a \end{pmatrix}\right]^{\frac{1}{2}}.$$

Use this fact to show that

$$|a + b\sqrt{-1}|\ |c + d\sqrt{-1}| = |(a + b\sqrt{-1})(c + d\sqrt{-1})|.$$

7. Show that

$$\begin{pmatrix} a & b \\ -b & a \end{pmatrix} = \sqrt{a^2+b^2}\begin{pmatrix} \dfrac{a}{\sqrt{a^2+b^2}} & \dfrac{b}{\sqrt{a^2+b^2}} \\ \dfrac{-b}{\sqrt{a^2+b^2}} & \dfrac{a}{\sqrt{a^2+b^2}} \end{pmatrix}.$$

Hence show that if one sets

$$\frac{b}{a} = \tan\theta \qquad \text{and} \qquad \sqrt{a^2+b^2} = r,$$

then

$$\begin{pmatrix} a & b \\ -b & a \end{pmatrix} = r\begin{pmatrix} \cos\theta & \sin\theta \\ -\sin\theta & \cos\theta \end{pmatrix}$$

and $a + b\sqrt{-1} = r(\cos\theta + \sin\theta\sqrt{-1})$.

BREAKING THROUGH CONTRADICTIONS: We have seen how matrices have enabled us to reconcile the contradictory demands embodied in the statement "there is a number x such that $x^2 = -1$." It is paradoxical that while mathematics has the reputation of being the one subject that brooks no contradictions (figures can't lie, et cetera) in reality, it has a long history of successful living with contradiction. This is best seen in the extensions of the notion of number that have been made over a period of 2500 years. From limited sets of integers, to infinite sets of integers, to fractions, negative numbers, irrational numbers, complex numbers, transfinite numbers, each extension, in its way, overcame a contradictory set of demands. A recent example of such a reconciliation occurred in the last generation when the classical notion of a function was extended in order to meet some conflicting requirements of modern theoretical physics.

These extensions are accomplished by immersing an original system of objects in a larger system, just as the real numbers were immersed in the 2×2 matrices to produce complex numbers. Although the contradiction remains unresolved at the original, more restricted level, it is completely resolved at the higher level that offers more freedom.

There is no doubt that mathematics has been continually revitalized by the challenge of contradiction and the subsequent extension of its notions. Why this occurs, and how it occurs, and whether or not a particular extension has any larger utility or significance is part of the fascinating history of the subject.

9.2 The Mathematics of Symmetry: Groups of Matrices

Here is an experience that is undoubtedly shared by all who have ever had a bedroom with wallpaper on the walls. Look at a spot on the wall so

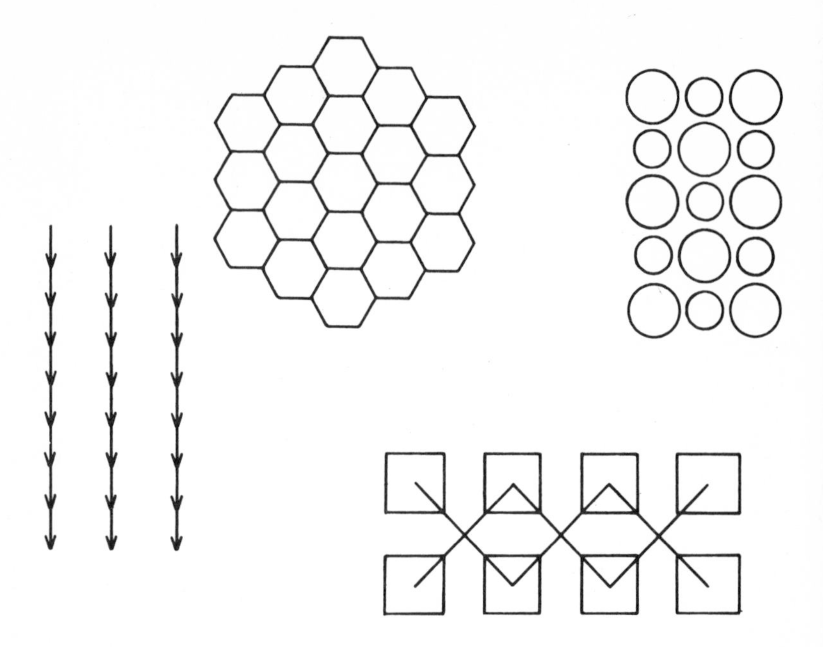

FIGURE 9.1 *Some Wallpaper Patterns*

that a pattern emerges (Figure 9.1). Focus a few inches to the right or to the left and the same pattern is there. Turn your head a bit: the same pattern. Look at the wall in the dresser mirror: the same pattern. What is the explanation? Wallpaper usually has a pattern with many *symmetries*, and symmetry of design means that the same design unit is seen over and over again in different positions.

Symmetry is a clue to much in nature, art, science, and mathematics. It has always made a strong appeal to the mathematician. About 1700 years ago, the mystic philosopher Plotinus wrote

"What geometrician or arithmetician could fail to take pleasure in the symmetries, correspondences, and principles of order observed in visible things?"

Despite this high regard, it was not until the nineteenth century that mathematicians found the language that was adequate for the proper discussion of symmetry. That language was the *theory of groups*. And one of the important tools in the theory of groups is matrix theory.

What characterizes the symmetry of a figure? It is the fact that certain simple transformations will turn the figure back into itself. This can be taken as the definition of the word "symmetry." For example, the stylized flower in Figure 9.2 will be transformed into itself if it is reflected about its central axis.

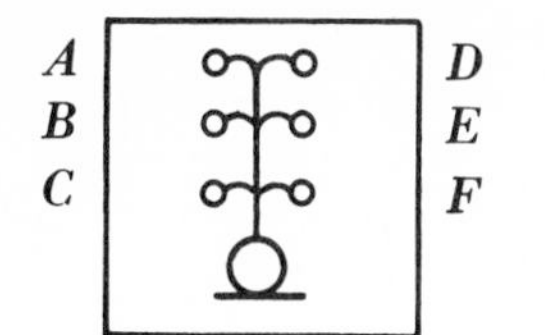

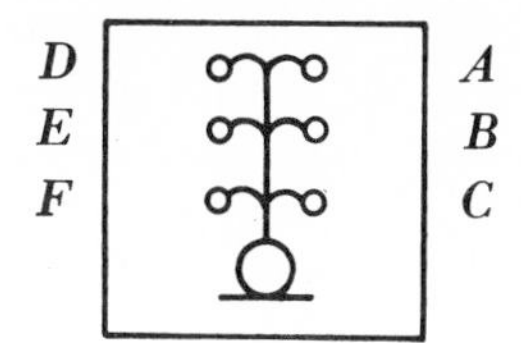

FIGURE 9.2

Each stem will fall on the corresponding stem, each flower on the corresponding flower, each leaf on the corresponding leaf. This kind of symmetry is known as *bilateral symmetry* and occurs frequently in design.

Decorative fretwork exhibits a different sort of symmetry. In Figure 9.3, which is imagined to continue indefinitely in both directions, the inner

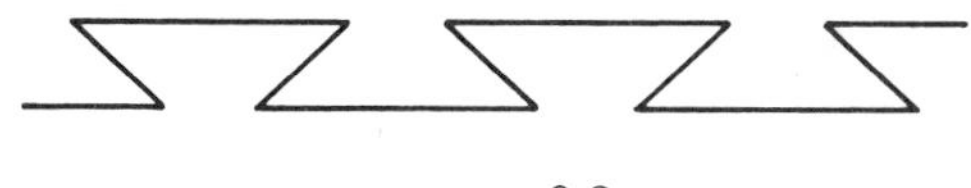

FIGURE 9.3

figure may be moved over one or several units of length and the whole figure will fall on top of itself. This type of symmetry or repetition is called *translational symmetry*.

Let us turn back to the flower. If we let the central axis of the flower be the y-axis, then a reflection in this axis is given by the equations

$$\begin{cases} x' = -x \\ y' = y \end{cases} \text{ with corresponding matrix } R = \begin{pmatrix} -1 & 0 \\ 0 & 1 \end{pmatrix}.$$

The flower is left unchanged by the reflection. It does not distinguish between $+x$ and $-x$.

Take a simple figure with bilateral symmetry and one whose equation is simple to deal with, the parabola $y = x^2$ (Figure 9.4).

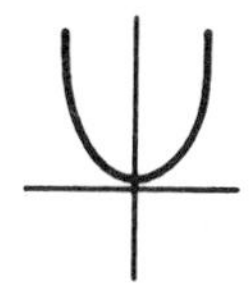

FIGURE 9.4

When we substitute into its equation the variables $\begin{cases} x = -x' \\ y = y' \end{cases}$, we obtain

$y' = (-x')^2 = (x')^2$. If we ignore the primes, we see that this is the same equation as the one we began with. Notice that this does not always happen. If we started with the equation

$$2x - 3y = 7,$$

this substitution would yield

$$-2x' - 3y' = 7.$$

By dropping the primes and rearranging the terms, we obtain

$$2x + 3y = 7.$$

This is *not* the same as the original equation; the original curve does not have bilateral symmetry about the y-axis.

Let us probe deeper. If we grip the axis of the flower or of the parabola between our thumb and forefinger, we might be inclined to spin it round and round. Every time the axis rotates 180°, one half of the flower occupies the position formerly occupied by its symmetrical half. Every time it is spun through 360°, the flower will be in its original position. What does this mean in terms of matrices? The matrix of the reflection R, followed by R once again, is $RR = R^2 = \begin{pmatrix} -1 & 0 \\ 0 & 1 \end{pmatrix}\begin{pmatrix} -1 & 0 \\ 0 & 1 \end{pmatrix} = \begin{pmatrix} 1 & 0 \\ 0 & 1 \end{pmatrix} = I$, or the identity transformation. The matrix of three reflections one after the other is $RRR = RR^2 = RI = R$. The matrix of four reflections would be $R^4 = (R^2)^2 = I^2 = I$, and so forth. The fact that $RR = I$ means that $R = R^{-1}$, and the geometrical interpretation of this is that the effect of a reflection can be undone by a further reflection.

All this information can be summarized by a multiplication table for the matrices R and I

	I	R
I	I	R
R	R	I

This table contains implicitly all that has just been said. The matrices I and R, together with their multiplication table, constitute an example of a mathematical system known as a *group*. We shall give a precise definition of a group in a later paragraph.

PROBLEMS

1. Describe in words the bilateral symmetries of each design in Figure 9.5.

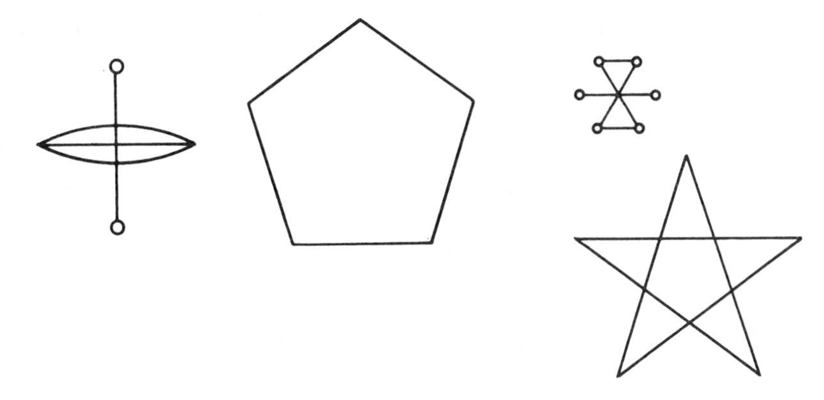

FIGURE 9.5

2. Which of the standard capital English letters has bilateral symmetry?

3. Find the equation of all straight lines that have bilateral symmetry with respect to the y-axis.

4. Show by a simple substitution that the curve $y = x^2 + 2x^4$ is symmetric with respect to the y-axis.

5. Is the curve $y = x^2 - 3x^3$ symmetric with respect to the y-axis?

6. Show that the curve $x = y^2 + 1$ is symmetric with respect to the x-axis.

7. Show that the curve $x^4 + y^4 = 1$ is symmetric with respect to both axes.

8. Show that the transformation

$$\begin{cases} x' = -x \\ y' = -y \end{cases}$$

changes the equation $xy = 1$ into itself. Interpret this geometrically.

9. Show that the transformation

$$\begin{cases} x' = x + 360° \\ y' = y \end{cases}$$

converts the curve $y = \sin x$ into itself. Interpret geometrically.

10. Show that the three expressions $x_1 + x_2 + x_3$, $x_1x_2 + x_2x_3 + x_3x_1$, $x_1x_2x_3$ retain their value if the numbers x_1, x_2, x_3 are permuted in any way. These functions are known as the *elementary symmetric functions* of x_1, x_2, x_3.

11. The curve $yx^2 = 8 - 4y$ is called the *Witch of Agnesi*. Show that it is symmetric with respect to the y axis. Plot the curve.

12. The curve $(x^2 + y^2)^2 = x^2 - y^2$ is called the *lemniscate of Bernoulli*. Show that it is symmetric with respect to both axes.

Let us next study Figure 9.6. What are the transformations that change it into itself? The figure is obviously unchanged by a counterclockwise revolution about the origin through 120° or through 240°. The first named transformation has the equations

$$\begin{cases} x' = (\cos 120°)x - (\sin 120°)y \\ y' = (\sin 120°)x + (\cos 120°)y \end{cases} \quad \text{or} \quad \begin{cases} x' = -\frac{1}{2}x - \frac{1}{2}\sqrt{3}\,y \\ y' = \frac{1}{2}\sqrt{3}\,x - \frac{1}{2}y. \end{cases}$$

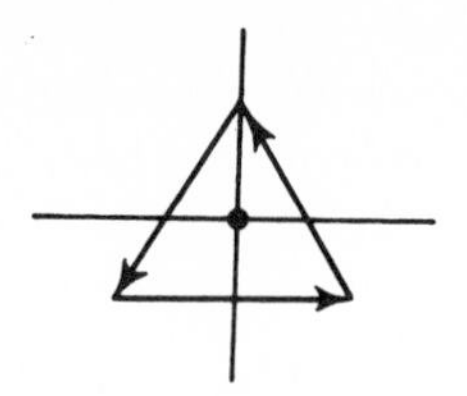

FIGURE 9.6

The matrix of this transformation is

$$R = \begin{pmatrix} -\frac{1}{2} & -\frac{1}{2}\sqrt{3} \\ \frac{1}{2}\sqrt{3} & -\frac{1}{2} \end{pmatrix}.$$

A rotation through 240° must have the matrix $RR = R^2$, and this is easily computed to be

$$R^2 = \begin{pmatrix} -\frac{1}{2} & \frac{1}{2}\sqrt{3} \\ -\frac{1}{2}\sqrt{3} & -\frac{1}{2} \end{pmatrix}.$$

Finally, note that $R^3 = RR^2$ must be the matrix of a rotation through 360°, and hence must be the same as I. Hence $R^3 = I$. Since $RR^2 = R^2R = I$, the inverse of R is R^2 whereas the inverse of R^2 is R.

The behavior of the matrices R and R^2 is summarized by this multiplication table:

	I	R	R^2
I	I	R	R^2
R	R	R^2	I
R^2	R^2	I	R

The matrices I, R, R^2, together with their multiplication table constitute a second example of a group.

PROBLEMS

1. Study, in a similar way to the text, the transformations that change the figure into itself. Draw up a multiplication table.
2. Do the same for the second design in Figure 9.5.

Definition: *A group of matrices is a set of square matrices (of the same order) that has the following properties:*

1. *If two matrices are in the set, so is their product.*
2. *The matrix I is in the set.*
3. *If a matrix is in the set, so is its inverse.*

The reader should now verify for himself that the two groups of matrices just mentioned do, in fact, satisfy these requirements.

A group of matrices may be presented in a concise form by means of a multiplication table. Across the top and down the left side, we write all the group elements. (If the group has an infinite number of elements, we have to imagine this to be carried out). In the body of the table we enter the corresponding products. We will then find that

1. Every entry in the body of the table is one of the elements of the group, that is, is one of the elements across the top or down the side. (This reflects group property 1.)
2. The matrix I is one of the elements. (This reflects group property 2.)
3. The matrix I appears in every row and in every column of the body of the table. (This reflects group property 3.)

Each of the three group properties has a definite meaning in terms of geometrical symmetry. Suppose that we have a certain figure. Call it F (Figure 9.7).

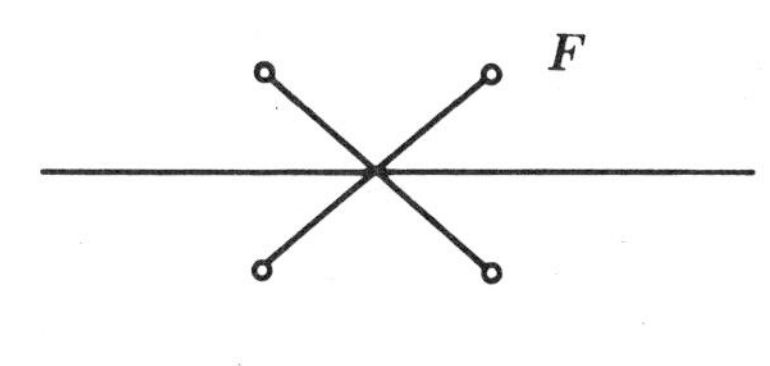

FIGURE 9.7

Suppose, now, that we think about *all* the linear transformations of the plane (rotations, reflections, et cetera) which are such that when they have been carried out, the figure F falls exactly on top of itself. To each such transformation there evidently corresponds a symmetry of the figure. Call the matrices of these transformations T_1, T_2, . . . and call the set of all these matrices $\mathcal{G}$. *Then* $\mathcal{G}$ *must be a group.* Here is the proof.

1. Let T_1 and T_2 be two matrices in $\mathcal{G}$. What will the combined transformation T_2T_1 do to the figure F? After T_1 is carried out, F falls on top of itself. After T_2 is carried out on this result, F falls on itself again. Hence T_2T_1 makes F fall on itself. T_2T_1 is therefore a member of $\mathcal{G}$. This establishes the first group property.
2. The identity transformation leaves everything unchanged. It certainly transforms F into F. Hence I must be a member of $\mathcal{G}$. This establishes the second group property.
3. If a transformation T changes a figure F into F, its inverse must change F back into F. Hence the inverse of the transformation T must be in $\mathcal{G}$. This establishes the third group property.

The symmetry of a figure F lies in the contrast between all possible transformations of the plane, and those transformations that leave F unchanged. The richer a figure F is in symmetries, the more involved is the structure of the related group $\mathcal{G}$ and its multiplication table.

On the basis of these few postulates, a vast mathematical theory has been constructed. Group theory has many uses in both pure and applied mathematics, but unfortunately we must terminate our presentation with this brief glimpse.

PROBLEMS

Prove that the following sets of matrices form a group. In Problems 1–3, give letters to the matrices and construct a multiplication table.

1. $\begin{pmatrix} 1 & 0 \\ 0 & 1 \end{pmatrix}, \begin{pmatrix} -1 & 0 \\ 0 & -1 \end{pmatrix}.$

2. $\begin{pmatrix} 1 & 0 & 0 \\ 0 & 1 & 0 \\ 0 & 0 & 1 \end{pmatrix}, \begin{pmatrix} 1 & 0 & 0 \\ 0 & 0 & 1 \\ 0 & 1 & 0 \end{pmatrix}, \begin{pmatrix} 0 & 1 & 0 \\ 0 & 0 & 1 \\ 1 & 0 & 0 \end{pmatrix}, \begin{pmatrix} 0 & 1 & 0 \\ 1 & 0 & 0 \\ 0 & 0 & 1 \end{pmatrix}, \begin{pmatrix} 0 & 0 & 1 \\ 1 & 0 & 0 \\ 0 & 1 & 0 \end{pmatrix}, \begin{pmatrix} 0 & 0 & 1 \\ 0 & 1 & 0 \\ 1 & 0 & 0 \end{pmatrix}.$

3. $\begin{pmatrix} 1 & 0 \\ 0 & 1 \end{pmatrix}, \begin{pmatrix} -1 & 1 \\ 0 & 1 \end{pmatrix}.$

4. All matrices $\begin{pmatrix} a & b \\ c & d \end{pmatrix}$ with $\begin{vmatrix} a & b \\ c & d \end{vmatrix} = 1.$

5. The set of all 3×3 matrices whose determinant equals ± 1.
6. The set of all $n \times n$ matrices that have inverses.
7. Interpret Problem 4 geometrically.

CHAPTER 10

Pippins and Cheese

"I will make an end of my dinner; there's pippins and cheese to come"—William Shakespeare

10.1 Additional Problems

1. Find the inverse of

$$\begin{pmatrix} 6 & 0 & 0 & 0 & 0 \\ 0 & 0 & 3 & 0 & 0 \\ 0 & -2 & 0 & 0 & 0 \\ 0 & 0 & 0 & 0 & \frac{1}{2} \\ 0 & 0 & 0 & -1 & 0 \end{pmatrix}.$$

2. Matrix square roots. A square matrix X is called a square root of a matrix A if $X^2 = A$. If $I = \begin{pmatrix} 1 & 0 \\ 0 & 1 \end{pmatrix}$, show that I and $-I$ are square roots of I. Show also that if a, b, and c are three numbers such that $a^2 + bc = 1$, then the matrix $\begin{pmatrix} a & b \\ c & -a \end{pmatrix}$ is a square root of I. Hence show that I has infinitely many square roots. How does this compare with the case of ordinary numbers?

3. If D is the diagonal matrix

$$\begin{pmatrix} a & & & & \\ & b & & & \\ & & \cdot & & \\ & & & \cdot & \\ & & & & \cdot \\ & & & & & p \end{pmatrix},$$

then

$$\begin{pmatrix} \sqrt{a} & & & \\ & \sqrt{b} & & \\ & & \ddots & \\ & & & \sqrt{p} \end{pmatrix}$$

is a square root of D.

4. If $\sqrt{B}$ designates a square root of B, show that $A\sqrt{B}\,A^{-1}$ is a square root of ABA^{-1}.

5. Consider the three simultaneous matrix equations $XY = A$, $YZ = B$, $ZX = C$. X, Y, Z, are unknowns. Show that if the matrix CBA has a square root, W, then a solution to this system is given by

$$X = AWA^{-1}B^{-1}, \qquad Y = BAW^{-1}, \qquad Z = WA^{-1}.$$

6. If $A = \begin{pmatrix} 1 & 1 & 1 \\ a & b & c \\ a^2 & b^2 & c^2 \end{pmatrix}$

then,

$$A^{-1} = \begin{pmatrix} bc^2 - cb^2 & b^2 - c^2 & c - b \\ ca^2 - ac^2 & c^2 - a^2 & a - c \\ ab^2 - ba^2 & a^2 - b^2 & b - a \end{pmatrix} / (b - c)(c - a)(a - b)$$

or

$$A^{-1} = \begin{pmatrix} b - c & 0 & 0 \\ 0 & c - a & 0 \\ 0 & 0 & a - b \end{pmatrix} \begin{pmatrix} -bc & b + c & -1 \\ -ca & c + a & -1 \\ -ab & a + b & -1 \end{pmatrix}$$
$$\div (b - c)(c - a)(a - b).$$

7. Verify that for any choice of quantities S, a, and b,

$$\begin{pmatrix} S + a + b & S - 2a & S + a - b \\ S - 2b & S & S + 2b \\ S - a + b & S + 2a & S - a - b \end{pmatrix}$$

is a magic square. Prove, conversely, that any 3×3 magic square with common sum $3S$ can be written in this form.

8. Verify that $(I + E)(I - E) = I - E^2$. Conclude from this, that if E is a matrix whose elements are small compared to 1, that $(I - E)^{-1}$ is

approximately $(I + E)$. Show that $I + E + E^2$ is an even better approximation to $(I - E)^{-1}$. Find an approximate inverse to

$$\begin{pmatrix} .98 & .03 \\ .02 & .97 \end{pmatrix}.$$

9. Determine integers x and y such that $\begin{pmatrix} x & y \\ 3 & 5 \end{pmatrix}$ has an inverse whose elements are all integers.

10. If $A^2 = A$, prove that $(I + A)^n = I + (2^n - 1)A$.

11. If $A^2 = I$, prove that $(I + A)^n = 2^{n-1}(I + A)$.

12. If J is a $p \times p$ matrix all of whose entries are 1, prove that

$$(J + I)^n = \left(\frac{(p + 1)^n - 1}{p}\right) J + I$$

13. If

$$T = \begin{pmatrix} 1 & 0 & 0 & 0 & 0 & \cdots \\ 1 & -1 & 0 & 0 & 0 & \cdots \\ 1 & -2 & 1 & 0 & 0 & \cdots \\ 1 & -3 & 3 & -1 & 0 & \cdots \\ 1 & -4 & 6 & -4 & 1 & \cdots \\ \vdots & & & & & \end{pmatrix},$$

then $TT' =$

$$\begin{pmatrix} 1 & 1 & 1 & 1 & \cdots \\ 1 & 2 & 3 & 4 & \cdots \\ 1 & 3 & 6 & 10 & \cdots \\ \vdots & & & & \end{pmatrix}.$$

The elements of this matrix are those in the Pascal triangle.

14. Compute T^2, where T is the matrix in Problem 13.

15. The three lines

$$\begin{aligned} a_1x + b_1y + c_1 &= 0 \\ a_2x + b_2y + c_2 &= 0 \\ a_3x + b_3y + c_3 &= 0 \end{aligned}$$

bound a triangle. Prove that the area of this triangle is the absolute value of

$$\frac{1}{2} \frac{\begin{vmatrix} a_1 & b_1 & c_1 \\ a_2 & b_2 & c_2 \\ a_3 & b_3 & c_3 \end{vmatrix}^2}{\begin{vmatrix} a_1 & b_1 \\ a_2 & b_2 \end{vmatrix} \begin{vmatrix} a_2 & b_2 \\ a_3 & b_3 \end{vmatrix} \begin{vmatrix} a_3 & b_3 \\ a_1 & b_1 \end{vmatrix}}.$$

Explain what happens when one or several of the factors in the denominator is equal to zero.

16. The most general 3×3 orthogonal matrix is given (with some exceptions) by

$$\frac{1}{1 + r^2 + s^2 + t^2}\begin{pmatrix} 1 + r^2 - s^2 - t^2 & 2(t - rs) & 2(s + rt) \\ -2(t + rs) & 1 + s^2 - r^2 - t^2 & 2(r - st) \\ -2(s - rt) & -2(r + st) & 1 + t^2 - r^2 - s^2 \end{pmatrix}.$$

Prove that for any values of r, s, and t, the above matrix is orthogonal.

17. Let E_{ij} be an $n \times n$ matrix whose elements are all 0 with the exception of the i, jth element which is 1.

Prove that $E_{ij}E_{pq} = \delta_{jp}E_{iq}$. Here, δ_{jp} is a constant equal to 1 if $j = p$ and equal to 0 if $j \neq p$.

18. If A is a square matrix and σ is the sum of the elements of A, prove that

$$JAJ = \sigma J.$$

19. If A and B are upper triangular matrices so are $A + B$ and AB. If k is a constant, kA is upper triangular. Hence, prove that if A is upper triangular, any polynominal of A (such as $3I - 7A + 15A^3$) is upper triangular.

20. If $P_1, P_2, \ldots, P_{n!}$ are the $n!$ permutation matrices of order n, prove that $P_1 + P_2 + \cdots + P_{n!} = (n - 1)!J$.

21. A *Markoff* matrix* of order n is a matrix (a_{ij}) whose elements a_{ij} satisfy the conditions

(1) $0 \leq a_{ij} \leq 1$

(2) $a_{i1} + a_{i2} + \cdots + a_{in} = 1$ for each $i = 1, 2, \ldots, n$.

Prove that the product of two Markoff matrices is also a Markoff matrix.

22. Let V_1 and V_2 be two fixed vectors. The equation $V \cdot V_1 = V_2 \cdot V_1$ represents a certain straight line. Keep V_2 fixed and vary V_1. For each V_1 a certain straight line results. What do these lines have in common? Try it out with $V_2 = \begin{pmatrix} 1 \\ 1 \end{pmatrix}$.

23. The vector V_1 has unit length. Prove that $(V_1 \cdot V_2)V_1$ is the projection of V_2 onto V_1.

10.2 Topics for Investigation

NORMAL MATRICES: Mathematicians who work with matrices distinguish a fairly large class of matrices which they call *normal.* A normal matrix is a square matrix A such that

$$AA' = A'A$$

---

*After Andrey Andreyevitch Markoff (1856-1922), a Russian mathematician who initiated an important branch of the theory of probability.

Show that the following matrices are normal:

(1) Symmetric matrices
(2) Diagonal matrices
(3) Orthogonal matrices, that is, matrices A such that $AA' = I$.
(4) Permutation matrices
(5) Pseudopermutation matrices

What can you say about the elements of a 2×2 matrix that is normal? Prove that an upper triangular matrix is normal if and only if it is a diagonal matrix.

ORTHOGONAL MATRICES: An orthogonal matrix represents a transformation that is the generalization to higher dimensions of two and three dimensional rotations.

Show that

(1) If A is orthogonal, so is A'.
(2) If A is orthogonal, then det A is either 1 or -1. Hint: Take the determinant of AA'.
(3) If A is orthogonal, then $A^{-1} = A'$. Hence A is nonsingular.
(4) If A is orthogonal, so is A^{-1}.
(5) If A and B are orthogonal, so are AB and BA.
    Interpret 4 and 5 geometrically.
(6) In an orthogonal matrix whose determinant equals 1, each element is equal in value to its cofactor.

JACOBI'S MATRICES: A Jacobi matrix (C. G. J. Jacobi 1804–1851) is an $n \times n$ matrix of the form

$$\begin{pmatrix}
1 & & & & & & & & & & \\
& 1 & & & & & & & & & \\
& & \ddots & & & & & & & & \\
& & & 1 & & & & & & & \\
& & & & \cos\theta & \cdots & & -\sin\theta & & & \\
& & & & & 1 & & & & & \\
& & & & \vdots & & \ddots & \vdots & & & \\
& & & & & & 1 & & & & \\
& & & & \sin\theta & \cdots & & \cos\theta & & & \\
& & & & & & & & 1 & & \\
& & & & & & & & & \ddots & \\
& & & & & & & & & & 1
\end{pmatrix}$$

All the elements of the matrix not indicated specifically are zero. Prove that a Jacobi matrix is an orthogonal matrix. Jacobi matrices are of considerable importance in the numerical determination of the characteristic roots of symmetric matrices.

DE MOIVRE'S THEOREM IN MATRIX FORM: de Moivre's Theorem says that $(\cos\theta + \sqrt{-1}\sin\theta)^n = \cos n\theta + \sqrt{-1}\sin n\theta$. Use the association

$$\cos n\theta + \sqrt{-1}\sin n\theta \leftrightarrow \begin{pmatrix} \cos\theta & \sin\theta \\ -\sin\theta & \cos\theta \end{pmatrix}$$

to infer that

$$\begin{pmatrix} \cos\theta & \sin\theta \\ -\sin\theta & \cos\theta \end{pmatrix}^n = \begin{pmatrix} \cos n\theta & \sin n\theta \\ -\sin n\theta & \cos n\theta \end{pmatrix}.$$

THE ALGEBRA OF COMMUTATORS: The matrix $AB - BA$ is known as the *commutator* of the square matrices A and B. Since A and B are not, in general commutative, the commutator will not generally equal zero.

Suppose that we write $AoB = AB - BA$, and regard the process of forming the commutator as a certain operation "o" performed on A and B. Prove that

(1) $AoB = -BoA$.
(2) $(tA)oB = Ao(tB) = t(AoB)$, t is a scalar.
(3) $Ao(B + C) = (AoB) + (AoC)$.
(4) $(A + B)oC = (AoC) + (BoC)$.
(5)* $Ao(BoC) + Bo(CoA) + Co(AoB) = 0$.
(6) $AoA = 0$.
(7) $AoI = IoA = 0$.
(8) If A and B are skew symmetric, so is AoB.

SPIN MATRICES: Wolfgang Pauli's theory of electron spin in quantum mechanics makes use of the four matrices

$$I = \begin{pmatrix} 1 & 0 \\ 0 & 1 \end{pmatrix} \quad X = \begin{pmatrix} 0 & 1 \\ 1 & 0 \end{pmatrix} \quad Y = \begin{pmatrix} 0 & -i \\ i & 0 \end{pmatrix} \quad \text{and} \quad Z = \begin{pmatrix} 1 & 0 \\ 0 & -1 \end{pmatrix}.$$

In the matrix Y, the symbol i designates $\sqrt{-1}$. Prove that these matrices have the following multiplication table:

	I	X	Y	Z
I	I	X	Y	Z
X	X	I	iZ	$-iY$
Y	Y	$-iZ$	I	iX
Z	Z	iY	$-iX$	I

*This is known as the *Jacobi identity*, and it has been said that every student of mathematics should verify it once in his life.

Show that $XoY = 2iZ$, $YoZ = 2iX$, $ZoX = 2iY$.

NONASSOCIATIVE OPERATIONS: For two square matrices of the same order, define a new operation "o" by means of the equation $AoB = AB'$. Show that this operation is not associative. That is, it is not always true that $(AoB)oC = Ao(BoC)$.

If $AoB = AB - BA$, find out whether this operation is associative.

QUATERNIONS: These are the 1835 invention of Sir William R. Hamilton who thought that they were the greatest thing in mathematics. Despite their applications in mechanics, in algebra, and despite the efforts of a society for the promulgation of quaternions (this is no joke!), the judgment of the succeeding generations has been more temperate.

A quaternion is a hypercomplex number. An ordinary complex number is of the form $a + bi$ and i is a symbol satisfying $i^2 = -1$. A quaternion is a number of the form $a + bi + cj + dk$ where a, b, c, d are real numbers and where i, j, and k are complex quantities that behave according to the multiplication table below.

	1	i	j	k
1	1	i	j	k
i	i	-1	k	$-j$
j	j	$-k$	-1	i
k	k	j	$-i$	-1

Thus, a quaternion is a real linear combination of the *four* quantities 1, i, j, and k. This accounts for the Latin root *quater* in the name. Two quaternions are added in an obvious fashion:

$$(a_1 + b_1 i + c_1 j + d_1 k) + (a_2 + b_2 i + c_2 j + d_2 k)$$
$$= (a_1 + a_2) + (b_1 + b_2)i + (c_1 + c_2)j + (d_1 + d_2)k.$$

They are multiplied by using the distributive law, and whenever products of the symbols 1, i, j, k appear, they are to be replaced by the value given in the multiplication table above. For example, the product of

$$(1 + i + j + k) \text{ by } (1 + i)$$

can be found as follows,

$$\begin{array}{l} 1 + i + j + k \\ 1 + i \\ \hline 1 + i + j + k \\ \quad + i \qquad\quad + i^2 + ij + ik \\ \hline 1 + 2i + j + k - 1 + k - j \\ = 2i + 2k. \end{array}$$

Prove that quaternions are not commutative by multiplying $(1 + i)$ by $(1 + i + j + k)$. Apart from this quirk, the quaternions satisfy all remaining requirements for a field.

Just as the complex numbers can be given a matrix representation as certain 2×2 matrices, the quaternions can be given a representation as certain 4×4 matrices.

Make the following association

$$a + bi + cj + dk \leftrightarrow Q = \begin{pmatrix} a & b & c & d \\ -b & a & -d & c \\ -c & d & a & -b \\ -d & -c & b & a \end{pmatrix}$$

In particular,

$$1 \leftrightarrow I = \begin{pmatrix} 1 & 0 & 0 & 0 \\ 0 & 1 & 0 & 0 \\ 0 & 0 & 1 & 0 \\ 0 & 0 & 0 & 1 \end{pmatrix}$$

$$i \leftrightarrow \mathcal{J} = \begin{pmatrix} 0 & 1 & 0 & 0 \\ -1 & 0 & 0 & 0 \\ 0 & 0 & 0 & -1 \\ 0 & 0 & 1 & 0 \end{pmatrix}$$

$$j \leftrightarrow \mathcal{G} = \begin{pmatrix} 0 & 0 & 1 & 0 \\ 0 & 0 & 0 & 1 \\ -1 & 0 & 0 & 0 \\ 0 & -1 & 0 & 0 \end{pmatrix}$$

$$k \leftrightarrow \mathcal{K} = \begin{pmatrix} 0 & 0 & 0 & 1 \\ 0 & 0 & -1 & 0 \\ 0 & 1 & 0 & 0 \\ -1 & 0 & 0 & 0 \end{pmatrix}$$

Use these matrices to verify the multiplication table just given.

Verify that $QQ' = (a^2 + b^2 + c^2 + d^2)I$. Evaluate det Q and see what identity results when the previous result is combined with the law of multiplication of determinants. Prove that if $Q \neq 0$, then

$$Q^{-1} = (a^2 + b^2 + c^2 + d^2)^{-1} \cdot (aI - b\mathcal{J} - c\mathcal{G} - d\mathcal{K}).$$

From this, infer a formula for $\dfrac{1}{a + bi + cj + dk}$.

MAGIC SQUARES AND MATRICES: A magic square is a square matrix whose row sums, column sums, and diagonal sums are all equal. A famous example of a magic square is

$$\begin{pmatrix} 16 & 3 & 2 & 13 \\ 5 & 10 & 11 & 8 \\ 9 & 6 & 7 & 12 \\ 4 & 15 & 14 & 1 \end{pmatrix}.$$

Here the elements of the matrix are the integers from 1 to 16. If A and B are magic squares, prove that $aA + bB$ is also a magic square.

A *pseudomagic* square is a matrix whose row sums and column sums are all equal. No requirement is made about the diagonals. Call this common sum d. A matrix A is a pseudomagic square if and only if $AJ = JA = dJ$. J is the matrix all of whose elements are 1. Prove this.

If A and B are pseudomagic squares, so is $aA + bB$. But more than this is true: the matrix AB is also pseudomagic. For, $AJ = JA = d_1J$, and $BJ = JB = d_2J$. Here d_1 and d_2 are the common sums in A and B respectively. Therefore,

$$(AB)J = A(BJ) = A(d_2J) = d_2(AJ) = d_2(d_1J) = d_2d_1J.$$

Similarly,

$$J(AB) = (JA)B = (d_1J)B = d_1(JB) = d_1(d_2J) = d_1d_2J.$$

By the principle noted above, the matrix AB must be pseudomagic.

If A is a pseudomagic matrix, what can be said about a polynomial in A?

Although the product of two pseudomagic matrices is pseudomagic, the product of two magic squares is not necessarily magic. Example:

$$A = \begin{pmatrix} 8 & 1 & 6 \\ 3 & 5 & 7 \\ 4 & 9 & 2 \end{pmatrix} \quad B = \begin{pmatrix} 6 & 1 & 8 \\ 7 & 5 & 3 \\ 2 & 9 & 4 \end{pmatrix} \quad AB = \begin{pmatrix} 67 & 67 & 91 \\ 67 & 91 & 67 \\ 91 & 67 & 67 \end{pmatrix}.$$

For further information, see the article by L. M. Weiner, *American Mathematical Monthly*, vol. 62 (1955).

FERMAT'S LAST THEOREM IS FALSE! (FOR MATRICES): Fermat's last theorem (which has not yet been proved by mathematicians) says that if n is an integer that is > 2, it is impossible to find three integers x, y, z, none of them zero, such that $x^n + y^n = z^n$. It turns out that a parallel statement for matrices is false. That is to say, we can find three matrices A, B, C, such that

(1) A, B, C have integer elements
(2) $A \neq 0$, $B \neq 0$, $C \neq 0$,

and we can find an integer $n > 2$ such that

$$A^n + B^n = C^n.$$

Moreover, $A^n \neq 0$, $B^n \neq 0$, $C^n \neq 0$.

Not only is the theorem false for matrices, but it is *totally* false. For we can find matrices A and B such that the equation $A^n + B^n = (A + B)^n$ is satisfied for *all* integers $n > 1$. What more can one ask for in this direction?

PROOF: Let A be idempotent, that is, let: $A^2 = A$.

$\left[\text{For instance } A = \begin{pmatrix} 2 & 1 \\ -2 & -1 \end{pmatrix}\right]$. Take $B = I - A$.

$\left[B = \begin{pmatrix} -1 & -1 \\ 2 & 2 \end{pmatrix}\right]$. Then $A^n = A$.

$B^2 = (I - A)(I - A) = I - 2A + A^2 = I - A = B.$

Hence

$B^n = I - A = B.$

$A^n + B^n = A + I - A = I = (A + B)^n.$

FERMAT'S LAST THEOREM AND PSEUDOMAGIC SQUARES: Let A be an $n \times n$ pseudomagic square with common row and column sum equal to d. Then

$$AJ = JA = dJ.$$

Set

$$B = \frac{d}{n} J \text{ and } C = A - \frac{d}{n} J.$$

Therefore

$$A = B + C.$$

Now,

$$BC = \frac{d}{n} JA - \frac{d^2}{n^2} J^2 = \frac{d^2}{n} J - \frac{d^2}{n^2} J^2.$$

But

$$J^2 = nJ, \text{ so that } BC = \frac{d^2}{n} J - \frac{d^2}{n} J = 0.$$

A similar computation yields $CB = 0$.

Hence

$$A^2 = (B + C)^2 = B^2 + BC + CB + C^2 = B^2 + C^2$$
$$A^3 = (B^2 + C^2)(B + C) = B^3 + C(CB) + B(BC) + C^3 = B^3 + C^3.$$

In a similar fashion, for any integer $n \geq 1$,

$$A^n = B^n + C^n.$$

Try this out with $A = \begin{pmatrix} 1 & 2 \\ 2 & 1 \end{pmatrix}$.

MAXWELL'S INFLUENCE MATRICES (see page 69): It would be interesting to devise a simple physical experiment to test the symmetry of the influence coefficients (that is, $d_{ij} = d_{ji}$).

The influence matrices have a number of remarkable properties. Here is one. Select two stations on the elastic body. Suppose that the body is not supported at these stations, so that a positive deflection can occur there when the body is stressed. Then if d_{11}, d_{12}, d_{21}, and d_{22} are the influence coefficients, the following determinant is positive:

$$\begin{vmatrix} d_{11} & d_{12} \\ d_{21} & d_{22} \end{vmatrix} > 0.$$

Use the formulas for the deflection of a cantilever beam under a concentrated load (page 71) and verify this inequality in this special instance.

This works with any number of stations $1, 2, \ldots, n$. If d_{ij} are the influence coefficients, then the determinant

$$\begin{vmatrix} d_{11} & d_{12} & \cdots & d_{1n} \\ \vdots & & & \vdots \\ d_{n1} & d_{n2} & \cdots & d_{nn} \end{vmatrix} > 0.$$

This is known as the property of *positive definiteness*, and is part of a larger and more general theory in mechanics. For a proof of the general fact, look at Biezeno and Grammel, *Engineering Dynamics*, vol. I, pp. 109–120.

THE MATHEMATICAL MICROSCOPE: The principles of the transformation of the plane can be put to use to make a "mathematical microscope." This is a device that will enable us to enlarge a curve in the vicinity of a point.

If the plane is subject to a uniform magnification of amount σ along both the x and the y axes, the equations of the transformation are

$$\begin{cases} x' = \sigma x \\ y' = \sigma y \end{cases} \quad \text{or} \quad \begin{pmatrix} x' \\ y' \end{pmatrix} = \begin{pmatrix} \sigma & 0 \\ 0 & \sigma \end{pmatrix} \begin{pmatrix} x \\ y \end{pmatrix}.$$

Suppose that $y = f(x)$ is the equation of a curve which we will assume passes through the point $x = 0$, $y = 0$. Under the transformation, the equation becomes

$$\frac{y'}{\sigma} = f\left(\frac{x'}{\sigma}\right).$$

By solving for y' and then omitting the primes, we obtain

$$y = \sigma f\left(\frac{x}{\sigma}\right).$$

This equation is the mathematical microscope. The quantity σ is the magnification. By selecting σ very large, we can magnify a curve in the vicinity of $x = 0, y = 0$. Here are some examples of how it works. The curve $y = x^2$ is a parabola that passes through $x = 0$ $y = 0$. It is drawn in Figure 10.1.

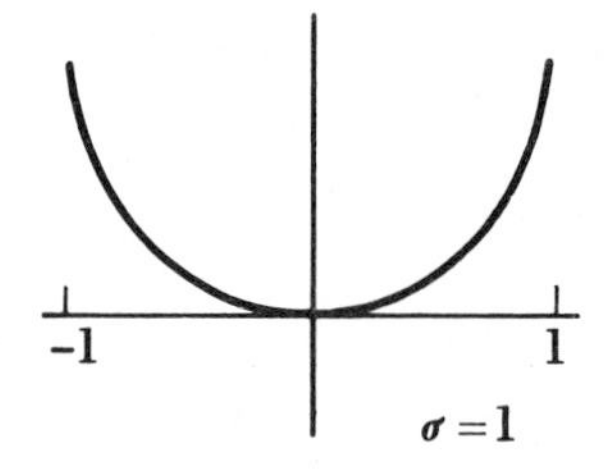

FIGURE 10.1

Hence $f(x) = x^2$. Now select a magnification $\sigma = 10$. Then the magnified curve is $y = 10\left(\frac{x}{10}\right)^2 = \frac{x^2}{10}$. This is drawn in Figure 10.2.

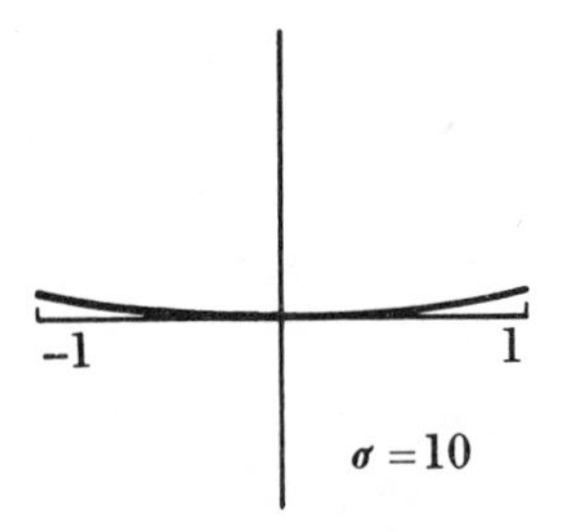

FIGURE 10.2

Notice that we obtain a parabola again, but very much flattened. If $\sigma = 100$, the magnified curve is $y = x^2/100$ which is practically indistinguishable from a straight line (Figure 10.3).

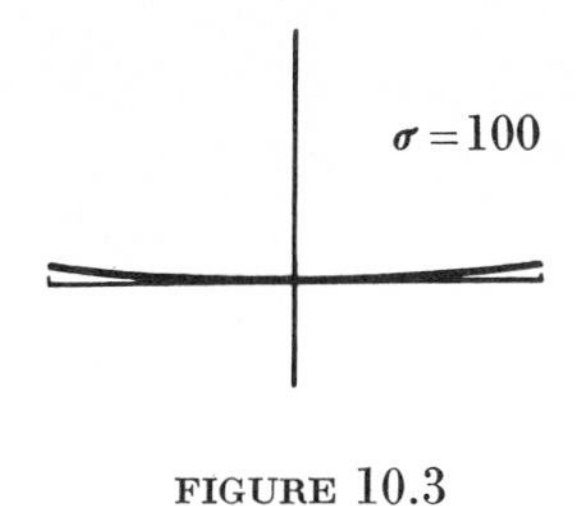

FIGURE 10.3

The reader should verify and explain that when the v-shaped curve in Figure 10.4 is subject to a magnification we obtain the same curve over again. (Figure 10.5.)

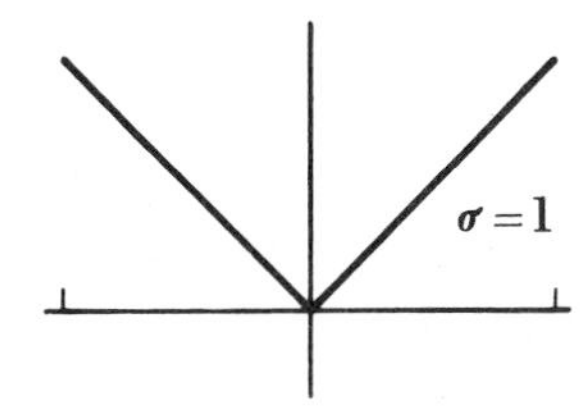

FIGURE 10.4

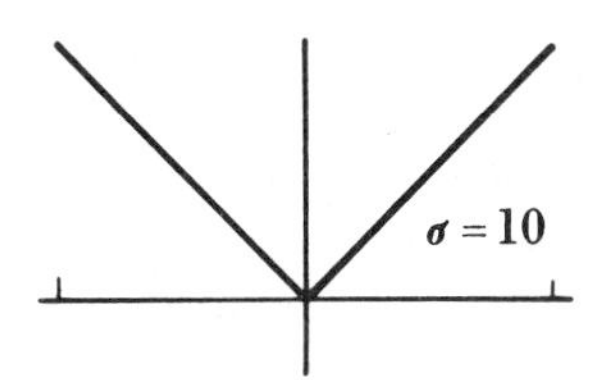

FIGURE 10.5

Apply the mathematical microscope to the following curves at $x = 0$, $y = 0$:

(a) $x^2 + (y - 1)^2 = 1$.
(b) $y = \sqrt{x}$.
(c) $y = x^2 - x$.
(d) $y = x^3 - 2x$.

In each of these cases, what line does the enlarged curve appear to be approaching as the magnification becomes greater and greater?

If a curve passing through the point $x = 0$, $y = 0$ is sufficiently smooth at that point, then the magnified curve will approach a straight line. This idea is developed rigorously in the differential calculus.

ROTATING THE ELEMENTS: Let Q designate the $n \times n$ matrix with ones on the nonprincipal diagonal and zeros elsewhere:

$$Q = \begin{pmatrix} 0 & 0 & 0 & \cdots & 0 & 1 \\ 0 & 0 & 0 & & 1 & 0 \\ \cdot & \cdot & \cdot & \cdots & \cdot & \cdot \\ 1 & 0 & 0 & \cdots & 0 & 0 \end{pmatrix}$$

Show that $Q' = Q$ and $Q^2 = I$. A is a given $n \times n$ matrix. Find simple relations between the matrix A and the matrices AQ, QA, QA', $A'Q$, QAQ, $QA'Q$. For example, QAQ is the matrix A rotated 180° counterclockwise.

HADAMARD MATRICES: It should not be thought that the frontiers of modern mathematics always involve such difficult things that they are completely remote from the high school student.* We shall mention a topic that has attracted a lot of attention in recent years, one that involves only the simplest ideas, and yet presents many unsolved problems.

Look at the following matrices

$$\begin{pmatrix} 1 & 1 \\ 1 & -1 \end{pmatrix}, \quad \begin{pmatrix} 1 & 1 & 1 & 1 \\ 1 & -1 & 1 & -1 \\ 1 & 1 & -1 & -1 \\ 1 & -1 & -1 & 1 \end{pmatrix},$$

$$\begin{pmatrix} 1 & 1 & 1 & 1 & 1 & 1 & 1 & 1 \\ 1 & -1 & 1 & -1 & 1 & -1 & 1 & -1 \\ 1 & 1 & -1 & -1 & 1 & 1 & -1 & -1 \\ 1 & -1 & -1 & 1 & 1 & -1 & -1 & 1 \\ 1 & 1 & 1 & 1 & -1 & -1 & -1 & -1 \\ 1 & -1 & 1 & -1 & -1 & 1 & -1 & 1 \\ 1 & 1 & -1 & -1 & -1 & -1 & 1 & 1 \\ 1 & -1 & -1 & 1 & -1 & 1 & 1 & -1 \end{pmatrix}.$$

These matrices have the following remarkable properties

(a) The elements of the matrices are either 1 or -1

(b) In each matrix, the elements in two different rows or in two different columns coincide in exactly half the number of positions. (Thus, the second and third rows of the second matrix are $1 \quad -1 \quad 1 \quad -1$ and $1 \quad 1 \quad -1 \quad -1$ respectively. The first and last elements coincide, while the

*For a recent collection of unsolved mathematical problems that have appeal for the professional and amateur alike, see "Tomorrow's Math" by C. Stanley Ogilvy, Oxford University Press, New York, 1962.

second and third elements differ.) Another way of expressing this property is by saying that the inner product of two different rows or two different columns is always zero. (Thus, in the second matrix, the inner product of the second and third rows is $(1)(1) + (-1)(1) + (1)(-1) + (-1)(-1) = 1 \quad -1 \quad -1 + 1 = 0$.)

Matrices that have these two properties are known as *Hadamard matrices* (after the French mathematician Jacques Hadamard (1865–1963)).

If such a matrix is designated by H and is of order n, then it is not at all difficult to show that Property (b) is expressed by the matrix equation

$$HH' = nI.$$

The main problem concerning Hadamard matrices is this: for what orders are there Hadamard matrices, and how do you construct them? At the present time (Nov., 1964) the answers to these questions are only partially known.

It should be clear that an Hadamard matrix must have an even order. But more than this is true: with the exception of the 2×2 case given above, an Hadamard matrix must have an order that is a multiple of four. Here is a simple, and ingenious proof of this fact. Let $n \geq 3$, and set

$$H = \begin{pmatrix} a_1 & a_2 & a_3 & \cdots & a_n \\ b_1 & b_2 & b_3 & \cdots & b_n \\ c_1 & c_2 & c_3 & \cdots & c_n \\ & & & \cdots & \\ & & & \cdots & \end{pmatrix}.$$

The a's, b's, and c's are either 1 or -1. Therefore,

$$a_1^2 + a_2^2 + \cdots + a_n^2 = n.$$

Since the inner products of different rows are zero, we have

$$\begin{aligned} a_1b_1 + a_2b_2 + \cdots + a_nb_n &= 0 \\ a_1c_1 + a_2c_2 + \cdots + a_nc_n &= 0 \\ b_1c_1 + b_2c_2 + \cdots + b_nc_n &= 0. \end{aligned}$$

Now notice the algebraic identity:

$$\begin{aligned} (a_1 + b_1)(a_1 + c_1) + (a_2 + b_2)(a_2 + c_2) + \cdots + (a_n + b_n)(a_n + c_n) \\ = (a_1{}^2 + a_2{}^2 + \cdots + a_n{}^2) + (a_1c_1 + a_2c_2 + \cdots + a_nc_n) \\ + (a_1b_1 + a_2b_2 + \cdots + a_nb_n) + (b_1c_1 + b_2c_2 + \cdots + b_nc_n). \end{aligned}$$

Hence, by substituting the above values for these four parentheses, we find that $(a_1 + b_1)(a_1 + c_1) + (a_2 + b_2)(a_2 + c_2) + \cdots + (a_n + b_n)(a_n + c_n) = n$. Since the a's, b's and c's are either 1 or -1, a moment's consideration shows that the product $(a_1 + b_1)(a_1 + c_1)$ must be either 0 or 4. The same is true of the other products: $(a_2 + b_2)(a_2 + c_2), \ldots, (a_n + b_n)(a_n + c_n)$. Therefore n, which equals the sum of these products, must be divisible by 4.

The present evidence seems to indicate that the reverse is also true: if n is a multiple of 4, then $n \times n$ Hadamard matrices can be constructed. But this has not yet been shown to be the case.

It is not difficult to devise methods for constructing Hadamard matrices when n is a power of 2. This was already done in 1867 by Sylvester. Examine the relationship between the three matrices given and see whether you can construct an Hadamard matrix of order 16. Hadamard matrices have been constructed for all multiples of 4 less than 200, with the exception of 116, 156, and 188. Hadamard matrices have interesting connections with the theory of numbers and geometry. A more recent surprising application is to the construction of optimum code words for communicating through space.

More information can be found in the following articles.

R. E. A. C. Paley, "On Orthogonal Matrices," *Journal of Mathematics and Physics*, vol. 12, (1933), pp. 311–320.

S. W. Golomb and L. D. Baumert, "The Search for Hadamard Matrices," *The American Mathematical Monthly*, vol. 70 (1963) pp. 12–17.

A. T. Butson, "Generalized Hadamard Matrices," *Proceedings of the American Mathematical Society*, vol. 13 (1962) pp. 894–898.

Further references will be found in these articles.

MATRICES AND FRACTIONAL TRANSFORMATIONS: In addition to linear transformations, matrices may be used to represent certain other kinds of transformation. If a, b, c, and d are constants, the transformation $x' = \dfrac{ax + b}{cx + d}$ which sends numbers x into numbers x' is known as a *fractional transformation*. Suppose we agree to represent this transformation by the matrix $\begin{pmatrix} a & b \\ c & d \end{pmatrix}$. Show that the matrix product corresponds to the product of two such transformations.

GENERAL INNER PRODUCTS: The inner product of $V_1 = \begin{pmatrix} x_1 \\ y_1 \end{pmatrix}$, $V_2 = \begin{pmatrix} x_2 \\ y_2 \end{pmatrix}$ was defined in Chapter 6 by means of $(V_1 \cdot V_2) = (x_1x_2 + y_1y_2) = V_1'V_2$. This inner product has the properties listed in the Theorem on page 220. It is of some interest to ask whether other definitions of the inner product can lead to a number that has these properties. This is indeed the case. Let the elements of the matrix $P = \begin{pmatrix} p_1 & p_2 \\ p_2 & p_3 \end{pmatrix}$ satisfy the two inequalities $p_1 > 0$, $\begin{vmatrix} p_1 & p_2 \\ p_2 & p_3 \end{vmatrix} > 0$. Define a new inner product $V_1 \cdot V_2$ by means of the equation $(V_1' \cdot V_2) = V_1 P V_2$.

Prove that this new inner product has all the properties as required. Show that the special selection $P = I = \begin{pmatrix} 1 & 0 \\ 0 & 1 \end{pmatrix}$ leads to the inner product already studied in the text.

THE TRACE: If A is a square matrix, the *trace* of A is defined as the sum of the elements on the principal diagonal. The trace of A is designated by $\text{tr}(A)$. For example

$$\text{tr}\begin{pmatrix} 3 & -1 \\ 2 & 7 \end{pmatrix} = 3 + 7 = 10.$$

Prove that:

1. $\text{tr}(A + B) = \text{tr}(A) + \text{tr}(B)$.
2. $\text{tr}(cA) = c\,\text{tr}(A)$, c is a scalar.
3. $\text{tr}(A) = \text{tr}(A')$.
4. $\text{tr}(AB) = \text{tr}(BA)$.

Is it true that $\text{tr}(AB) = [\text{tr}(A)]\,[\text{tr}(B)]$?
Contrast the properties of the function $\text{tr}(A)$ with those of $\det A$. The trace has the important property that

5. $\text{tr}(A^{-1}BA) = \text{tr}(B)$.

Prove this in the case of 1×1 and 2×2 matrices.

THE PANTOGRAPH: A lazy tongs, or pantograph, consists of four rods of equal length, hinged together at A, B, C, and D (Figure 10.6).

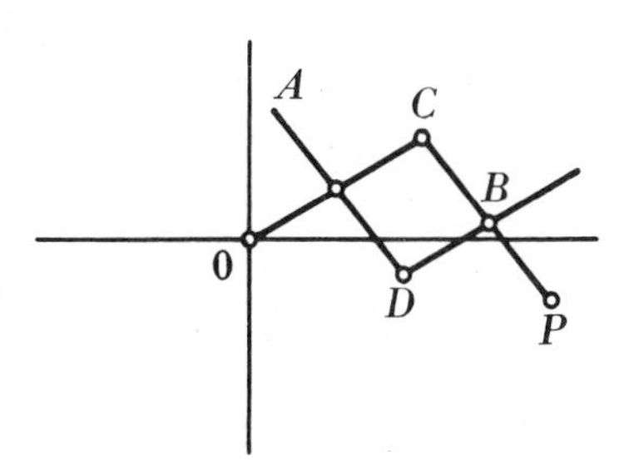

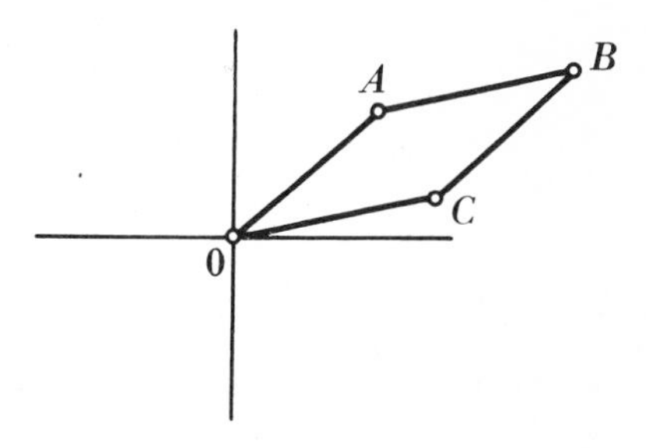

FIGURE 10.6

1. A and B are the midpoints of the respective rods. O is hinged at the origin of a coordinate system. Find the transformation that takes D into P. Express with matrices.

2. In the linkage on the right, $OA = AB = BC = CO$, and OA is fixed. Find the transformation that takes C into B.

A DOZEN DISCOVERIES THAT SHOOK THE MATHEMATICAL WORLD: Working with noncommutative multiplication may put us in mind of other mathematical inventions or discoveries that proved upsetting in their day. Here is my list. Every serious student of mathematics ought to acquire some understanding of what each is about.

DISCOVERY	DISCOVERER
1. The existence of an infinity of positive integers.	Known in antiquity. But as late as 250 B.C. Archimedes still finds it necessary to show how to write and give names to very large numbers.
2. Existence of irrational numbers.	Pythagoras (around 500 B.C.).
3. Impossibility of squaring the circle.	Generally acknowledged to be the case by the mathematicians of antiquity, but not proved conclusively until the work of F. Lindemann in 1872.
4. Euler's Formula: $e^{\pi\sqrt{-1}} = -1$.	Leonhard Euler (1707–1783). But apparently some preliminary rumbles of it are found in the work of Roger Cotes (1682–1716).
5. Impossibility of solving the Quintic Equation in closed form.	Conjectured by Ruffini (1765–1827). Proved by Nils Henrik Abel (1802–1829).
6. Representation of a general function in a series of sines and cosines.	Jean Baptiste Joseph Fourier (1768–1830).
7. Existence of non-Euclidan geometries.	Discovered independently by Bolyai (1802–1860) and Nikolai Lobatchewski (1793–1856).
8. Existence of noncommutative algebras.	The quaternions (1835) of Sir William Rowen Hamilton (1805–1865). Matrices.
9. Nonexistence of extremal solutions in the calculus of variations.	Karl Weierstrass (1815–1897).
10. Nondenumerability of the real numbers.	George Cantor (1845–1918).
11. Existence of logical paradoxes in set theory.	Bertrand Russell (1872–) and others. Around 1900.
12. Existence of unprovable propositions.	Kurt Gödel (1931).

Numbers 1, 11, and 12 have not yet been fully accommodated in mathematical thinking.

TRUE OR FALSE: The conjecture has been made that since matrices do not commute, XY may be specified as one matrix whereas YX may be specified as a totally different matrix. That is to say, if A and B are given square matrices we can find square matrices X, Y such that $XY = A$ and $YX = B$. True or false? Hint: Take determinants.

MATRIX CRYPTOGRAPHY: Cryptography is the art of sending secret messages. One of the most primitive methods for concealing the meaning of words is to replace each letter by a different letter or a different symbol. We might, for example, agree to write B for A, C for B, . . . , Z for Y, and A for Z. With this code the message PUT OUT THE CAT BEFORE YOU LEAVE would be sent as QVU PVU UIF DBU CFGPSF ZPV MFBWF. A code such as this one is called a simple substitution code.

Encoding a message is equivalent to subjecting that message to a certain transformation. Decoding a message is equivalent to subjecting the message received to the inverse transformation. We should naturally deal with nonsingular transformations for if the transformation were singular, we should not be able to decode the message unambiguously.

The principal difficulty with simple substitution codes is that they preserve the frequencies of letters and of groups of letters. This makes it easy to break the code. A way around this difficulty is to deal with blocks of letters and to allow the whole block to have a coded image. Matrix theory provides an interesting way of doing this. What follows can be regarded as an exercise in pure mathematics and nothing is implied as to whether the method has any practical significance.

Suppose, first of all, that each letter is given a numerical value, for example, $A = 1$, $B = 2$, . . . , $Z = 26$. Divide the message into groups of three letters, thus: *PUT OUT THE CAT BEF ORE YOU LEA VEX*. The added X rounds out the triplets. Now use the matrix

$$\begin{pmatrix} 14 & 8 & 3 \\ 8 & 5 & 2 \\ 3 & 2 & 1 \end{pmatrix}$$

as a multiplier for each of the triplets. (The reason for using this matrix will be explained below). Thus, since $P = 16$, $U = 21$, $T = 20$, *PUT* would be coded as 452 273 110 since

$$\begin{pmatrix} 14 & 8 & 3 \\ 8 & 5 & 2 \\ 3 & 2 & 1 \end{pmatrix}\begin{pmatrix} 16 \\ 21 \\ 20 \end{pmatrix} = \begin{pmatrix} 452 \\ 273 \\ 110 \end{pmatrix}.$$

OUT would be encoded as 438 265 107 since

$$\begin{pmatrix} 14 & 8 & 3 \\ 8 & 5 & 2 \\ 3 & 2 & 1 \end{pmatrix}\begin{pmatrix} 15 \\ 21 \\ 20 \end{pmatrix} = \begin{pmatrix} 438 \\ 265 \\ 107 \end{pmatrix}.$$

Note that while *PUT* and *OUT* have two letters in common, the encoded messages are totally different. To decode, we use the inverse matrix.

Since

$$\begin{pmatrix} 14 & 8 & 3 \\ 8 & 5 & 2 \\ 3 & 2 & 1 \end{pmatrix}^{-1} = \begin{pmatrix} 1 & -2 & 1 \\ -2 & 5 & 4 \\ 1 & -4 & 6 \end{pmatrix},$$

we can compute

$$\begin{pmatrix} 1 & -2 & 1 \\ -2 & 5 & -4 \\ 1 & -4 & 6 \end{pmatrix}\begin{pmatrix} 452 \\ 273 \\ 110 \end{pmatrix} = \begin{pmatrix} 16 \\ 21 \\ 20 \end{pmatrix} = \begin{pmatrix} \text{P} \\ \text{U} \\ \text{T} \end{pmatrix}$$

$$\begin{pmatrix} 1 & -2 & 1 \\ -2 & 5 & -4 \\ 1 & -4 & 6 \end{pmatrix}\begin{pmatrix} 438 \\ 265 \\ 107 \end{pmatrix} = \begin{pmatrix} 15 \\ 21 \\ 20 \end{pmatrix} = \begin{pmatrix} \text{O} \\ \text{U} \\ \text{T} \end{pmatrix}.$$

To make the code breaking harder, we can use larger blocks of letters. To make the decoding process simple, we need to use as a multiplier a matrix that has integer elements and whose inverse also has integer elements. Otherwise we might get into problems with the round-off of computation.

Here is one way such matrices can be obtained. Let T be a matrix that is upper triangular, has integer elements, and has 1's on the main diagonal. The matrix T^{-1} is also of this form and is easily computed. Then, the matrix TT' has integer elements and

$$(TT')^{-1} = (T')^{-1}\,T^{-1} = (T^{-1})'\,T^{-1}.$$

Since T^{-1} has integer elements, so does $(T^{-1})'$, and hence also $(TT')^{-1}$. This is the way the multiplier used above was obtained. We start with

$$T = \begin{pmatrix} 1 & 2 & 3 \\ 0 & 1 & 2 \\ 0 & 0 & 1 \end{pmatrix}$$

and compute

$$T^{-1} = \begin{pmatrix} 1 & -2 & 1 \\ 0 & 1 & -2 \\ 0 & 0 & 1 \end{pmatrix}.$$

Now

$$TT' = \begin{pmatrix} 14 & 8 & 3 \\ 8 & 5 & 2 \\ 3 & 2 & 1 \end{pmatrix}$$

and

$$(TT')^{-1} = \begin{pmatrix} 1 & 0 & 0 \\ -2 & 1 & 0 \\ 1 & -2 & 1 \end{pmatrix} \begin{pmatrix} 1 & -2 & 1 \\ 0 & 1 & -2 \\ 0 & 0 & 1 \end{pmatrix} = \begin{pmatrix} 1 & -2 & 1 \\ -2 & 5 & -4 \\ 1 & -4 & 6 \end{pmatrix}.$$

For further information on matrices and cryptography the reader is referred to L. S. Hill, "Concerning Certain Linear Transformation Apparatus of Cryptography," *American Mathematics Monthly*, vol. 38, p. 135; W. F. Friedman and C. J. Mendelsohn, "A Bibliography of Cryptography," *American Mathematics Monthly*, vol. 50, p. 345; J. Levine, "Some Applications of High-Speed Computers to the Case $n = 2$ of Algebraic Cryptography," *Mathematics of Computation*, vol. 15 (1961), pp. 254–260.

If A is a matrix with integer elements and if $\det A = +1$ or -1, we can prove, using Cramer's rule, that A^{-1} also has integer elements. The converse is also true: If A has integer elements and A^{-1} has integer elements then $\det A = +1$ or -1. Hint: $(\det A)(\det A^{-1}) = 1$.

MULTIPLICATION OF DETERMINANTS: Give a geometrical interpretation for the multiplication rule for 3×3 determinants. Complete proofs are not necessary.

LEVEL SPIRITS: Certain numerical processes are nothing but linear transformations in disguise. Take a look at the following numerical game. Write down three numbers at random; say

$$8, 64, 32.$$

Average the first and second and replace each by this average. Leave the third number alone:

$$36, 36, 32.$$

Average the second and third and replace each of these by this average. Leave the first number alone:

$$36, 34, 34.$$

Average the third and first and replace these by the average. Leave the second number alone:

$$35, 34, 35.$$

We can carry out this process over and over:

$$\begin{matrix} 34\tfrac{1}{2} & 34\tfrac{1}{2} & 35 \\ 34\tfrac{1}{2} & 34\tfrac{3}{4} & 34\tfrac{3}{4} \\ 34\tfrac{5}{8} & 34\tfrac{3}{4} & 34\tfrac{5}{8} \\ 34\tfrac{11}{16} & 34\tfrac{11}{16} & 34\tfrac{5}{8} \\ 34\tfrac{11}{16} & 34\tfrac{21}{32} & 34\tfrac{21}{32}. \end{matrix}$$

This game can be visualized in the following way. Take three glasses, each containing different amounts of water (Figure 10.7).

FIGURE 10.7

Adjust the first two glasses until the water in both is the same height (Figure 10.8).

FIGURE 10.8

Adjust the second two until the water is at the same height. Continue doing this.

(1) How can we predict the result after n steps?

(2) In the number game worked out, the values seem to be settling down to $34\frac{2}{3}$ which is the average of the initial numbers 8, 64, 32. Can we prove that this is really the case?

INSCRIBED QUADRILATERALS: Start with a quadrilateral, mark the midpoints of the sides, and join them consecutively. A second quadrilateral (actually, a parallelogram) results. Find the midpoints of its sides and draw the third figure. Keep this process up. Where will it all end?

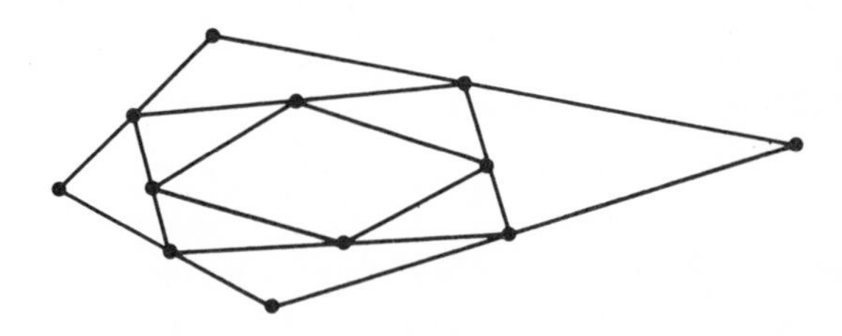

FIGURE 10.9

THE QUAKER OATS BOX: The Quaker Oats box has on its side a picture of a Quaker holding a Quaker Oats box in his hand. This box, in its turn, has a picture of a Quaker holding . . . .

Work with the simplified version in Figure 10.10 and determine the point toward which the boxes converge.

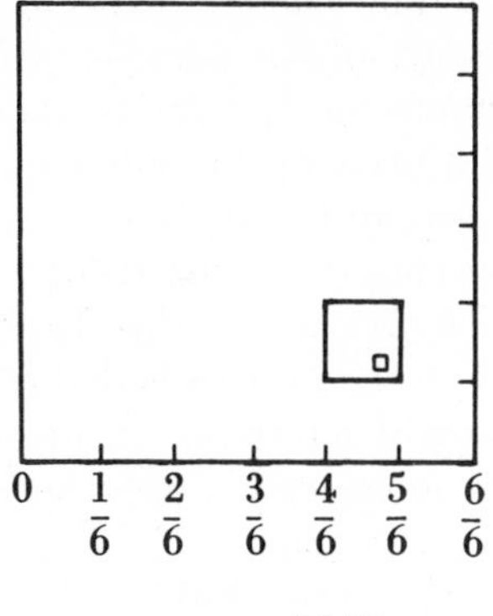

FIGURE 10.10

THE LORENTZ TRANSFORMATION: The Lorentz transformation (H. A. Lorentz) is of fundamental importance in the theory of relativity. In one space variable x, and time variable t, the transformation is

$$x' = \frac{x - vt}{\sqrt{1 - (v/c)^2}}, \qquad t' = \frac{t - xv/c^2}{\sqrt{1 - (v/c)^2}}.$$

The quantities v and c are constants: v is the velocity of a particle and c is the velocity of light. The quantity v is always $< c$. Show that this transformation can be written in the form

$$\begin{pmatrix} x' \\ t' \end{pmatrix} = \frac{1}{\sqrt{1 - (v/c)^2}} \begin{pmatrix} 1 & -v \\ -\frac{v}{c^2} & 1 \end{pmatrix} \begin{pmatrix} x \\ t \end{pmatrix}.$$

Show that the transformation is nonsingular, and find its inverse.

EVENTS: A pair of numbers (x, t) is called an "event." If (x_1, t_1) and (x_2, t_2) are two events, the distance between them is defined by the quantity $(x_1 - x_2)^2 - c^2(t_1 - t_2)^2$. If (x_1', t_1'), (x_2', t_2') are the Lorentz transformation of two events, show that the distance between (x_1', t_1') and (x_2', t_2') is the same as between (x_1, t_1) and (x_2, t_2).

10.3 Historical and Biographical Notices

The subject of matrices and the subject of determinants are, as we have seen, closely related. Historically, determinants came first. The Chinese had an inkling of the notion of determinant around 1300, and the distinguished Japanese mathematician Takakazu (1642–1708) knew about them. As far as the West is concerned, determinants make their appearance in a correspondence between Leibnitz and de l'Hospital in 1693. But this correspondence was not published until much later and the actual development of the theory of determinants was not firmly under way until 1750 when Cramer (of Cramer's Rule) takes up the subject.

These days there is a strong tendency to turn things around and to present determinants as a chapter in the theory of matrices—just as we have done in this book. The reason for this, to quote the words of A. S. Householder, an authority on the subject, is that although "much of matrix theory originated in the form of determinantal identities, . . . many determinantal relations become more readily apprehended when seen as interpretations of relations among matrices."

Felix Klein, the Grand Mogul of Mathematics at the beginning of the twentieth century reported, "Cayley once said to me, in converstation, that if he had to give fifteen lectures on the whole of mathematics, he would devote one of them to determinants." If Cayley were alive today, there is no doubt what he would do; he would give one of his fifteen lectures on matrices, and make a passing remark about determinants.

A story is told that when Hamilton—to whom some of the early insights of matrix theory are due—first came across the noncommutativity of matrix multiplication, he found it very hard to believe and to accommodate into his thinking. Shocks occur from time to time in mathematics. (See page 330). But over the years, we have gotten used to them and are less responsive. When Pythagoras and his school discovered that not all numbers were rational, they were greatly shocked at the discovery, and are reputed to have offered up a hecatomb of cattle as a sacrifice to the gods. I do not recall hearing that Hamilton slaughtered any cattle in honor of his noncommutative algebras. This, perhaps, is an example of what some ancient Romans meant when they said that the golden age of history was in the *past*, in the days of the gods and the giants, and since that time, history has been running down. Mathematics could well afford to recapture some of the primitive enthusiasm of its past.

Josiah Willard Gibbs (1839–1903) was the person most instrumental in popularizing vector analysis. Gibbs was a mathematical physicist who taught for many years at Yale and was noted for his contributions to thermodynamics. Gibbs himself very modestly attributed the notion of vectors to his predecessors.

There is a very excellent scientific biography of Gibbs written by R. E. Langer in *The American Mathematics Monthly*, vol. 46, p. 75.

Some of Gibbs' predecessors who worked on linear algebra include the

American, Benjamin Peirce, his son Charles Santiago Sanders Peirce (1832–1914), and the German mathematician, Hermann Grassmann.

Hermann Grassmann (1809–1877) was a mathematician who taught at the Gymnasium in Stettin. His major work, *Ausdehnungslehre* (that is, the theory of extension) lay neglected for many years. This was due in part to the fact that he was in advance of his times, but more probably to the fact that his exposition was very difficult to understand. The quality of communication is as important in mathematics as in other fields, and much brilliant mathematics undoubtedly lies buried in the obscurity of language.

Apropos of Grassmann's difficult style, the following anecdote, making use of chemical notation, is told. The English mathematician and paradoxer A. De Morgan is reputed to have said to Hamilton: "I should like to hear about Grassmann—whom I am not likely to read. Between ourselves, I am disappointed with Germans—almost always. I have a new theory—take it. German intellect is an excellent thing, but when a German product is presented, it must be analyzed. Most probably it is a combination of intellect (I) and tobacco smoke (T). Certainly I_3T_1 and I_2T_1 occur; but I_1T_3 is more common, and I_2T_{15} and I_1T_{20} occur. In many cases metaphysics (M) occurs; and I hold that $I_aT_bM_c$ never occurs without $b + c > 2a$."

Biographies and portraits of Hamilton, Cayley, and Sylvester can be found in *Men of Mathematics* by Eric Temple Bell, Simon and Schuster, New York, 1937.

10.4 Bibliography

General Texts on Matrix Theory and Linear Algebra

1. R. V. Andrée, *Selections from Modern Abstract Algebra*, Holt, Rinehart and Winston, New York, 1958.

2. G. Birkhoff and S. Maclane, *A Survey of Modern Algebra*, Macmillan, New York, 1941.

3. John G. Kemeny, J. L. Snell, and C. L. Thompson, *Introduction to Finite Mathematics*, Prentice-Hall, Inc., New York, 1957.

4. Marvin Marcus, *Basic Theorems in Matrix Theory*, National Bureau of Standards Applied Mathematics Series No. 57. This is an up-to-date compendium of results in matrix theory. It can be purchased for 15¢ from the Superintendent of Documents, U. S. Government Printing Office, Washington 25, D. C.

5. L. Mirsky, *An Introduction to Linear Algebra*, Oxford University Press, 1955.

6. D. C. Murdoch, *Linear Algebra for Undergraduates*, John Wiley, New York, 1957.

7. School Mathematics Study Group, *Introduction to Matrix Algebra*, Yale University Press, New Haven, 1961.

Particular Topics

MATRICES: There is a nice semipopular article on matrices in *Mathematics, Queen and Servant of Science* by Eric Temple Bell, McGraw-Hill, New York, 1951. Chapter 6: "Oaks from Acorns."

ORIGINAL ARTICLES: If you are something of an antiquary and would like to see what some of the original articles look and sound like, get *Source Book in Mathematics* by David Eugene Smith, McGraw-Hill, New York, 1929. The following original articles relevant to matrix theory are reprinted there: Leibnitz on determinants, Hamilton on quaternions, Grassmann on Ausdehnungslehre, and Sylvester on Higher Space.

NOTATION: The development of notations for determinants and matrices can be found in Volume 2 of *A History of Mathematical Notations*, Open Court, by Florian J. Cajori, Chicago, 1929, pp. 87–105.

LINEAR SYSTEMS: SOLVING LINEAR SYSTEMS OF EQUATIONS: There is a vast literature on this subject. A popular account of some of the uses and difficulties associated with the solution of linear systems of equations will be found in Section 22 of "The Lore of Large Numbers" by P. J. Davis, vol. 6, *New Mathematical Library*, New York, 1961. To learn something about the size of the subject take a look at the article "Solving Linear Equations Can Be Interesting" by George E. Forsythe, *Bulletin of the American Mathematical Society*, vol. 59 (1953) pp. 299–329.

ELIMINATION METHOD: The Gauss-Jordan elimination method worked out in detail for an electronic computer can be found in Chapter 2 of *Mathematical Methods for Digital Computers*, A. Ralston and H. S. Wilf, Editors, John Wiley, New York, 1960.

DETERMINANTS: Though the theory of determinants appears to be a mathematical stepchild these days, it is a stepchild that apparently everyone loves. How else can one explain the existence of a vast literature on determinants and the fact that they are currently employed over and over again in many branches of mathematics. To obtain some idea of the size of the literature on determinants, see Thomas Muir's summary work entitled *The Theory of Determinants in the Historical Order of Development*. This book was reprinted by Dover, New York, in 1960 in two fat volumes and covers determinants from Leibnitz' day to about 1900.

VECTORS: For applications of vectors to mechanics, the reader should consult books on physics. For example, *Physics*, Physical Sciences Study Committee, D. C. Heath Co., Boston, 1960. For the use of vectors to prove certain theorems of plane geometry, see pp. 1–25 of *Vector and Tensor Analysis* by Louis Brand, John Wiley, New York, 1947.

MATRICES, GRAPHS, NETWORKS: Seshu and Reed, *Linear Graphs and Electrical Networks*, Addison-Wesley, 1961. Not an easy book, but a book that will raise one's horizons considerably.

SYMMETRY: The reader who would like to read a very fine essay on symmetry in nature, art, science, and how it ties up with mathematics. should get *Symmetry* by Hermann Weyl, Princeton University Press, Princeton, N. J., 1952.

DIFFERENCE EQUATIONS: *Introduction to Difference Equations*, Samuel Goldberg, John Wiley, New York, 1958. This book develops the simple portion of the theory of difference equations. It is easy to read and is full of illustrative examples from economics, sociology, and psychology. These examples, and many of them are of recent origin, show how a little mathematics can go a long way in explaining certain social and economic phenomena. Although matrix theory is not stressed here, it is presented.

MACHINE PROOFS: To follow up the remark on page 26 about the possibility of proving theorems by machine, see the popular article by D. H. Lehmer entitled, "Automation and Pure Mathematics" that appears in the book, *Applications of Digital Computers* edited by Walter F. Freiberger and William Prager, Ginn and Co., 1963. To follow up the remark about the identity of mathematics and logic, read "Are logic and mathematics identical" by L. Henkin, *Science*, vol. 138 (1962) pp. 788–794.

ABSTRACT ALGEBRA: "The Fundamental Properties of Algebra," E. V. Huntington in *Monographs on Modern Mathematics*, J.W. A. Young, ed., 1911. This is an old article, but still worth reading.

Index

BCDEFGHIJ 0698765
PRINTED IN THE UNITED STATES OF AMERICA

ABOUT THE AUTHOR

PHILIP J. DAVIS is Professor of Mathematics at Brown University in Providence, Rhode Island. He received his Ph.D. from Harvard University and from 1951–58 was on the staff of the National Bureau of Standards in Washington, D. C. During the period 1958–63 he served as Chief, Numerical Analysis Section of the Bureau of Standards.

Professor Davis has written a large number of articles on topics having to do with numerical analysis and interpolation and approximation theory. His books include *The Lore of Large Numbers* (1961) and *Interpolation and Approximation* (Blaisdell, 1963).

In 1963, the Mathematical Association of America awarded him the Chauvenet Prize for his expository paper on the history of the gamma function.